THE NEW NATURALIST

A JOURNAL OF BRITISH NATURAL HISTORY

CONTENTS

Woodlands

The Western Isles of Scotland

Migration

The Local Naturalist

12 colour photographs and 175 illustrations in black and white

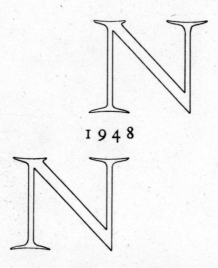

1948

EDITOR: JAMES FISHER • ASSISTANT EDITOR: ELISABETH ULLMANN

COLLINS   *St. James's Place*   LONDON

THE NEW NATURALIST

A JOURNAL OF BRITISH NATURAL HISTORY

NOTHING is easier than to hail, in the first editorial of a new publication and in an atmosphere of grandiloquence, the dawn of a new movement—and then, readily, to accept the guiding role in the movement.

We who place the NEW NATURALIST before you, do not believe that there is a *new* movement in British natural history. We are aware that the careful study of natural history has been cultivated, in Britain, for longer, and with greater zeal, than in any other country in the world. The animals and plants of Britain are better known than any others. Our natural history movement, is, in fact, a very old one; indeed, it is now a tradition. It has been part of the tradition, moreover, that the observation of British plants and animals, and the making of collections and records of them, should be largely in the hands of enlightened amateurs— so, in nearly every subject, from birds to molluscs, from ferns to Protozoa.

IS THERE A NEW SITUATION?

This great movement—this great stream—has changed in the present century in remarkable ways. It has changed in width and depth, as education has spread through all society, and as leisure has come to those who had little of it before; and it has changed in direction. For it can now truthfully be said that, at least in those subjects which have been the special province of the amateur (particularly the studies of birds, butterflies, and flowering plants), the basic museum work has been done. By this we do not mean that there is no more interesting museum work to do: but the common classification and naming of the species has been so completely finished, and is so ably presented in text-books, that the observer may fearlessly turn his mind to the study of animals and plants at home; where they live. For some years, now, we have been working in an age of field-studies. The word "ecology" is now freely used in ordinary conversation among naturalists; not long ago it fell on deaf ears, or from self-conscious lips.

It is the object of the *New Naturalist* organisation to serve the field-workers with books, and with this journal. Its publications are ecological, and do not attempt to replace existing text-books, or books of identification or reference. Some of its main books, which chiefly deal with the ecology of communities, or with aspects of geology and weather, have already appeared; some of its monographs, which deal with the ecology of individual species, are shortly to appear. The NEW NATURALIST will have a more general mission, though its bias will also be towards the living thing and its home in Britain, and towards the study of evolution.

CAN WE BE TOO SCIENTIFIC?

The NEW NATURALIST, then, will be primarily scientific. We hope that the articles in it will, without exception, describe some aspect of the nature of Nature. Some writers to-day complain that "modern natural history" is "too scientific", as if by being scientific it ceased to be poetic or artistic or whatever else they want it to be. This attitude, which is regrettably common, reflects a confusion of mind. Do these people really believe that the search for truth is less important than the search for poetry or art or aesthetic satisfaction or "happiness"? Do they not understand that the purest source of these imponderables is in the realms of fact, and that the establishment of facts is most simply done by the ancient methods of logical science? Once facts are despised, fancies replace them; and fancies are poisonous companions to the enjoyment and appreciation of Nature.

Here in Britain we have enough natural history

March in a Hertfordshire wood. The Winter aconite, Eranthis hyemalis, *has been cultivated in England for about four hundred years, and is now naturalised in many places*

John Markham

to write about for ever—even if we refrain from writing purely for entertainment, or purely for profit, or purely to inflict on the reader the personality of the writer. Indeed, as a small European country, we have a fauna and a flora which are remarkably rich, considering our size. These living things in Britain will provide research problems and research material to biologists for centuries to come. If the biological staffs of our universities, museums, and government research departments were ten times as great, it would still be years before we could see much exhaustion of the problems of animal and plant distribution, ecology, and life-history, to be found in these magnificent islands, with their varied landscape and climate.

THE ISLAND BIOLOGISTS

Our task, then, will be to publish the discoveries and conclusions of these island biologists, so that the reader may wonder and ponder on them. If this gives him the interest and joy that a man has at the truth honestly explained, we shall have done our duty. We shall try, as far as possible, to persuade research biologists to write, for us, the results of their own researches, or syntheses of the general conclusions of the biological schools to which they belong: and we will ask them to write their articles at their own level; to explain their work as if they were explaining it to a circle of friends or acquaintances of the same intellectual calibre, but without the special vocabulary of the subject. These special vocabularies are, after all, only scientific shorthand, and it will be no hardship for research workers sometimes to write in longhand!

It is clear, then, that we do not wish to make the NEW NATURALIST a Popular Paper. We have no desire to make, of natural history, a simple entertainment; or to make something that would be no more than an educational introduction to biology. Our ambition is a different one; it is to capture the British natural history, and to transform it into lines of type, and blocks, and coloured inks. This is, of course, an impossible ambition—but it is the only one we can fairly hold! We do not intend to be devoted to the pursuit of "Nature" (which is a noun whose meaning can be vastly obscure) or to the mere exploration of the "Country" (which is a noun with a half-baked,

week-end sound to it). We welcome nature-lovers and country-goers as travellers with us, in spite of the difficulties of understanding, sometimes, what they are about, what it is they love, or why they go!

TOPICAL—OR EPHEMERAL?

The production of a journal of this sort is not easy, and we shall probably make a lot of mistakes. We hope, however, to avoid the cardinal error of haste. We have been under some temptation, considering the present (possibly temporary) awakening of public interest in natural history, and its vast popularity, to rush in with a monthly publication. But we should be topical, not ephemeral; and we should not try to outstrip the supply of learned articles.

We therefore aim to publish the NEW NATURALIST every quarter. This editorial introduces the first four quarters, the first annual volume. We intend to publish future quarterly numbers separately as soon as it is possible to do so. Meanwhile we shall preserve the succession of annual volumes.

Nearly every number of the NEW NATURALIST will be a special number, devoted to some subject of moment. Our first number is about Woodland; our second, about the Western Isles of Scotland; our third, about Migration; our fourth, about Local Natural History. Future numbers, in future volumes, might deal with National Parks or Nature Conservation or the Sea or Mountains or the West Country; or any of an almost infinite number of subjects which will, in due course, become topical and present themselves. From time to time we will have a general number, a Miscellany. We shall particularly seek striking and interesting colour photographs of British animals, plants, earth-structure, or weather.

REGULAR FEATURES

Apart from the half-dozen articles, or so, upon the main subject of the number, we intend to have various occasional features. Since some of these must, by their nature, be very topical (such as reviews of current books, radio, and films) we cannot print them in this present volume in anything but token form. But ultimately we hope to have a regular contribution from a prominent amateur naturalist, in which he writes as he pleases about events in natural history, looked at from the amateur's point of view. In this feature, he will uphold the amateur's place in the scheme of things, and he will watch the amateur's interests, and show how they can best be served. Naturally, we shall have book reviews; and we shall also watch the natural history journals. As far as we know, no naturalist journal has so far reviewed films or radio: we hope to remedy this omission.

In this volume we devote some considerable space to the engagements and activities of local societies throughout Britain. The local natural history societies of Britain are remarkable. They are very numerous, and some are very large. Most are modest and far from wealthy; working quietly but keenly without any publicity. Nobody knows *exactly* how many there are, and, though they often have arrangements with their neighbours, they have not, as a whole, yet made much effort to integrate their activities. Nobody wishes to hurry or push them away from the healthy regionalism which is one of the features of British democracy, and it will certainly not be our policy to try to do so. Thanks to the Amateur Entomologists' Society, we have been able, in this volume, to publish a list of them, and maps to show how the country is at present covered by them. How far, to-day, does the amateur know what services are at hand, what people and things are ready and fit to help him with his natural history?

In bringing out the NEW NATURALIST, we do not believe our project to be unreasonably ambitious. Britain is the home of naturalists, and—in spite of spreading towns and cities—a modest oasis of Nature. If we can make a volume which, in style and contents, is worthy of observers and observed, we shall have succeeded.

Scarlet flycaps in a Hertfordshire wood

John Markham

Woodlands in Perthshire   Aerofilms Ltd.

THE NEW NATURALIST

A JOURNAL OF BRITISH NATURAL HISTORY

SPRING

WOODLANDS

CONTENTS

THE NEW NATURALIST   3

THE WOODLANDS OF ENGLAND AND WALES   8

H. GODWIN, F.R.S.: *British Forests in Prehistoric Times*   11

A. G. TANSLEY, F.R.S.: *British Woodlands*   16

R. MELVILLE: *The British Elms*   36

MONICA SHORTEN: *Grey Squirrels in Britain*   42

E. B. FORD, F.R.S.: *Woodland Butterflies*   47

PHILIP E. BROWN: *Woodland Tits*   52

M. K. COLQUHOUN: *Woodland Bird Communities*   57

STEPHEN POTTER: *Books and the Amateur Naturalist*   67

EDITOR: JAMES FISHER • ASSISTANT EDITOR: ELISABETH ULLMANN

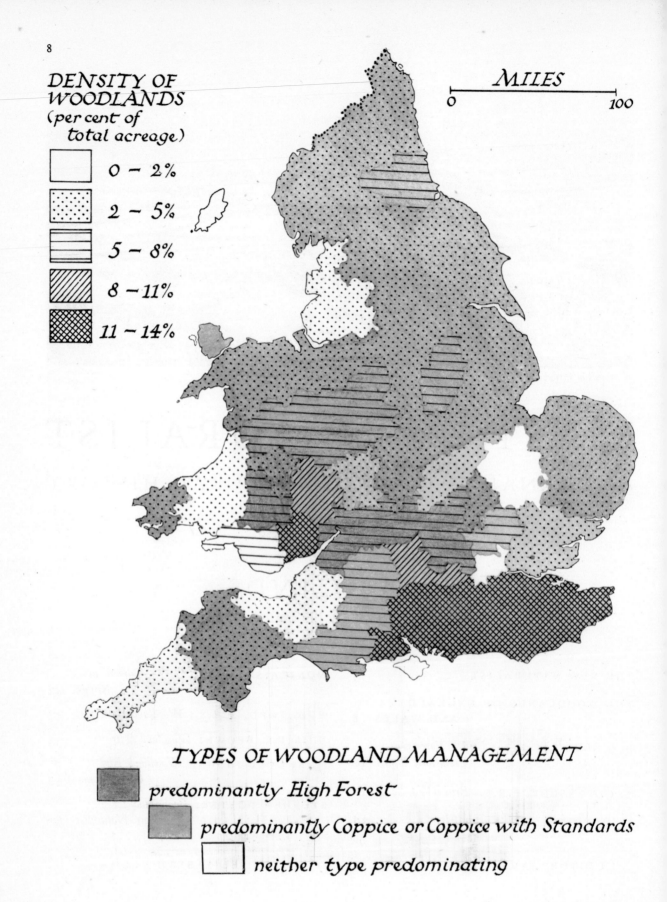

8

DENSITY OF
WOODLANDS
(per cent of
total acreage)

0 ~ 2%

2 ~ 5%

5 ~ 8%

8 ~ 11%

11 ~ 14%

MILES
0   100

TYPES OF WOODLAND MANAGEMENT

predominantly High Forest

predominantly Coppice or Coppice with Standards

neither type predominating

THE WOODLANDS OF ENGLAND AND WALES

A summary compiled by JEANNE FITZPATRICK

The only complete census of British woodland was conducted by the Forestry Commission in 1924. In 1939 they started to repeat this measurement, but the work was interfered with by the war: enough was done, however, to indicate some of the changes that had taken place in the intervening years.

Since the Middle Ages, Britain's trees have been steadily cut down or burned; for timber, for fuel, to clear ground for cultivation or dwellings, or to get rid of wolves. By 1924 Scotland, England and Wales were each about five per cent woodland; and relatively little of this small woodland area was composed of the natural climax forest. Those counties which remained most densely wooded were Hampshire, Kent, Surrey, Sussex, and Monmouth. Sussex had the highest density of woodland of all, Middlesex had the lowest.

The 1924 census recorded the main types of woodland management, the most important divisions being into coppiced woods and high forest and, within high forest, into hardwoods and softwoods. In England East Yorkshire, Nottinghamshire, and Buckinghamshire had mostly high forest (over 70 per cent of their woodland), and under 10 per cent of their woodland coppice. The counties with great amounts of coppice including "coppice with standards" were Kent (three-quarters) and Sussex (nearly two-thirds).

Hardwoods, in 1924, were more than holding their own in the high forests of England and Wales against the competition of the faster-growing softwoods. In only nine counties had the acreage of softwood overtaken that of hardwood. These counties were, in England, Somerset, Hampshire, Surrey, Norfolk, and Northumberland; in Wales, Glamorgan, Carmarthen, Cardigan, and Caernarvon. Since 1924 the situation has materially changed, in favour of softwoods. The actual figures for 1924 were:—

	ENGLAND		WALES	
	Acres	% of Total Woodland	Acres	% of Total Woodland
A. Economic, or potentially economic, High Forest comprising:	754,077	46·2	113,003	44·6
Conifer*	195,231	12·0	46,940	18·5
Hardwood	338,456	20·7	43,957	17·4
Mixed	220,390	13·5	22,106	8·7
Coppice, and Coppice with Standards	485,229	29·7	35,331	13·9
Scrub	87,410	5·5	34,934	13·8
Felled	194,742	11·9	62,182	24·5
B. Uneconomic (amenity beds, parks, etc.)	109,529	6·7	8,011	3·2
Totals	1,630,987	100·0	253,461	100·0

In 1943 the Forestry Commission estimated that (after considerable wartime felling) there were, in England, Wales, and Scotland, about two million acres of productive timber. The present plan is that another three million acres should be brought under cultivation and grow crops of trees, during the next fifty years. This will give us about double the amount of woodland which we enjoyed in 1924, probably with interesting consequences to our flora, fauna, and scenery; and possibly even to our climate.

* *This includes plantations of exotic conifers as well as natural and semi-natural woods.*

H. GODWIN

BRITISH FORESTS IN PREHISTORIC TIMES

WE do not expect to be able to understand a nation without knowing its history, and the story of a man's childhood and upbringing help us greatly to comprehend his character. Similarly those complex interesting communities, the natural forests of this country, cannot be fully understood without consideration of their origin in past times.

Twenty thousand years ago Europe was in the grip of a great Ice-Age, and though the southern parts of Britain were free from actual ice-sheets, the evidence of frost-disturbed soils shows that even there a severe, and indeed arctic, climate generally prevailed in which forest growth was almost certainly absent. Whence, when, and in what order, came to the British Isles the trees which made up the almost continuous mantle of forest cover which we know existed here in early historic time? Our ability to answer satisfactorily such questions rests upon a remarkable scientific technique elaborated in the past two or three decades and spoken of as "palynology", or more simply, "pollen-analysis".

Our forest trees are very largely pollinated by the wind; and when we see the golden showers of pollen shed from a shaken pine-branch, or from the dangling hazel catkins, we can realise in what vast amounts these grains are committed to the air. Few indeed reach the stigmas of the female flowers and discharge their normal biological function. The great majority sink to earth and are lost sight of; but grains also fall into lakes in great quantities and sink down to be buried in the soft muds of the bottom, or reach the water-logged surfaces of fens and peat-bogs where they become incorporated in the growing deposits. In such materials, devoid of oxygen, the living cell-contents of the grains disappear, but their fatty outer membranes remain and can be preserved for thousands (and indeed for millions) of years; that is to say for periods of time extending back far beyond the great Ice-Age.

Beneath the microscope, pollen grains are objects of considerable beauty and diversity, some smooth, others corrugated, ridged, or spiny, with pores variable in number, size, and disposition, with wall thickenings of different character and extent. Such features permit us to identify the pollen of the different genera of plants; and this can be done with equal ease for fossilised pollen, provided only that the various kinds of mineral and organic debris among which it occurs can be removed and prevented from obscuring the field of vision. New chemical and mechanical methods of treating muds, peats, and silts allow this to be done easily, thanks to the great resistance of the pollen membranes to the severest chemical treatment. We find ourselves able to recover from a piece of peat or mud no larger than a wheat-grain some hundreds of pollen-grains identifiable under the microscope. In the ordinary way some of these will be the pollen of herbs, and some of trees; depending on the vegetational cover of the neighbourhood when the sample was laid down.

If a vertical series of samples, an inch or two apart, is taken through any deep and continuously formed deposit, and the pollen in them is identified, we can reconstruct the history of the vegetation in that place. We shall find, in the changing proportions of the different pollen types throughout the series, a reflection of the changes which have gone on in the plants of the landscape throughout the formation of the deposit. It is customary, within each sample, to count 150 tree-pollen grains, and to express the amount of each pollen type as a percentage of this total. The hazel pollen and that of herbaceous plants (the non-arboreal pollen) is also usually expressed as a percentage of the arboreal pollen, although not reckoned in this total. In any given series the drift of the pollen-percentages is shown in what we refer to as a pollen-diagram, and it will be evident that the vertical scale represents not only depth, but also time. Although the pollen of certain trees such as the yew, apple, and rowan is preserved badly or not at all, so many of the important forest-trees have well-preserved pollen that pollen-analysis can be made to yield a reasonably complete picture of former forest history.

Our knowledge naturally depends upon the number and position of the sites from which pollen-analyses have been made; these are fairly frequent and well-spread in England and Wales, but as yet very infrequent in Scotland. In Ireland much extremely valuable work has been done, but we know of it in only general terms until the results have been published. All the same, enough has been done to confirm a parallel drift of forest history for these islands throughout post-glacial time, although there have always been the same kind of regional differences that are evident to-day.

The period which might be roughly placed between 18000 B.C. and 8500 B.C. is known as the Late-Glacial, and during this the first stages

of glacial retreat took place. The pollen-diagrams and other plant remains show that tundra vegetation, dominated by sedges and grasses (but with abundant dwarf-birch, arctic willow and associated arctic-alpine herbaceous plants) covered our countryside even as far south as Cornwall and the Lea Valley, north of London. In these open landscapes grazed such large mammals as the Giant Irish Deer (*Cervus megaceros*), Reindeer, Elk, and to judge from the Continent near by, probably also the Wild Horse and Bison, with perhaps even the Mammoth. It is likely that they were hunted by the last races of Palaeolithic man. The increased warmth led to the spread of tree-birches, aspen, and possibly pine, during what proved to be but a passing phase. The cold returned and this incipient woodland vanished, to be replaced by arctic tundra, probably locally sprinkled with birch in the south of Britain and treeless farther north.

At last, the general and permanent climatic improvement set in, and the Post-Glacial period opened with rapid recession of the ice-sheets and rapidly succeeding vegetation changes. Tree-birches covered the country with open forest, and

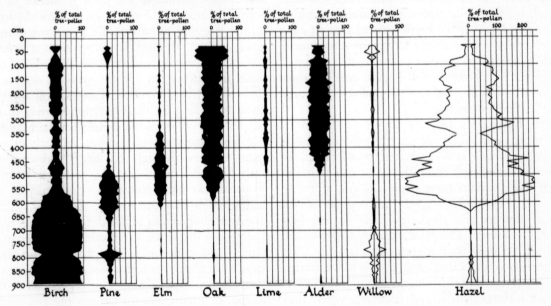

A typical pollen-diagram through the deposits of Hockham Mere, a deep drained lake in Norfolk. It covers a very large part of late-glacial and post-glacial time, and upon examination the changing proportions of the different tree-pollens from base to top will be seen to indicate the general drift of forest history described in the text. The latest phase of reversion of woodland history is only weakly shewn at this site. (The figures on the left indicate distance from the surface of the lake deposits down to the sand of the lake basin.)

in the south more favourable places held pine, with traces even of elm, oak, and hazel. It is still unknown whether these warmth-demanding trees survived the glaciation in Britain itself, whether they lived upon now submerged land south of our present coast-line, or whether they immigrated from the Continent over the dry bed of the North Sea.

With continued climatic improvement, spread of warmth-demanding trees became general. It led first to replacement (or admixture to a considerable degree) of birch by pine, and the abundance of hazel pollen at this time is higher than it has ever been since. Especially in the west, hazel pollen values greatly exceed those for the total tree-pollen, and indicate widespread hazel-scrub, possibly of the character of that still natural in western Ireland. This phenomenal expansion of hazel coincides with the establishment of elm, oak, and lime as substantial components of the forest-cover in the lowlands of England. They soon equalled or excelled the pine in abundance. From Ireland the lime-tree was absent, and, like beech and hornbeam, seems not to have been a natural forest tree there at any time in the post-glacial period.

The elm extended before the oak, and in Ireland was remarkably abundant; after oak followed the lime and small amounts of alder, but pine retained its hold and the mixed-oak forest was not yet everywhere dominant. These were the forest conditions during the so-called Boreal period, during which the Baltic was a fresh-water lake discharging across southern Sweden, the North Sea was rapidly reaching its present extent, and Mesolithic man fished and hunted the country with weapons of wood, flint, bone, and antler. It appears that most of the giant mammals became extinct when their open pastures gave place to this continuous dense woodland; and that the forest *was* dense we learn from the paucity of non-tree pollen in the pollen-diagrams.

At about 6500 B.C., which is taken as the end of the Boreal period, the further climatic amelioration was indicated by recession of the pine, and by the mixed-oak-forest trees becoming totally dominant, together with the alder which increased greatly in abundance, and which was an important and general feature of our natural oak-woodlands from this time onwards. Now

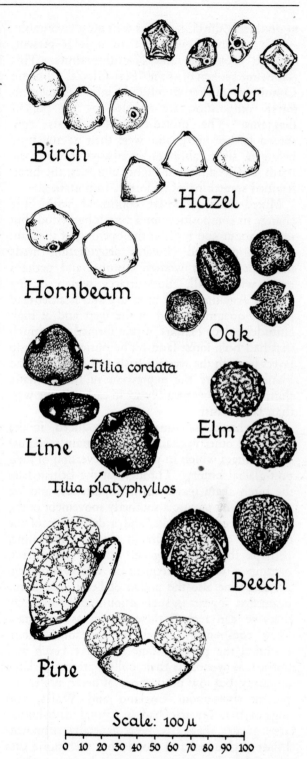

Scale: 100μ

0 10 20 30 40 50 60 70 80 90 100

Pollen grains of those British trees and shrubs most commonly preserved in peats or muds, drawn to the same scale. (1μ = one thousandth of a millimetre)

undoubtedly the climate was at its most favourable, and it continued warmer than it is at present, through Mesolithic and Neolithic times. This is the time spoken of as the "Post-Glacial Climatic Optimum" during which only minor changes in forest composition are revealed by the pollen-diagrams. The mixed-oak-alder forests now spread farther north and west than at any time before or since, although as always towards the north and west, and at higher altitudes, the birch retained something of its former importance.

Mixed-oak-alder forest continued with little change in composition for a very long period, but round about 500 B.C., at the opening of the Iron Age, a profound climatic deterioration made itself felt all over western Europe, and perhaps more widely still. Bog-surfaces which during Bronze Age times had been dry and heather-clad became quagmires, and in the west and at high altitudes a deep blanket of peat formed over much that had been forest land. The buried tree-stump layers beneath the western Irish and the Highland blanket-peat are the expression of this climatic shift, which quite possibly set in earlier in the west than farther east.

The change in climate also produced, in the forest and other vegetation types, certain recognisable changes which in part are a reversion of their post-glacial history. Throughout the British Isles the birch again increased in importance; and we may certainly picture a southerly movement of the climatic vegetation belts, and a depression of the tree-limit on our mountain slopes. The lime, perhaps the most exigeant of the forest trees, became much less frequent in our woodlands. At this time also the pollen of beech and horn-beam first appears in such amount and continuity that we can reckon these genera as important forest components. Only in the south-eastern counties, the present home of native beech and hornbeam woods, is their pollen present in large amounts; but low proportions of beech pollen are present throughout England and Wales, and suggest that the tree had a natural distribution area greater than has been generally supposed. Finds of charcoal and wood from prehistoric sites prove that the tree was native at least as early as the Bronze Age.

With the establishment of the alder-oak-elm-birch (beech) period the forest condition of early

historic time had been achieved, and from this time forward the hand of man, always destructive, was heavy upon the forest land. Throughout the millennia between the onset of glacial retreat and the advent of the Romans, the forests were great natural communities directly under climatic control, and it is thus we have regarded them. They constituted the environment of prehistoric man, dominated his life and determined his economy. His escape from their control was gradual, but finally, of course, he dominated our forests and all but extinguished them. It has been one of the triumphs of recent pollen-analytic investigations to detect and record the beginnings of this process in Neolithic, Bronze Age, and Iron Age times, and this has proved possible through the recognition of cereal pollen (as a category of grass pollen), and of the pollen of certain weeds of cultivation, among them particularly the rib-wort plantain (*Plantago lanceolata*). These pollen types in England, as in Denmark, first appear in Neolithic times, although they become far more abundant in the succeeding Bronze and Iron Ages. Disturbances of the smooth drift of the tree-pollen curves indicate how clearance by fire and axe made space for a shifting cultivation, and there can be no doubt that grazing animals tended to prevent re-colonisation of ground won from the forest. In the extensive Brecklands of East Anglia, home of dense pre-historic settlement, the pollen records have now shown that the great heaths of grass, sand-sedge, and ling had their origin at this period and in this way.

It will be apparent how much more is yet to be learned of the history of our woodlands, but the outline of their story is beginning to emerge, and we now understand the methods by which the picture can be completed.

REFERENCES:

G. ERDTMAN (1943) *An Introduction to Pollen Analysis.* Michigan, U.S.A., Waltham.

H. GODWIN (1934) *Pollen Analysis: an outline of the problems and potentialities of the method.* The New Phytologist, vol. 33.

H. GODWIN (1940) *Pollen Analysis and Forest History of England and Wales.* The New Phytologist, vol. 39.

Bole of old yew tree at Kingley Vale, near Chichester, Sussex. The trunk is formed of multiple stems that grow up fused together. The age of these great yews is commonly 500, and up to 1,000 years

John Markham

A. G. TANSLEY

BRITISH WOODLANDS

MANY years ago, when I was teaching botany at Cambridge, an able student asked me why I treated British woodlands as part of the natural vegetation of the country. "Surely," he said, or words to that effect, "they are all, or almost all, planted." Intelligent though he was he had some difficulty in grasping the thesis on which my teaching was based, but eventually saw that it was supported by the facts then available. We can now add that it is abundantly confirmed by all the research that has since been carried out.

Briefly, the history of our woodlands, as we now know it, is this. Originally the British and Irish forests were a natural extension to these islands of the great forests of Europe, modified to some extent by our insular climate. Their particular story begins as soon as the repressing influence of the last phase of the Great Ice Age passed away and the general climate became suitable for the growth of trees. At that time—about 10,000 years ago—Britain was a peninsula of the European continent, and as the ice retreated, trees from Europe must have spread north-westwards over the great land bridge that stretched across what is now the southern part of the North Sea, the Straits of Dover and the eastern part of the Channel. It is quite possible, even likely, that there were already some trees in this country, trees that had survived the last cold phase from the preceding warmer (interglacial) period, for the ice sheets and glaciers of the last phase did not cover eastern England. But whether surviving here or spreading from the Continent or both, there was extensive colonisation of the land by certain trees both before and after the final insulation of Britain through transgression of the sea across the old land bridge.

These trees were at first mainly birch and pine, which formed the bulk of the first forests and penetrated to Scotland and Ireland. Besides these there were willows and alders on the great tracts of waterlogged land and round the shallow meres left behind by the melting of the ice. Later, as the climate got damp as well as warm, oak accompanied by elm, and in the south lime, increased and came to dominate most of the English and some of the Scottish forests; and in the wettest periods there was a great deal of alder. Later still there was a spread of beech and hornbeam in the south, but the limits of distribution of these last trees are not yet fully known. Nor have we an exact knowledge of the post-glacial history of ash, though it was to play an important part in later forests. Birch and pine always formed a major part of the Scottish forests. Oak, beech, ash, alder, birch, and pine have been the dominants of the native British woodlands from those times until now.

When the original tree colonisation was being completed man had not yet disturbed the native vegetation to any great extent. He was still a hunting and food-collecting animal, and it was not till he began to sow crops and to keep flocks and herds—in this country about 4,500 years ago—that he began to fell trees not only for construction, tools and firewood, but to make room for his sheep and cattle. The small and scattered populations of those times did no more than touch the fringes of the great forests, and it was many centuries before England was gradually changed from a forest-covered to a pastoral and arable country. Eventually, during the Middle Ages, necessary timber had to be imported in increasing quantity, until in the Modern Period we had to get from abroad the great bulk of what we needed.

It was not till the sixteenth century that a general dearth of timber began to make itself felt, and in the seventeenth the last reserves of the English forests were used up, largely because of the heavy demands of smelting and glass-making. In the second half of that century not enough

R. J. Lythgoe

A natural oakwood on the slope of an Old Red Sandstone hill near the Upper Lake, Killarney. The shrub layer of this wood, consisting entirely of holly, is shown in the photograph on page 22

sound oak could be found in the country for the needs of the navy. Systematic planting of trees for timber began in a small way, especially in Scotland, in the fifteenth and sixteenth centuries, and was afterwards considerably extended, though it has never been adequate to the country's needs. There were many competing uses for the land, and the people as a whole have never been what is called "forest-minded". The planting that was done, actively in the eighteenth century and considerably in the nineteenth, was carried out almost entirely by specially keen landowners.

The Scottish lords and lairds were particularly enthusiastic planters, and vied with one another in establishing new forests. The great bulk of these plantations were of their native pine, which was very successful, but oak and elm and a little beech were also planted in Scotland, as well as the alien sycamore, first mentioned in Britain in the sixteenth century. In the eighteenth there were added spruce, a little silver fir, and a good deal of larch, which often did very well, and was used as a substitute for oak. The English planted more hardwoods in proportion, especially oak, the dearth of which had been particularly felt, but also a good deal of Scots pine, larch, and some spruce.

The Scottish and north English plantations were often on open moorland, which may or may not have borne woodland formerly, but in the south largely on the sites of old woodland which had been felled or thinned. When planting began in the sixteenth and seventeenth centuries there was a fair amount of native English woodland remaining, though only a fraction of the original extent. At the end of the seventeenth century a contemporary estimate gives a figure which was substantially below 16 per cent of the land area of England and Wales; it is impossible to say how much below because "parks and commons" were lumped with woodland in that figure. At the beginning of the twentieth century, woods and plantations occupied only just over 5 per cent of England and Wales, the lowest figure in Europe.

The kinds of native British woodland existing when planting began were certainly of the same broad types that colonised the country in post-glacial prehistoric times, fragments of which still exist, though mostly in a more or less modified state—oakwood, beechwood, ashwood, alder-wood, birchwood, and in the Scottish Highlands pinewood. Mixed woods (apart from mixed plantations) do exist in Britain, but they are not characteristic, almost all our native woods being dominated by a single species of tree, though other species are usually present among or below the dominants. That is why we naturally speak of an oakwood or a beechwood, though birches, ashes, wych elms, and other trees such as holly, yew, wild cherry, crab apple, and mountain ash may be associated with the dominants. This relative purity of dominance in our woods is not, as many people seem to assume, originally the result of planting with one kind of tree, but of the success in competition of a particular species in given conditions of climate and soil. It is perfectly true that very many, if not most, of our woods have been replanted, often with the same kind of tree of which they were originally composed, notably in the case of oak and beech woods. In other cases a different tree has been substituted, sometimes a native tree, such as ash on the site of an original oakwood or beechwood, sometimes a foreign tree such as larch or spruce; and where such replanting has been done the purity of the wood is of course directly due to this. A wide comparison of the woods composed of native deciduous trees over considerable stretches of country enables us to say with confidence what is the natural dominant tree and to separate those woods which have had their origin in the planting of some other kind.

When an old native wood dominated by a particular species is clear-felled and replanted with the same species, it acquires, as the trees grow to maturity, much of the character of a natural wood.

Nature does not distinguish between oaks of the same species, whether they sowed themselves as acorns or were planted as saplings. There is, however, one marked difference between a natural self-regenerating wood, which has been left entirely alone, i.e. a "virgin" wood, and a planted wood. In the former there are always old trees, the parents of the younger ones, and sometimes three or four generations are represented, besides the debris of old dead trees and fallen branches. This gives diversity to a virgin wood which is not found in one that has been planted. But if in the natural wood there has been felling and a taking out of the older trees, a certain uniformity or approximate uniformity in the age of the trees is introduced. Another cause of even age in naturally developed woods is the occurrence of certain years when specially large quantities of seed are ripened and self-sown. The wood may come to consist very largely of trees from this particular year, the offspring of other years having been mostly destroyed as seeds or seedlings by their many enemies such as mice and voles.

In these ways a wood which has been regularly exploited by selective felling comes to approximate in character to one which has been planted with the same kind of tree on the site of an old natural wood, and in the absence of written records it may be difficult or impossible to distinguish between them. Both these kinds of wood, different as is the actual origin of their trees, we call "semi-natural", because they both have been modified by man's interference but retain nevertheless many of the characters of a natural wood, such as the general nature of the undergrowth, which, in a planted wood, partly survives from the preceding natural wood and partly colonises it afresh.

Virgin woods are almost absent from a country like our own which has been intensively exploited for many centuries. Fragments of virgin wood-land are only found in remote places where the difficulty of access or of removing the wood has protected them, or the growth of the trees is so poor that they are of little or no value. The great majority of our deciduous woods composed of native trees are semi-natural in the sense defined, and that is the justification for considering hem as part of the natural vegetation of the country. Plantations of foreign trees such as the foreign conifers with which the Forestry Commission

May in the Spey Valley; a mixed stand of birch and juniper at Inchriach in Inverness-shire— a plant association typical of parts of the Highlands

John Markham

R. J. Lythgoe

Edge of High Wood near Burwash, East Sussex. Pedunculate standard oaks in open canopy: dense coppice of hornbeam (right and centre) and hazel (left)

intends to cover much of the country, are in a completely different category. They are entirely "artificial" woods, whose undergrowth, where any is present, is usually widely different from that of a natural or semi-natural wood.

We may now turn to consider the different kinds of native woodland.

OAKWOODS

Oakwood is the natural woodland over the greater part of Britain. In post-glacial times, following the prevalence of birch and pine, it spread over most of the lowland plains and into the valleys of the west and north. Till the beginning of the Modern Period great oak forests occupied much of the Midland and Essex plains and of the Kent and Sussex Weald, largely on

clay soils, which, because of their intractableness, were among the last to be used for cultivation. Broadly speaking one may say that except on the most sterile sands, on shallow limestones, and on permanently wet soils, oak is the natural dominant in our climate up to an altitude of 1,000 to 1,500 feet, except in places constantly exposed to violent winds. It has been repeatedly shown that on all the clays, loams, and the better sands, oaks colonise abandoned arable or grassland and establish oak-wood, wherever there are enough parent trees in the neighbourhood to produce the necessary seed.

There are two kinds of native oak in Britain—the common or pedunculate, and the durmast or sessile oak. The former has its acorns on long slender stalks, while in the latter the acorns are sessile or on short thick stalks; there are also certain differences in the leaves. The pedunculate oak is the familiar tree of the southern, eastern, and

A heavily thinned pedunculate oakwood, Gravetye Manor, Sussex, in April: rather sparse coppice of hazel and sallow, wood anemone in full flower and dominant in the field layer

midland woods and hedgerows; the sessile oak dominates the woods of the valleys and hillsides of the west and north, though it also occurs, either alone or mixed with the pedunculate, on the sandy soils of south-eastern England. The two trees are very much alike in general form and when they grow together abundant hybrids are produced.

The most familiar type of oakwood in the English lowlands is "coppice-with-standards" (Photos, pp. 20 and 21). In this there are well-spaced spreading oaks (about twelve to the acre is an average number) and an undergrowth, typically of hazel, which is cut to the stools once every ten or twelve years. This is a man-made type of wood formed from original oak forests where hazel was the dominant shrub in the undergrowth. Most of the young trees were cut out, those that were left being able to spread so that, when mature, their ultimate twigs just touched those of the neighbouring trees. The curved timber of the heavy main branches developed under these conditions was useful for shipbuilding. The "open canopy" of foliage formed by the well-spaced trees allows more light to penetrate than does the dense "close canopy" formed by trees growing close together and forming dense narrow crowns at their tops. The additional light reaching the shrubs below promoted their luxuriance so that a continuous shrub layer was produced, sprouting vigorously when coppiced. The "smallwood" of hazel and other shrubs was, and is, used for hurdles, fences, stakes, pea- and bean-sticks, and so on.

Coppice-with-standards has been the traditional form of regularly exploited oakwood in the English lowlands for some centuries and was often planted on open ground; but with the disappearance of wooden ships the spreading, short-boled,

Elizabeth Cowles

Dense shrub layer of holly in the oakwood shown on page 17. Ivy climbing the oak trunks

John Markham

Foxgloves in flower and bracken on the edge of an oak-wood on light soil

heavy-branched oaks lost their value. Many such woods are now neglected; felled or dead oaks are not replaced, and the coppice is not cut at the proper time. Though the smallwood is still useful many coppices are now mainly used as fox coverts or pheasant preserves.

Besides the oaks and hazels other trees and shrubs, self-sown, are commonly found in oak-hazel coppices — ash, birch, crab apple, wild cherry, and field maple, with the shrubs dogwood and guelder rose. All of these are commonly coppiced along with the hazel. Hawthorn is often found in woods, but it is not a woodland shrub, and growing in shade its leaves are thin, the spines are poorly developed, and it does not flower. In parts of the south-east, hornbeam is abundant and is usually cut with the coppice (Photo, p. 20), though when allowed to grow up it makes a good tree. Oak itself is sometimes coppiced, and in

some parts of the country there are considerable areas of oak coppice, the bark of which was used for tanning leather before chemical tanning was introduced.

The periodic cutting of the coppice has a marked effect on the vegetation of the floor of the wood. The sudden access of light stimulates the growth and especially the flowering of the herbs, and to this we owe the glorious sheets of primroses, wood anemones (Photo, p. 21), blue-bells, and wood violets appearing in the second or third and subsequent years after the coppice is cut. As the shrubs grow up and their canopy closes in towards the end of the coppicing cycle the herbaceous vegetation often becomes sparse and many of the plants cease to flower.

Besides the gregarious early spring-flowering species there are a number which flower in later spring or through the summer, such for instance as

wood-sorrel, wood sanicle, wood avens, willow-
herb, St. John's-wort, herb-Robert, enchanter's
nightshade, and many others.

The trees, the shrubs and the herbs growing
on the floor of a wood form three "storeys" or
"layers" of vegetation, and in most English woods
there is a fourth, the moss layer, usually only an
inch or two high. The development and density
of the lower layers of woodland vegetation
depend on those of the upper, because of the
varying amount of light penetrating the canopy.
When the tree foliage is dense in a close-canopy
wood, so that the light below the trees is dim (as
for instance in a beechwood) shrubs are absent
or very sparse and poorly developed. Under old
thick coppice there is no continuous layer of
woodland herbs ("field layer") and when the
herbs are densely packed there is little room for
mosses. In very wet climates where the air is
nearly always damp the moss layer is very thick
and the field layer poor or almost absent, as in the
Killarney woods (Photo, p. 30).

Oakwoods, as we have seen, inhabit a wide
range of soils, from heavy clays to medium sands
in the lowlands, and the varying soils produced
by the old hard rocks of the northern and western
hillsides. These soil differences have a marked
effect on the structure and composition of the
wood. We can distinguish four main types of
oakwood depending on soil characters, though
there are many transitions between them.

(1) Oakwoods on clays and loams which are
well aerated and have a medium water content.
The trees are well grown and the dominant hazel
is accompanied by a variety of other shrubs. The
field layer includes primrose, sanicle, dog's
mercury, wild strawberry, bluebell on the lighter
loams, wood anemone, and lesser celandine
among spring flowers, with the later-flowering
wood buttercup, wood sedge, creeping bugle,
wood avens, perforate St. John's-wort, common
willow-herb, and many others.

(2) Oakwoods on somewhat acid, drier soil
have few shrubs, and a field layer in which
bracken fern is prominent, associated with bluebell and wood soft-grass. Many of the species
found in (1) are absent and are replaced by such
plants as foxglove (Photo, p. 22) barren straw-
berry, wood-sage, earthnut, upright St. John's-
wort.

(3) Heathy oakwoods on very acid sands and
similar soils. The oaks are often poorly grown,
there is abundance of birch, and shrubs are practically absent. The field layer consists of heath
plants such as bilberry, with heather in well-
lighted places, heath grasses, heath bedstraw, and
tormentil.

(4) Very wet oakwoods, often waterlogged in
winter on heavy clay or with a high water table,
often have an abundance of alder. Sallows are
conspicuous among the shrubs. In the field layer
tufted hair-grass with long, narrow, harsh, finely
serrated leaves is usually conspicuous, with large
sedges—the drooping sedge and the great stooled
sedge—several species of rush, water figwort,
creeping buttercup, stinging nettle, cleavers, and
sometimes meadowsweet—not flowering in the
shade.

BEECHWOODS

The British beechwoods have a much more
restricted distribution than the oakwoods. In late
prehistoric times beech seems to have extended
farther north and west, though it never reached
Ireland, but existing native beechwoods are confined to the south, and mainly the south-east, of
England.

There is still a certain amount of mystery surrounding the history of the beech in England,
partly turning on Julius Caesar's remark that the
Gallic trees were present in England except beech
and fir. Fir, i.e. spruce, was certainly absent, but
we now know, from the presence of its pollen in
the peat, that beech had been in East Anglia, and
much farther north and west, long before Caesar's
invasion, and Caesar certainly traversed country
which is now one of the main centres of native
beechwood. One writer has suggested that the
tree was originally located farther north, and
migrated to the south-east after Caesar's time, but
that is not very easy to believe. The present limits
of clearly native, aggressively wood-forming beech
in England round off its Continental distribution
very naturally (the same may be said of the even
more restricted south-eastern distribution of hornbeam). It is plausible to suppose that the general
failure of beech to form natural woods over wider
areas of England may be due to the fact that

R. J. Lythgoe

Finely grown beechwood, more than 100 feet high, on the deep loam of the Chiltern plateau. The field layer is mainly dominated by bramble, but many other species are present: shrubs are almost absent

H. Godwin

Poorly grown beechwood with crooked stems of no great height on an acid gravel soil adjoining Burnham Beeches. The floor of the wood is covered with leaf litter, interrupted by large cushions of the beautiful silvery-green moss Leucobryum glaucum

"good mast years" when enough ripe seed is produced to give large crops of seedlings only occur at fairly long intervals and that the cooler summers of the west and north check the setting and ripening of seed. Beech *can* however grow well and ripen seed in the east of Scotland, where beechwood self-sown from planted trees has established itself in some places in Aberdeenshire.

The main existing areas of native beechwood are on the chalk to the north, south and west of the Weald, on the chalk of the Chiltern Hills, and on the oolitic limestone of the Cotswolds. There are one or two outliers of apparently native beechwood in the Wye Valley and in South Wales, mostly on Carboniferous Limestone. Over the rest of the country almost all the beech is in plantations, though isolated trees may conceivably be descended from native beech when it was spread more widely through England.

The concentration of beech on limestone soils has led to a widespread notion that the tree is a "lime lover". It is true that our most characteristic beechwoods are the "hangers" on the shallow, highly calcareous soil of the chalk escarpments and valley sides, but the finest beech actually grows on good deep loams overlying the chalk plateaux, not at all calcareous (Photo, p. 24), and the tree can also establish woods on highly acid sands and gravels, as at Burnham Beeches (Photo, p. 25), in Epping Forest, and at many places in and around the Weald. On heavy soils beech is at a disadvantage compared with oak, and it cannot stand waterlogging.

Beechwood is perhaps the most beautiful of all our native woodlands. The smooth grey column-like boles supporting a canopy of foliage, a delicate tender green in May, darkening in high summer, and turning to a glorious bronze in October, the general absence of shrubs, giving an emptiness to the wood which allows of long vistas, the thick persistent carpet of leaf litter, a warm brown through most of the year changing to a rich purple when it is soaked by winter rains—all combine to give the beechwood its peculiar attractiveness. Most beechwoods are notable for the variety of larger fungi that spring from the abundant humus, especially in autumn. Two examples of these are shown in the photographs on pp. 30 and 31.

The different types of beechwood depend essentially on differences of soil.

(1) The "hangers" of the chalk escarpments and valley sides. The surface of the soil is covered with leaf litter except on very steep slopes or where the wind has free access. The litter is gradually converted below into black humus, below which comes a layer of highly calcareous mineral soil before the weathered surface of the chalk rock is reached at a depth of 12 to 16 inches. The humus and mineral soil are filled with the fine branches of the surface beech roots associated with fungal hyphae called "mycorrhiza" which play an important part in nutrition; anchoring roots strike down into the fissures of the chalk. This very complete penetration by beech rootlets leads to a severe drain on the soil water content so that in the summer the soil often becomes very dry, and this is one important cause of the frequent sparseness or even absence of a field layer, especially in young woods with closely set saplings. The denseness of the canopy also contributes by cutting off light from the floor of the wood. In older woods where many of the young trees have been suppressed and the canopy has begun to open out, the ground often becomes completely covered with herbaceous vegetation.

Beechwood is typically very pure, but occasional trees of whitebeam, or of ash (poorly developed), are found in the canopy. Shrubs are practically absent except in openings, but below the beech canopy there is often a layer of yew or holly—both evergreens which can use the light in spring before the canopy of beech foliage is developed.

The common dominants of the field layer are dog's mercury and wood sanicle, the former on the gentler slopes with deeper soil, the latter on the steeper gradients where the soil is very shallow. Ivy, creeping on the ground and rooting at intervals in the humus, often covers the ground in very deep shade, besides ascending the trees. Mercury and sanicle, like the evergreen ivy, do much of their vegetative growth in spring before the canopy of foliage cuts off the light. Associated with these plants are many other common oak-wood species, but some are specially characteristic of chalk beechwoods. Among these are sweet woodruff, hairy violet, early-flowering wood violet, wall lettuce, and melic-grass. Less common but very characteristic are columbine, Solomon's seal, green hellebore, and spurge laurel, the last-named an evergreen dwarf shrub

---

Bear's garlic (ramsons) in full flower dominating the field layer of a damp hazel copse in May. A few stinging nettles in the foreground

John Markham

W. J. B. Blake

Ashwood on the steep rocky slopes of limestone in Dovedale, Derbyshire (the spruces on the right are planted)

with shining laurel-like leaves. Most characteristic of all, and either confined or nearly confined to chalk beechwoods, are certain orchids —common helleborine, white helleborine, and the rare narrow-leaved helleborine. Besides these the colourless saprophytic bird's-nest orchid, and its fellow saprophyte the "bird's-nest" (not an orchid) flourish in the deep humus and in deep shade since they have no chlorophyll (the green pigment of leaves) and are independent of light for making their food. Though mosses are numerous in species the moss layer is never continuous, as it often is in oakwoods, since the deep leaf litter is not easy for mosses to colonise.

(2) Beechwoods on deep loam are almost confined to the western South Downs and the plateau of the Chiltern Hills, and here the trees are of better growth than in the escarpment woods including some of the finest beech timber in the country (Photo, p. 24). The persistent leaf litter is several inches deep. Again there is a dearth of shrubs but sometimes a layer of holly below the beeches. Yew is not common. Oaks are locally frequent, whereas they are quite absent from typical escarpment woods, for these deep fertile loams are for the most part equally suitable for oak and beech. Beech tends under natural conditions to dominate the wood because it casts a deeper shade and equals oak in potential height growth, but on some rather heavier loams oak has the advantage. Ashes are occasional in the canopy, and on the Chilterns wild cherry (gean).

Two of the most characteristic dominants of the field layer are bramble and wood-sorrel, and there is a wide variety of accompanying plants, much wider than in the escarpment woods.

(3) Beechwoods on acid sands and gravels have a totally different flora from the woods on

John Markham

Ashwood establishing itself in the fissures of a limestone terrace

chalk soils and good loams. Where fertility is specially low the trees are badly grown, of low stature and often crooked (Photo, p. 25). Oaks and mountain ashes (rowans) sometimes accompany the beeches, and birches freely colonise gaps. Holly is occasional to frequent, alder-buckthorn and common sallow occur, and honeysuckle, though not frequent, is the characteristic climber. Ivy, hazel, field maple, and ash are absent altogether. The field layer is often absent, and where present is poor both in species and individuals. Bilberry, though not flowering, is sometimes dominant, or bracken where the shade is not too deep. Heather comes in where there is ample light. Wood soft-grass, wavy hair-grass, wood-sage, and a few other species are characteristic. The moss layer is discontinuous and consists of a few species which habitually grow on acid soils. The most conspicuous is the silvery-green *Leuco-*

bryum which forms large handsome cushions (Photo, p. 25).

It is doubtful if this type of beechwood is permanent, the dry peaty soil surface being very unfavourable as a seed bed.

ASHWOODS

Ash is an abundant tree throughout the country, common in woods dominated by other trees, especially on wet ground, but avoiding acid soils. It flourishes on shallow limestone soils and since it fruits much more freely and distributes its seeds more widely it colonises such soils earlier than beech, by which it is ultimately suppressed within the southern areas where beech is an aggressive tree. To the north and west of this region, ash has no comparable competitor, and

R. J. Lythgoe

Oakwood at Killarney near the upper limit of trees. Owing to the constantly damp air, tree trunks and boulders are covered with a thick carpet of mosses. There are very few flowering plants: a solitary foxglove and some rushes are seen in the foreground

S. C. Porter

Puffballs, Lycoperdon gemmatum, *in a beechwood*

John Markham

An open pinewood with bilberry field layer: Rothiemurchus forest

S. C. Porter

A mushroom-like fungus, Cantharellus infundibuliformis, *at the base of a beech tree*

H. Godwin

Buckthorn carr (fenwood) at Wicken Fen, Cambridgeshire, with the same plants (not flowering in the deep shade)
as are found in an alderwood: fen fern, comfrey, yellow flag, stinging nettle, are shown

here it forms permanent ashwoods on limestone soils, notably on the Carboniferous Limestone, by far the most extensive of the British limestones apart from chalk. These limestone ashwoods are best developed in the Derbyshire dales (Photo, p. 28), to a less extent in West Yorkshire, North and South Wales, and on the Mendip Hills, but wherever native woodland is present on lime-stone soils outside the beechwood region it is ashwood.

The most characteristic accompanying trees are wych elm, and in the south, whitebeam and yew. Field maple and aspen also occur, but birch is quite absent except at high altitudes. The shade cast by the ash canopy is much lighter than that of beech or even oak, and typically there are well-developed shrub and field layers. The com-monest shrubs are hawthorn and hazel, which are abundant almost everywhere in and about ash-

woods. Of the "lime loving" shrubs dogwood, spindle, buckthorn, privet, and elder are more or less frequent, and wayfaring tree in the south. Ivy is abundant, as it is indeed in all native British woods except those on poor acid soils.

The field layer varies with the amount of water in the soil. On the damper soils ramsons (bear's garlic, Photo, p. 27) and lesser celandine are often dominant, accompanied by such species as broad-leaved bell-flower, melancholy thistle, water avens, spotted and butterfly orchids, globeflower, and a number of other more widely distributed plants of damp soils. On drier ground dog's mercury with the delicate moschatel sheltering between its sturdy shoots, is a widespread dominant, and in the driest places, such as fresh limestone scree, ground ivy and wood-sage often dominate con-siderable stretches, while lily-of-the-valley and stone bramble also form societies. The handsome bloody cranesbill and the very rare baneberry are other striking ashwood plants.

Ashwood readily establishes itself on limestone talus fallen from the crags of a limestone gorge, but also in the fissures of limestone rock, including those of the flat limestone pavements that are found in several parts of northern England and in western Ireland (Photo, p. 29). These vertical cracks are freely colonised by woodland plants before the trees arrive, and when the trees grow up they overshadow the blocks between the fissures so that these become covered with mosses and later by a complete field layer of woodland plants.

Ashwood also occurs on the soil derived from basic igneous rocks, which, like limestone soil, is rich in nutritive salts and gives an alkaline reaction. Towards the upper limit of ashwoods which ascend above 1,000 ft., birch, which is absent from the woods at low levels, becomes associated with ash and eventually replaces it.

ALDERWOOD

We know from the great abundance of pollen grains preserved in peat that woodland dominated by the common alder, or in which the tree played an important part, was very extensive from middle post-glacial times when the climate became much wetter until late historical times when draining and clearing of wet low-lying land had done away with most of its natural habitats. To-day little alderwood remains but fragments in undrained hollows of marshy ground and belts along stream-sides and round ponds and lakes.

Among the best-developed English alderwoods are those on the fens of East Norfolk on the edges of some of the Broads. These have hardly been interfered with at all so that they are practically virgin woods. With the dominant alder are associated birch and ash, and of shrubs sallow, the two buckthorns, guelder rose, and sometimes hawthorn, spindle, and privet. The preponder-ance of lime-loving shrubs is explained by the fact that the fen peat is fed by water draining from the chalk. Of low shrubs red and black currant and gooseberry are very characteristic of these fenwoods. The field layer includes a wide variety of fen plants, and others, such as stinging nettle, which can tolerate excess of water in the soil. Fen fern, yellow flag, hemp agrimony, the two loosestrifes, red and yellow, comfrey (Photo, p. 32), and the great stooled sedges are generally conspicuous though they can rarely flower, and of climbers, nightshade, bindweed, and hop as well as ivy.

The fen woods are sometimes based on peat actually floating on water, and there are always numerous pools scattered through them. The air is constantly damp, so that the trunks and branches of the trees and shrubs, sometimes up to the growing twigs, as well as the many fallen dead branches, are apt to be covered with lichens and mosses. These untouched fen woods give in fact a very good picture in miniature of a wet tropical virgin jungle.

BIRCH AND PINEWOODS

Birch and pine woods may be considered together as they are naturally associated in much the same climates and soils. The two birches—the white or "silver" birch and the hairy birch (not always hairy!) with browner bark—are very common trees all over the country on dry and wet soils alike, though they are rarely found on limestones. Their small, dry, one-seeded, winged fruits are produced and dispersed by the wind in vast numbers, so that the seedlings spring up over extensive tracts of sandy heath in southern England where birchwoods, often preceding oak-woods, are common. In the north of England and Scotland, birchwood often fills up gaps in the valley-side oakwoods and forms a fringe on their upper limits (Photo, p. 34, and coloured plate, p. 19). Where oakwoods are absent, frag-ments of birchwood are often the only natural woodlands remaining after the extensive de-forestation of recent centuries. The constant browsing of sheep or red deer tends to prevent their regeneration and many are derelict. These birchwoods have little in the way of a flora of their own. Rowan is the principal tree accompanying birch and there are few shrubs. The field layer of a close birchwood consists mainly of those oak-wood plants which can stand the increased alti-tude, but in loose birchwoods the field layer is generally of plants of the surrounding moorland,

Robert M. Adam

Birchwood with bracken undergrowth

such as heather, bilberry and the moorland grasses, the light shade of the scattered trees having little effect on the general vegetation. As in all woods pasturing leads to the dominance of grasses in the field layer.

Our native "Scots pine", which is really one of the commonest species of European pine, though the northern forms belong to distinct races, was a widespread dominant throughout Britain in more than one post-glacial epoch. Superseded by oak in the south pine maintained itself in great Scottish forests till most of it was destroyed by ruthless exploitation, and regeneration was largely stopped by grazing. Little remains of these once magnificent forests, but there are still a few spots in the Highlands where regeneration is still taking place.

Pine grows naturally on much the same soils as birch, and the two trees are constantly seen together, both on our southern English sandy heaths and in the Scottish Highlands, especially on sands and gravels left by the moraines of old glaciers. Pinewoods cast a deep shade and are usually very pure. The field layer is typically heathy, bilberry or cowberry being common dominants with heather on the edges and in gaps (Photos, pp. 31 and 35). There are a few plants such as species of wintergreen and certain orchids which occur only in old native pinewoods or on heaths on the sites of pinewoods that have now disappeared.

In the south of England, just as in the Highlands, pine is associated with birch, and having been extensively planted, invades heath in mass in the same way. The floor of a southern pinewood is commonly almost bare, covered only with a thick litter of pine needles which decay very slowly.

Robert M. Adam

Open pinewood with juniper and heather and a birch on the left

REFERENCES:

A more or less arbitrary selection from the very numerous books and papers dealing with British woodlands.

MARK L. ANDERSON (1932) *The Natural Woodlands of Britain and Ireland.* Oxford, Department of Forestry.

MILLER CHRISTY (1924) *The hornbeam (Carpinus betulus L.) in Britain.* Journal of Ecology, 12: 39–94.

E. A. ELLIS (1933–4) *Wheatfen Broad, Surlingham.* Transactions of the Norfolk and Norwich Naturalists' Society, Vol. 13. (Broadland alderwoods.)

J. L. HARLEY (1937) *Ecological observations on the mycorrhiza of beech.* Journal of Ecology, 25: 421–3.

C. E. MOSS (1913) *Vegetation of the Peak District.* Cambridge, University Press. (Limestone ashwoods and "siliceous" oakwoods.)

ROBERT PAULSON (1926) *The beechwood: its canopy and carpet.* Transactions of the South-east Union of Scientific Societies for 1926: 24–37. (Beechwoods on acid soil only.)

P. W. RICHARDS (1938) *The bryophyte communities of a Killarney oakwood.* Annales Bryologiques, Vol. 11: 108–30.

E. J. SALISBURY (1916–18) *The oak-hornbeam woods of Hertfordshire.* Journal of Ecology, 4: 83–120, 6: 14–52.

E. J. SALISBURY and A. G. TANSLEY (1921–22) *The Durmast oakwoods of the Silurian and Malvernian strata near Malvern.* Journal of Ecology, 9: 19–38.

A. G. TANSLEY (ed.) (1911) *Types of British Vegetation.* Cambridge, University Press.

A. G. TANSLEY (1939) *The British Islands and their Vegetation.* Cambridge, University Press.

A. G. TANSLEY (1945) *Our Heritage of Wild Nature.* Cambridge, University Press.

A. S. WATT (1919) *On the causes of failure of natural regeneration in British oakwoods.* Journal of Ecology, 7: 173–203.

A. S. WATT (1923–25) *On the ecology of British beechwoods with special reference to their regeneration.* Journal of Ecology, 11: 1–48, 12: 145–204, 13: 27–73.

A. S. WATT (1931) *Preliminary observations on Scottish beechwoods.* Journal of Ecology, 19: 137–57, 321–59.

A. S. WATT (1934) *The vegetation of the Chiltern Hills, with special reference to the beechwoods and their seral relationships.* Journal of Ecology, 22: 230–70, 445–507.

R. MELVILLE

THE BRITISH ELMS

THE majority of people in Britain probably think there is only one kind of elm in the country; or, at any rate, they do not go beyond distinguishing the Wych elm, with its large, very rough leaves, often with three points on the top, from the rest, lumped together as "elms". In reality there are eight fairly well marked species, a number of local races and a tangle of hybrids, very difficult to classify. In recent years an intensive study of our elm populations has been begun, and we are gradually coming to see how their variation, distribution, and origin may be linked together to make a coherent story.

When the ice receded after the last Ice Age, which reached its maximum about 25,000 years ago, elms were among the first trees to arrive in Britain. The common Wych elm, *Ulmus glabra*, was most likely the first comer, for it is the hardiest of them all, extending farthest north of all the elms in Europe. It is found throughout the length and breadth of Britain, and is almost the only elm planted in our woodlands. When left to itself the Wych elm, in common with other elms.

Wych Elm, U. glabra

prefers the valley bottoms. It can often be seen hugging the banks of the streams in Wales and the Welsh marches and in many a Scottish valley. The farther north one goes the more constantly does it cling to the valley bottoms and the smaller is its stature. The broad alluvial plains of the south provide the most favourable conditions for its growth. Here it makes a round-headed tree a hundred feet or more in height, with the branches splaying fountainwise from a short stocky trunk. Under the milder climate of the south, it ranges over hill and dale and interbreeds with nearly all of our native elms: the hybrids often have the habit of the Wych elm, but differ much in the shape of their leaves. The leaves of the Wych elm itself vary somewhat in shape, but they appear to do so in a regular manner. In the north and west of the country the species is represented by individuals with comparatively long, narrow, lance-shaped leaves. As one proceeds towards the south and south-east, broader and broader leaf shapes are encountered. Some of the southern individuals have leaves which, except for the tip, are almost circular in outline. The picture is by no means clear in the south, however, as there the natural distribution of the tree has been most interfered with by man.

The English elm, *U. procera*, is more familiar to the countryside of England than the Wych elm. It is found in great abundance in the south, but thins out when it reaches Yorkshire, and is probably only a planted tree in Scotland. The crown is erect and of noble proportions, gently lobed, with the trunk commonly clothed with adventitious shoots that give it the familiar mossy appearance when seen at a distance. In a quiet and unobtrusive way the English elm has entered as much into the lives of our people on land as the oak has upon the sea. The timber is used for the seats of Windsor chairs, for weather-boarding

Ulmus procera, *the English elm, planted for an avenue at Harefield, Middlesex; in late April when the new leaves are growing fast*

L. James

houses, farm carts and waggons and, in the final act, for coffin boards. Before the days of metal pipes, London's water was piped through hollowed logs of the English elm.

The failure of the English elm to produce viable seed has led to a common belief that it is not a true native, and the suggestion that it was introduced by the Romans to provide supports for vines. Recent investigation has not brought to light any evidence in favour of these ideas; on the contrary, the tree appears to be endemic. It maintains itself by vegetative methods of propagation; under favourable conditions, the far flung roots with their numerous suckers will produce a copse from a single tree within a few years. Nor is the species completely sterile, for I have, at present, several seedlings raised from seed hand-picked from the trees in 1945. The principal reason for the failure of seed to develop is the early season at which the flowers bloom. In mild winters the English elm is in flower by mid-January, and invariably pays the penalty of its precociousness when flowers or young fruits succumb to the next cold spell. Only when persistent cold weather retards flowering until about the beginning of March, and continuous mild weather follows, is there much chance of seed maturing. Apparently seeds are produced freely in warmer climates, for in 1912 Henry obtained a supply from trees growing in the gardens of the royal palace of Aranjuez in Spain, whence they had been imported from England about 150 years previously. Possibly the more Continental conditions of post-glacial times allowed the progenitors of our tree to fruit more abundantly.

Several other elm species grow in the southern half of England where they are confined to more restricted areas. The Cornish elm, *U. stricta*, stiffly erect, stands sentinel along many a Cornish hedgerow. It finds its way eastwards to the Dorset coast and is represented by local varieties in southern Hampshire and the Channel Islands.

Cornish Elm, U. stricta

In Cornwall the leaves are relatively narrow, but they increase in breadth and in the complexity of their teeth on traversing the full range of the species to the Channel Islands. The Cornish elm, therefore, exhibits a fairly regular change in leaf

Cornish Elm, U. stricta

shape from west to east in much the same way as the Wych elm does from north to south. Graded variation of this nature is not uncommon among both animals and plants. It may affect various characters such as *form* in elm leaves; *colour* of the coal-tit in which yellow pigmentation increases from the Continent across Britain to Ireland; *size*, as in the length of the leaves of cedars—

English Elm, U. procera

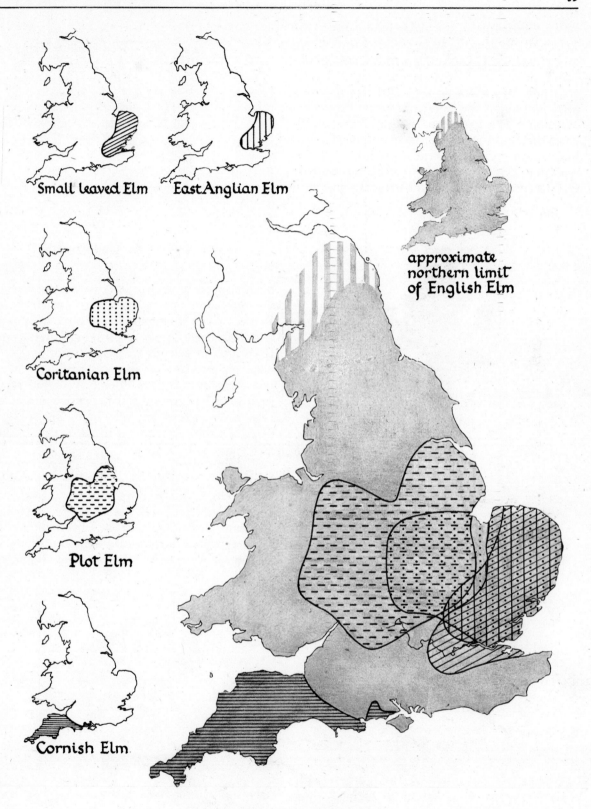

Small leaved Elm

EastAnglian Elm

Coritanian Elm

Plot Elm

Cornish Elm

approximate
northern limit
of English Elm

The Distribution of the British Elms

which increases from the Atlas mountains to the Lebanon and Himalayas; or *physiological characters*, such as vitamin C content, which increases northwards in the native rose species. Such regular gradations in a character are called clines, with a prefix to indicate the nature or relationships of the variation. The gradations in leaf shape of the elms, that are related to their geographical distribution, are referred to as topoclines. When topoclines exist they may be regarded as evidence that the species is native to the territory concerned.

East Anglian Elm, U. diversifolia

Plot Elm, U. Plotii

Another truly British elm is the Plot elm, *U. Plotii*, in old age matched by no other for character and individuality. The trunk is erect

Plot Elm, U. Plotii

and of magnificent proportions bearing at irregular intervals a few short spreading branches from which long whip-like streamers dangle. In youth

the leading shoot arches over, giving at a distance the impression of some giant green ostrich plume. Where the tree is common, as in some parts of the middle Trent valley, it is a striking feature of the landscape. It extends westwards into the Welsh marches, eastwards to the fens, and southwards into the upper Thames valley. A second small-leaved elm, as yet unnamed, shares some of the curious features of the Plot elm, but lacks its graceful habit. It is found in the lower Thames valley and East Anglia.

The richness of the elm flora increases on proceeding eastwards into East Anglia. Three other species, in addition to the Wych, English, and small-leaved elms, are found there. The East Anglian elm, *U. diversifolia*, has symmetrical leaves as well as the lop-sided foliage usual among elms, and they are borne haphazardly on different

East Anglian Elm, U. diversifolia

shoots or the same shoots. The smooth-leaved elm, *U. carpinifolia*, is a species widely distributed in Europe, but with us is confined to the eastern

Smooth-leaved Elm, U. carpinifolia

counties, except when planted. Hitherto, the third species has been confused with the smooth-leaved elm, but a formal description of it is

Smooth-leaved Elm, U. carpinifolia

to be published shortly. It is to be called the Coritanian elm after an ancient British tribe, the Coritani, that formerly inhabited part of its area of distribution. The habit of the tree is reminiscent of the smooth-leaved elm, but the smooth, bright green leaves differ markedly in shape, and are the most asymmetrical of any British elm.

With the possible exception of the English elm, the East Anglian species interbreed and their hybrid offspring are fertile and can cross again. The result is such a maze of forms as almost to defy classification, were it not for certain regularities in their distribution. There are, of course, numerous isolated hybrid trees, but notably in Essex and the adjacent parts of Hertfordshire, groups of related hybrids occupy some of the valleys, forming distinct local races. Often on passing over the brow of a hill from one valley to the next the elm population changes.

It is reasonable to assume that the local races of elm occurring in East Anglia have originated since the last Ice Age. The limit of the ice field then reached about the level of the Wash, so that it is unlikely that any elms survived. Evidence from the analysis of the tree pollens in peat deposits suggests that elms became abundant in southern England about 6000 to 7000 B.C. They must have been invaders from the Continent, coming across a land bridge where now the Channel and the North Sea stand. Much of the southern part of Britain must have been densely wooded by 6000 B.C., and in East Anglia each valley had a little community of elms that remained more or less isolated from those of neighbouring valleys. Although the pollen of elms is wind-borne, the greatest chance of pollination is from neighbouring trees. Thus by partial isolation began our local races of elm. Possibly the varieties of the Cornish elm, now restricted to Cornwall, south Hampshire and the Channel Islands, began their differentiation about this period, and completed it after isolation by water or by inhospitable sandy soils. Further study may yield more definite evidence on the fascinating question of the speed of evolution in this group of plants.

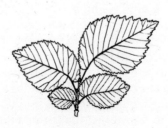

Coritanian Elm

MONICA SHORTEN

GREY SQUIRRELS IN BRITAIN

THE attention of the public has once again been called to the increase in numbers and range of the American grey squirrel (*Sciurus carolinensis*) in Great Britain. Before the war the growing menace of this introduced species had already been noticed with alarm, and a society was formed to enlist help in keeping down its numbers; with every year, however, the animal's distribution has become more widespread, and as the squirrel population becomes denser, more and more complaints of the damage done in woodland, farms, and gardens are heard.

The story of the introduction of the grey squirrel into this country is by now well known; scattered records exist from as early as 1830, but the main series of introductions began in 1889 and continued until 1929. In 1930 the first survey of their distribution was made by A. D. Middleton; this was followed up by a further survey in 1935, and another in 1937 in co-operation with B. T. Parsons. Each inquiry showed them to be spreading. The latest survey was completed in 1945 by the author, and again tells the same story. The accompanying map shows the present situation.

The Government is now lending its support to the control of the grey squirrel. Agricultural Executive Committees in the counties affected have been authorised to direct the formation of "Squirrel Clubs" which are issued with free cartridges. The return of more keepers to estates all over the country should help the scheme; and public interest aroused by numerous articles in the newspapers makes the recording of further increase in territory easier. Even if the grey squirrel cannot be exterminated it can at least be controlled.

It is to be hoped that the lesson afforded by the introduction of the rabbit into Australia, the sparrow in America, the grey squirrel in Great Britain and South Africa (to mention only a few of the many examples) has been learnt. The folly of putting down a foreign species in a country without first having considered all the possible consequences is inexcusable to-day. The spread of the grey squirrel could have been forecast with some accuracy. It is a vigorous and hardy animal, resistant to disease, versatile in food habits; in its native country it flourishes in a variety of habitats and climates, some very similar to those found in our country. At the time that the main introductions were made, the British red squirrel (*Sciurus vulgaris leucurus*) was suffering, and continued for some time to suffer, from the effects of an epidemic which greatly reduced it in numbers. The grey squirrel found a suitable habitat, especially in oak-hazel and beech woodland, showing its greater boldness by settling in open park-like habitats near houses and people as well as in the woods themselves. The habitat was poorly defended against such a sturdy and versatile newcomer. No natural predators of importance exist here that might control the numbers of the squirrel, and the degree of cultivation of the country provides the squirrel with the opportunity of robbing if the acorn or beech-mast crop is poor. Added to these factors, the squirrel was allowed to multiply in peace during the first few decades after its introduction.

It is unfortunate that so little precise information exists on the territory occupied by our native red squirrel before and just after the introduction of the grey. The present distribution has been mapped from a survey done during 1944-5; and this shows a very sparse, and possibly over-estimated population in the south and the midlands. Observers in these areas have forgotten what the red squirrel looks like, and some are known to have mistaken young brownish-hued grey squirrels for our own species. Large numbers are found only in Wales and Scotland. Sickness,

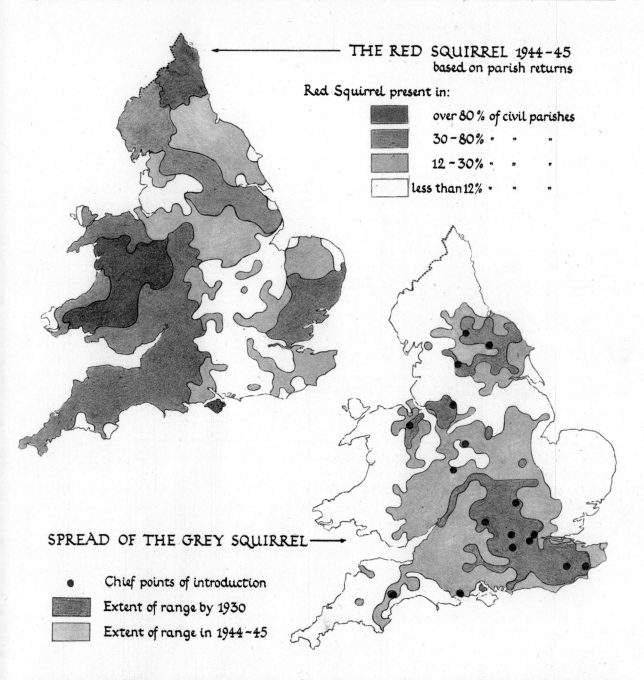

THE RED SQUIRREL 1944–45
based on parish returns

Red Squirrel present in:

over 80 % of civil parishes
30–80 % " " "
12–30 % " " "
less than 12 % " " "

SPREAD OF THE GREY SQUIRREL →

• Chief points of introduction
Extent of range by 1930
Extent of range in 1944–45

and large-scale felling which deprives them of food, cover, and nesting sites, undoubtedly contributed to the decline of the red squirrel. This decline has been recorded from places where the grey squirrel has never been seen; it would be unwise, therefore, to lay all the blame on the grey, so insultingly misnamed, "tree-rat".

The most obvious signs of grey squirrels in a winter woodland are the large round dreys built in the forks of the trees. These winter dreys are usually over a foot in diameter, and although their appearance from the outside may be rather rough and untidy, they are well constructed, and remain dry and clean inside throughout their occupation. The outer shell is made with twigs cut while the leaves are still on (unlike the dreys of the red

squirrel, where leafless twigs are used); this material is usually taken from the nest tree, but not always. The lining is made with grass, dry leaves, dead moss, bracken, and sometimes sheeps' wool. The drey rarely has an entrance that is easily seen; it seems that the squirrel builds loosely at the top of the drey near the trunk of the tree, and that the "door" is closed again after each entry. These dreys may be found 20-50 feet above the ground; but have been found as low as 8 feet and as high as 80 feet; they may be used for four or five years, with occasional re-buildings. Sometimes three or four juvenile squirrels are found occupying an old winter nest together; it is probable that the litter keeps together after leaving the parents, and its members take over an old drey sooner than build a new one for the first winter.

Another type of drey is used in the summer; this is made with green leafy twigs, and is not as solid and round in shape as the winter nest. It is usually found out on a limb, not close to the trunk of the tree. Several of these "bowers" may be built and used in a summer, for the need to escape from fleas and lice will often arise.

If grey squirrels only lived in dreys their extermination would perhaps be possible. Unfortunately the grey squirrel also makes use of hollow trees to nest in, and often enlarges and takes over old woodpecker holes. Holes caused by the rotting of the tree where a branch has snapped off are maintained by constant gnawing of the scar-tissue, and an entrance of about three inches in diameter, greasy and muddy round the edges, tells of squirrel occupation. Once a squirrel has reached the safety of such a shelter, there is little the hunter can do. Rabbit holes, too, are used as temporary shelter from pursuit. Many a squirrel hunter gets the impression that his quarry carries a map in his head of all the rabbit buries in the area; the squirrel will cross rapidly from tree to tree until suddenly it drops quickly to the ground and vanishes. A brief search at this point almost invariably reveals rabbit holes. If the squirrel has been wounded, a visitor to the holes in a day's time will often discover the squirrel dead in the mouth of the hole.

It is possible to detect the presence of grey squirrels in a woodland quite apart from the dreys. An inspection of the young sycamore

John Markham

A grey squirrel's winter drey in a Hertfordshire wood

trees within reach of the grey squirrel will often show them to have been stripped of the bark for several feet—sometimes many branches are stripped, all on one side only; but sometimes the damage extends right round the branch, which dies as a consequence. Beeches, maples, and willows are attacked in a similar way. Several theories exist as to why the squirrel does this; the attack is usually made between April and August, and squirrels have been seen licking the sap and eating the inner bark; perhaps this is done when there is a drought and the springs and pools are dry; perhaps the bark is taken for the vitamins and drugs contained in it. The bark of Scots pine is taken for nesting material in some areas. Where there are oak, ash, walnut, and chestnut trees between the age of eight and twenty years, these, too, may be barked. Leaders of young spruce and larch are sometimes found cut off by the squirrel, also the young green buds of sycamore

The grey squirrel, Sciurus carolinensis, *one of many man-made additions to the British fauna*

John Markham

trees. In a wanton way the animal cuts far more material than it bothers to eat.

The grey squirrel has two breeding seasons in the year; the first and main season is from January to early April, the second from June to August. It is not yet known what percentage of the females have two litters in a year, but the figure is probably low. Young born in the spring breed for the first time the following spring, and the summer young in the next summer breeding season. The average number of young per litter varies from year to year; in 1930, Middleton reported a figure of 4·2, in 1945 the figure for the area round Oxford was three, with very few records exceeding this average; in 1946, two was the average number, although a few cases of four and five young were recorded. No cases of more than five young being found in a litter have been reported in this country, although in America six have been found at a time. Single young are not uncommon.

After a gestation period of 30-40 days, the young are born blind and naked. At this early stage they already have a piercing call, and can be heard at once if the drey is disturbed. They measure about four inches from nose to tail tip. At about 33 days their eyes open; by this time their entire body is covered with hair, and their tail bears a coat of very silvery hairs 4 mm. or so in length. The young begin to venture outside the drey when seven or eight weeks old, but are still suckled by the mother, although they also chew bark and buds. Young squirrels weighing 280 g. (at birth they weigh about 17 g.) taken in May were found to have some milk in the stomach. The weight of a mature grey squirrel may be anything between 500 and 700 g. The length of life in the wild state is probably anything up to six years; in captivity it may be as much as fourteen.

It is probable that the young of a litter stay together until they are sexually mature; whether they are driven out by the parents and take over an unoccupied drey, or whether the parents themselves move, is still uncertain. Cases of whole families occupying the same drey throughout the summer and autumn have been reported.

Grey squirrels do not hibernate during the winter. During very wet or windy weather they may stay in the drey for twenty-four hours; but it is doubtful whether this time is ever greatly exceeded. Even when there is snow on the ground grey squirrels may be seen foraging for food; for, contrary to the beliefs of many, no hoard of food is laid up in drey or hollow tree to last through the winter. The squirrel certainly buries nuts and other items of food; but almost always singly, and near the place where the food is found. This burying activity is most amusing to watch; the squirrel will run round nosing the ground with the nut in its mouth, apparently searching for a satisfactory burial place. Sometimes it will start to dig, then pause, pick up the food again, and move off to search for another place. Eventually it will settle down to dig, the food held in its mouth, scooping away leaves and earth to a depth of about an inch with both front paws. The food is then vigorously pushed down into the hole with its mouth, and the squirrel sits back on its haunches and gathers together loose earth and leaves which it drags over the hole and pats down with both paws. Then it returns to fetch other food, and the procedure is repeated at another spot.

The recovery of these buried stores appears to be largely a matter of scent. The squirrel at first remembers clearly where it has put the food, for on the arrival of another squirrel it will rush to the burial place and pat down the surface, making threatening noises and giving every appearance of agitation. After a longer period it is likely that the general position of the burial ground is remembered, and squirrels may be seen moving slowly about the area, nose to ground, before they start digging. If they are disturbed, the place where they have started to scoop is in most cases found to be very near to, or directly over, a buried nut. In the autumn, when there is plenty of food about, burying activity is very marked; and the squirrels appear to be in a state of great excitement. I have seen a squirrel so disturbed by the presence of another near by at this time, that it dug up a recently buried nut and chased the other with it in its mouth, growling and attempting to pounce at it. Only when it was again alone did it re-bury the nut.

REFERENCES:

MONICA SHORTEN (1946) *A Survey of the Distribution of the American Grey Squirrel and the British Red Squirrel in England and Wales in 1944-45.* Journal of Animal Ecology, 15: 82-92.

A. D. MIDDLETON (1930) *The Ecology of the American Grey Squirrel in the British Isles.* Proc. Zool. Soc., London. 809-43.

E. B. FORD

WOODLAND BUTTERFLIES

S. Beaufoy

The Hedge Brown

L. H. Newman

The Wood White

S. Beaufoy

The White Admiral

LESS than two dozen species of butterflies inhabit the woods and forests of Britain, yet this small group shows great diversity in the structure, life-histories, and habits of its members. Their geographical distribution is extremely unequal, and many of them are absent from districts to which, superficially, they appear well suited. Woodland is not sharply separated from other types of country, and some of the insects adapted to it can extend their range into neighbouring thickets and along tree-lined roadsides. Moreover, several of the typical butterflies of our hedgerows, such as the Hedge Brown, *Maniola tithonus*, have colonised this artificial habitat from the rather similar conditions provided by the sunny fringes of woods, which are their true home; while they may also make their way into the more open glades, so penetrating far into the forest.

Woodland butterflies therefore do not form a well-defined group, for some rarely venture into the open countryside, while others may often be found there. Here in Britain only one species is adapted to spend its whole life under a thick canopy of trees. This is the Wood White, *Leptidea sinapis*, which in its restricted haunts may be seen making its way with weak yet persistent flight through dense undergrowth, generally ignoring the sunny pathways and clearings which it may chance to cross. Though it belongs to the great family Pieridae, which contains the ordinary Cabbage Whites and "Yellows", such as the Brimstone, it is a member of a peculiar section of that group, the subfamily Dismorphiinae, which is almost entirely restricted to Central and South America. Only three out of the 101 known species occur elsewhere, and here in England we have this one representative of them. The Wood White is also widespread in Europe and Asia. The structure of the Dismorphiinae, for example the arrangement of the nervures or struts which

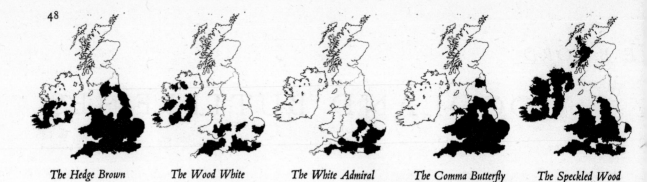

The Hedge Brown   The Wood White   The White Admiral   The Comma Butterfly   The Speckled Wood

support the wings, is highly characteristic, so that the true affinities of the Wood White were suspected long ago. Yet independent evidence on its classification has lately been obtained from a study of its chemistry. The white and yellow colours of all the Pieridae are built up from uric acid, produced by the insects themselves; but in the Dismorphiinae alone, flavones are also present in a number of the species. These are plant pigments, never manufactured by animals, and are absorbed by the caterpillars with their food. They contain no nitrogen and are responsible for flower colours ranging from ivory to deep yellow. The presence of flavone pigment in the Wood White has now been established, so confirming its inclusion among the Dismorphiinae, a group so remote from the rest of our fauna. The butterfly is restricted to scattered localities in the southern Midlands and the south of England. Formerly it occurred in Cumberland and Westmorland, but it is now extinct there. Indeed, thirty years ago this insect had vanished from many of its former haunts, but for a considerable time past it has continued to spread and extend its range once more.

Here we are faced with a remarkable situation. Not only the Wood White, but a number of other woodland butterflies have become steadily commoner during the last quarter of a century, and have greatly increased their range. Three other species may be specially mentioned in this connection.

Up to the middle of last century, the beautiful White Admiral, *Limenitis camilla*, was abundant in many of the woods of southern England. Gradually it became more localised, until restricted to the New Forest and a few isolated woodlands in the neighbouring counties and in Suffolk, from which, however, it has once more spread extensively. The Comma butterfly,

S. Beaufoy

The Comma Butterfly

S. Beaufoy

The Speckled Wood

S. Beaufoy

The Large Tortoiseshell

49

The Scotch Argus   The Chequered Skipper   The Purple Hairstreak   The White-letter Hairstreak   The Purple Emperor

The Purple Hairstreak   S. Beaufoy

The Purple Emperor   S. Beaufoy

Polygonia c-album, which somewhat resembles the familiar Small Tortoiseshell, but has a deeply indented margin and a white comma-like mark on the lower surface, has a comparable history. It gradually became localised to the Gloucester, Hereford, and Monmouth area, from which it has now spread throughout the Midlands and south of England. The insect is one which strays far outside woods, maintaining itself along hedge-rows and in gardens, where it feeds on nettle, hop, or currant, though woodland is certainly its original home. The Speckled Wood, *Pararge aegeria*, never became as localised as the species just mentioned, but in England its range was reduced to the south-western counties and a few other scattered localities, from which it has now spread extensively. This is one of our few butter-flies which prefer shade to sun, and it may be found along wooded lanes and hedgerows as well as in the depths of the forest.

These and other species all became gradually more restricted in range during the latter half of last century, but have spread once more during and after the First World War. Yet there has been everything to discourage them from doing so. The very time that these woodland butterflies have been increasing their range coincides with the most rapid destruction to which our forests have ever been exposed, and with a policy of planting little but conifers which is disastrous to the wild life of our islands. Some powerful over-riding influence must dictate such curious changes in distribution. Indeed, a study of Scandinavian glaciers has lately demonstrated a cycle of exten-sion and retreat of the ice roughly corresponding with the fluctuations in the distribution of these butterflies. It probably indicates widespread climatic trends, detectable only by special means, to which they have responded.

Moreover, the climatic changes of the past, as

well as of the present, have left their mark upon the insects of these islands. During the last glacial period, the fourth of the "Great Ice Age", various northern or alpine forms were able to spread into Britain, and these cannot now survive in the climate of southern England. One such species, the Scotch Argus, *Erebia aethiops*, though a grass feeder, is only to be seen among scattered trees or along the sunny edges of woods or glades, It is found no farther south than northern England, where it is exceedingly local, but it becomes progressively commoner through Scotland and is abundant in the Highlands. There, too, we meet with isolated colonies of several species, familiar in southern England, which were cut off in a few favoured localities during the last ice age, where they had survived since the previous warm interglacial period. Thus the Speckled Wood, which disappears north of the Mersey and Humber, except for a small colony in Westmorland, is to be met with again in Argyll and Inverness. Also the little Chequered Skipper, *Carterocephalus palaemon*, occurs in England only from Northamptonshire to Lincolnshire; but it exists also in western Inverness where, in isolation, it has evolved into a slightly different race. It is an active insect, delighting in bright sunshine, but never found outside woodland rides, where it flies among the grasses which its caterpillars eat.

Indeed it is curious that so many woodland butterflies feed upon low-growing plants, or else on bushes, such as sallow or sloe. In fact only three normally feed on trees: the Purple Hairstreak, *Thecla quercus*, upon oak, and the White-

letter Hairstreak, *Strymonidia w-album*, and the Large Tortoiseshell, *Nymphalis polychloros*, upon elm. All butterflies must pass the winter in a quiescent state. This may occur in any one of their stages: egg, caterpillar, chrysalis, or perfect insect. Two of the species which hibernate as caterpillars have to make special provision for their winter sleep. These are the White Admiral and the Purple Emperor, *Apatura iris*, which feed respectively on honeysuckle and sallow. Both spend the winter on a leaf, which they are careful to bind to the stem with silk so that it shall not fall in autumn; a notable instance of adaptation.

Though some of our woodland butterflies are common, others are local or rare, and we may well fear for their continued existence. Nor should we be lulled into a false sense of their security by considering that certain species are getting commoner to-day; for this is probably a cyclic phenomenon, and they will become rare again. The chief menace which they will have to face is the destruction of forests and the disastrous replacement of deciduous trees by conifers. Only in a few special instances are the activities of collectors a source of danger to the butterflies of Britain.

REFERENCES:

E. B. FORD (1946) *Butterflies* (2nd impr.) The New Naturalist, London, Collins.

F. W. FROHAWK (1934) *The Complete Book of British Butterflies*. London, Ward Lock & Co.

R. SOUTH (1941) *The Butterflies of the British Isles* (3rd edition). London, Frederick Warne.

THE LONG-TAILED FIELD-MOUSE

The long-tailed field-mouse, or wood-mouse, Apodemus sylvaticus, *is the most successful British rodent. It is found from gardens to mountain-tops, from Kent to St. Kilda, from Cornwall to Shetland. It is the only mouse of Ireland, besides the house-mouse.*

It lives in most habitats; for instance, it is the commonest rodent of woodland; is found frequently (with house-mice) in corn-stacks, (with short-tailed voles) on grassland and moor and (with bank voles) on islands and in gardens. It often invades houses in the autumn. In Shetland and the Hebrides large, dark, long-tailed Apodemus *are found which are thought by some to be of the same species, and by others relics of some previous* Apodemus *which escaped the Ice Age in those regions. In England another large* Apodemus *is found, A.* flavicollis, *the yellow-necked mouse, which overlaps altogether with the range of* A. sylvaticus.

The wood-mouse, Apodemus sylvaticus; *a highly successful and adaptable rodent, common in British woodlands, and in other habitats*

John Markham

PHILIP E. BROWN

WOODLAND TITS

THE family Paridae, the family of the tits, is a very successful group of small, bold, adaptable birds which is found almost the world over. In Britain three genera of this family are represented: *Parus*, by the great tit, blue tit, coal-tit, crested tit, marsh-tit and willow-tit; *Aegithalos* by the long-tailed tit; and *Panurus* by the bearded tit.

Few of our birds are better known than some of the tits since, though small, they are conspicuous in colour and behaviour; and, though probably of woodland origin, they are not now by any means confined to woods. A good number can be seen in gardens, even in the suburbs of large towns; five species have been recorded in Inner London. It is easy to attract great and blue tits to a garden bird-table and also, in suitable localities, the marsh- and coal-tits; and they will readily breed in suitable nest-boxes. Great and blue tits are among the very few birds capable of solving a problem like that of getting at a lump of fat suspended on a piece of string. This some of them will do by hauling up a length of the string with their beaks, standing on the slack with one of their feet, hauling up another length and so on until they gain the prize. Perhaps the tits stand rather high in the scale of avian intelligence, which may possibly account for the way in which some of them have quickly learnt the trick of pecking a hole in the cardboard disc on a milk-bottle and sipping up the cream.

Within thirty feet of where I am writing this in my Hampshire home there are three different species of tits, all incubating eggs. A blue tit is sitting in the wall of the house where a conveniently loose brick six inches from the ground has provided the ideal home. Near by in an elm a great tit occupies a box eight feet above ground, and some thirty-five feet up a hole in the same tree shelters a marsh-tit (an abnormally high site and a relatively uncommon kind of tree to select). The blue tits

originally prepared to nest in the box, and had in fact placed lumps of moss in it over the course of several days, when the great tit decided to take it over (apparently without any real opposition) causing the smaller birds to go elsewhere. The great tits took about ten days to complete the nest, and during this period the hen roosted in the box every night, often entering it for the last time more than an hour before sunset. Usually the cock bird will roost in the box with the hen during nest-building, but this was not so in this case as the cock regularly spent the night under the roof of a shed some twelve feet away.

The great tit is "dominant" over the blue tit, as may be often seen at the bird-table as well as in this matter of commandeering nest-boxes. The smaller bird appears to give way without making any real demur. At least one case is on record, however, where a hen blue and a hen great tit both nested in the same box, showing no hostility to each other, and both successfully bringing off their broods.

Sometimes a blue tit will lay one or more eggs in a nest before it is usurped by a pair of great tits. The hen of the new pair of owners then lays her own clutch, incubating these together with the blue tit's, and finally rearing a mixed family. I once had an instance of a pair of coal-tits being ousted from a nest-box after laying the first egg. The blue tits which took over successfully reared one young coal-tit in their family of nine.

Some very interesting results have been obtained by Hugh Kenrick and others from systematic colour-ringing of tits in a comparatively small area such as a large garden. Colour-ringing makes it possible to recognise each individual bird not only at the nest-box but elsewhere and at other seasons of the year. Working in a comparatively small area Kenrick found that of his blue tits three-eighths were resident all the year round,

Eric Hosking

Willow-tit, nesting in alder, Norfolk. Owing to its like-ness to the marsh-tit the status of this species in Britain is still somewhat obscure

Eric Hosking

Marsh-tit. Its glossy head distinguishes it from the willow-tit, whose head, as the photograph shows, is matt

Eric Hosking

Great tit: a common species which feeds on the ground more than other tits, nesting in a Suffolk wood

John Markham

Blue tit: the commonest and most widespread of the British tits, a tree-top species for most of the day

one-eighth were present only in the summer, one-quarter winter-residents and one-quarter winter-transients. He also found that while some pairs mated together in successive years, others had different partners in different years. Of course it must be borne in mind that the life of a blue tit is short, and some pairs must inevitably be broken up by the death of one partner. The evidence obtained from ringed birds shows that very few survive for five years, and the average life of a tit is not more than a year or two.

Generally speaking, the various species of tits are separated ecologically: that is, they *tend* to be restricted to different habitats. This applies even to the great and blue tits, which may appear on superficial observation to overlap completely with one another. The great tit is more a bird of the hedgerows, gardens, and orchards than is the blue tit, especially outside the breeding season, when the latter bird seems to favour woods and copses. Even where the two species are in woodland together, the great tit tends to keep lower down than the blue. In North Hampshire I have for several winters past made counts of a large number of tit flocks, and the following table will give some idea of the part which the environment plays. For each of the habitats it is assumed that there are ten blue tits in the flock, the figures for the other species showing the relative numbers in which, on the average, they occur. The sign " <1 " (less than 1) shows that the species occurs but in very small numbers.

Eric Hosking

In the ancient relict pine-forest of the Spey Valley, and in a few other parts of the Scottish Highlands, is found the crested tit. It remains confined to its old haunts, and to neighbouring conifer plantations

anything approaching the proportion of the blue, probably because of all five species it least exhibits the tendency to flock. The marsh-tit only approaches the numbers of the blue tit in oak-

HABITAT	BLUE TIT	LONG-TAILED TIT	GREAT TIT	COAL-TIT	MARSH-TIT
Hedgerows, gardens, and orchards ..	10	9	4	1	2
Pure oak woods	10	13	3	2	7
Mixed "broad-leaved" and "narrow-leaved" woods	10	11	2	8	3
Pure "narrow-leaved" woods	10	10	1	30	<1

It will be evident at a glance that the coal-tit is very greatly affected by the presence or absence of narrow-leaved trees, and it is easily the dominant bird in the conifer woods, constituting sixty per cent of the flocks. The great tit is never present in woods, and is very casual in the conifer woods. In all four habitats the blue tit and the long-tailed tit occur in remarkably even proportions, but they occupy different strata, the long-tails tending to feed in the lower secondary growth.

Counts next winter may show some marked differences. It may be premature to say that the great and blue tits have not been affected very badly by the severe weather early in 1947. There is, however, no doubt that many long-tailed tits have died. Fortunately, like most other tits, they lay a large clutch of eggs, averaging eight or nine, and their powers of recovery are considerable. The crested tit—the rarest of our tits—is confined to the Spey valley area of Scotland. The severe weather of last winter has probably affected this bird also, but the greatest threat to its status may be the felling of timber, which has been going on in that area on a large scale. Nevertheless, the species has recently spread in some directions.

Flocks of tits are rarely met with from March to June; they are usually very small, though often of mixed species and are probably non-breeders. Family-parties of eight to twelve long-tailed tits are frequent in late May and June, for this species

nests earlier than the others. Mixed flocks may be met with from July onwards and they increase in numbers until November and December, when flocks of over 100 birds are not uncommon. This has been clearly shown by some forty observers, widely scattered over the country, who sent me a great number of flock-counts. At the turn of the year flocks tend to break up, presumably as the members seek territories in which they will afterwards breed. Probably most members of these flocks are young birds of the year, for most of the old birds appear to retain their territories all the year round and do not wander far. This may be one reason why the size of a flock varies in very short intervals of time. Certainly the winter flocks disintegrate late in the afternoon, small parties of the birds seeking their own particular roosts. Most of the tits go to bed at sundown, and they do not usually emerge until sunrise or a few minutes after.

Long-tailed tit at its round, covered nest in a mixed Suffolk hedgerow

Eric Hosking

M. K. COLQUHOUN

WOODLAND
BIRD COMMUNITIES

CERTAIN soils, such as the very heavy clays of Sussex and Kent, are not suitable for ordinary cultivation, yet an orchard or woodland may flourish. The reason for this is largely mechanical. The stiff clays can only be worked for a few days in the year, even by the heaviest machinery, and unless the organic manures and vegetation are covered they cannot decompose into the humus which is so essential to plant life. Woodlands are of course not usually cultivated by man, but their requirements of carbon, hydrogen, and nitrogen have to be met if they are to survive, and they are in fact met from the decaying vegetation of the woodland floor. The work of decomposition is largely carried out by the smaller animals, who utilise the leaves and other waste vegetation, and whose mobility enables them to keep the soil friable and porous with more effect than any machine stirring the soil occasionally.

The fauna of the woodland floor is of greater importance than is generally realised. From counts in a square metre it can be estimated that there are up to 40 million Acarina (mites) and 28 million Collembola (springtails) per acre in a beech wood. Nearly all these mites and all the springtails live on decaying organic matter, and play an important part in establishing and maintaining the wood. In addition, there are of course the earthworms, whose numbers are less spectacular, but whose relatively large size makes them the most important animals in the wood. The link between soil and vegetation filled by worms, now known to all, was first stated concisely by Gilbert White, a century before Darwin published his work.

As the wood was able to develop by reason of the animal life in the soil, which in its turn obtained its food from the discarded vegetation of the wood, a new habitat was formed for other animals. Insects particularly, with their need for

humidity, fitted well into the forest environment, a fact which has aided the evolution of many species. Looking back with the wisdom of man, vertebrate flight seems inevitable, whether it was to escape the climbing predators or whether it was to take advantage of the food supply offered by the countless insects which swarmed on the vegetation and in the air.

Thus, most woodland birds are insectivorous. In the tropical rain forests trees and shrubs are able to flower or fruit throughout the year, and the proportion of fruit- and seed-eating birds is higher than in Britain. In Britain some species avoid the winter altogether by migration, while others become necessarily omnivorous in order to survive a season in which insect life is dormant. To the human eye, the amount of insect life available in summer, even allowing for the needs of the nestlings, is out of all proportion to that available in winter, when it is noticeable that the majority of species are searching for food throughout the hours of daylight. As invertebrate life withdraws from the winter, presenting as small a surface area as possible to the lower temperatures, the lack of insect bulk must be partly responsible for the ceaseless searching indulged in by some species. It is noticeable that the blackbird, who, in mild weather, is able to drag bulky and nutritious earthworms from the ground, appears to have more spare time for preening, fighting, or even singing, than the blue tit who is constantly eating something—presumably insect eggs—invisible to man.

For the blue tit does not eat earthworms. As the first birds became adapted for flight, which happened (it is assumed) in the forests, new species began to branch out in various directions, and adaptation and specialisation began. Insects had taken to the air and birds, too, began to feed in flight. Those birds that remained in the forests developed in different ways; just as each

The stock-dove, here seen at a nesting-hole in Yorkshire, is a bird of old woodland or parkland, abundant in central and southern England and Wales
T. M. Fowler

Eric Hosking

The blackbird is probably the most abundant land-bird in Britain, and a typical member of the woodland bird community

Eric Hosking

A wren's nest in a holly tree: the wren is a dominant bird in the shrub layer of British woodland

individual in a class of school children has its own character, so each species has its own adaptations. Moreover, just as competitive selection rules the school examinations so also it rules the habits and adaptations of birds; and natural selection must be keen in a British deciduous wood during the winter months.

Some of these adaptations are obvious. The woodpecker, primarily a specialist, can hammer away at a stout tree, in order to reach the wood-boring insects, without any ill-effects to itself, its tail being used as a limb to support the weight of its body. This seems a tedious and laborious way of feeding compared with that of the blackbird, but the latter's sensitive bill has its limitations. A hard frost makes the ground impenetrable, and only a meagre supply of soft berries remain between the blackbird and starvation, while the woodpecker is still successfully tapping its way round the wood. Mortality of the blackbird can be very high in prolonged hard weather, but the woodpeckers, or, at least, the spotted woodpeckers, do not appear to suffer to any appreciable extent. The green woodpecker *did* suffer considerably in the terrible weather of February 1947; this species depends as much on ground-living ants as on tree-trunk insects, and the ant-hills were frozen so stiff that even the woodpecker's bill could not penetrate them.

Specialisation, of course, has its limitations. The tree-creeper feeds on the bark fauna, and its bill has gradually become curved and slender so that it can reach insects hiding in the crevices. The bird works upward, flying first to the base of a tree and then running up the bole in a spiral movement, searching for insects as it goes; it then flies to the base of another tree and begins again, so working its way through the wood. I remember

Eric Hosking

Eric Hosking

Green woodpecker: this bird has excavated its hole in an elm in a hedge. Green woodpeckers are common in woodland, but also in parkland and open country

Great spotted woodpecker at its nesting-hole in a silver birch. This species is probably the most woodland-living of the woodpeckers

The trunk climbers: all these birds are adapted for vertical bark-climbing. All have sharp claws, and bristly tails

Eric Hosking

Eric Hosking

Lesser spotted woodpecker. This small woodland and parkland species excavates holes for its nest—this one is in a greengage tree in an orchard

Tree-creeper. The creeper is a universal British woodland bird; it nests in cracks or behind loose bark, and does not excavate a hole

which are used as props. The woodpeckers are shown approximately half size, the creeper just over two-thirds

noticing a swarm of flies dancing in the spring sunshine a foot or two from a large oak. An ascending tree-creeper also saw them, put its head back and was just able to reach the nearest fly; it then climbed the tree for a few more yards, before flying down to the base of the same tree and repeating the manœuvre. It carried out these movements some half-dozen times, expending more energy on feeding than would be provided by the food it had caught. A swallow would have fed on this swarm by flying through it at great speed; a flycatcher would select the most convenient perch and make little sorties into the dancing flies. The last method would appear to be the most sensible, but the flycatcher, as its English name reveals, is a specialist. It, too, has its limitations, for it is not able to find the food on which the tree-creeper lives through the winter, so that when the adult flies are no longer hovering in the sunshine it migrates to a warmer country.

Occasionally a species can take a short cut without having to climb the long evolutionary ladder, although the highly developed specialist is often living dangerously near to extinction, since it may not be able to adapt itself to a sudden change in the environment. The bills of the green and the great spotted woodpecker are similar; during thousands of years they have become adapted for feeding on wood-boring insects. Yet the green woodpecker now uses this bill for digging at ant hillocks, and a large proportion of its food consists of ants. There is also a difference in habitat, which may have preceded the change in feeding, the green woodpecker being found more in parkland, or even open country, while the great spotted woodpecker inhabits the denser woods. It would probably be disadvantageous for the bird to become entirely dependent on ants, since, as we have seen, it suffers severely when the ground becomes frost-bound. On the other hand the great spotted woodpecker will have to adjust itself to changes brought about by a developing forestry in Britain.

Just as the bole and branches are explored by the woodpeckers and tree-creepers, the twigs, stalks, and leaves are searched by the various tits and species like the chaffinch, which come in to breed when leaves are present and food is abundant. The nuthatch is not included with the woodpeckers because its food is not the same, as is

revealed by its name derived either from the English "hack" or the French "hacher" (as in "cross-hatch"). The acorn or hazel is carried to a crevice which is used as a vice during the subsequent hammering. Among the seed-eaters the crossbill is an obvious specialist, its chief food being pine and larch cones in coniferous woods: the hawfinch is adapted for feeding on kernels and seeds. Finally there developed the birds which prey on other birds as well as on the small mammals on the woodland floor; these are the diurnal hawks and the nocturnal owls. Both of these have curved beaks for tearing at flesh, but while the hawks have developed a swift flight for hunting their prey, the owls have developed in the opposite direction, a loose soft plumage making their flight slow and silent so that they can approach unnoticed a sleeping or slow-moving prey.

Every part of the wood is therefore "covered" by one or more species of bird, just as the soil itself is covered by the wood. It is useful to think of a bird fauna as a unit, just as the parts of an oak make one whole; this makes it easier to recognise that if anything happens to one species others may be affected. The oak leaf is completely unlike the bole of the oak, but if the leaves are frosted the growth of the trunk is slowed. The analogy may, of course, be carried further, for the caterpillar, which (when in sufficient numbers) has the power to defoliate the tree, is in that sense a part of it and therefore so also is the bird which feeds on the caterpillar. A bird is part of a *community* of living things which live in the same habitat, and which are, to a greater or lesser degree, interrelated.

Because all species of birds do not have *obvious* adaptations it would be unwise to assume that none exists. While the crossbill has been developing its extraordinary beak, and the owl its silent flight, there has been ample time for each species in the community to develop in an individual direction. Before searching for the less obvious adaptations it is desirable to recognise clearly the composition of the community of which the species are a part. The writer and a colleague have suggested that in the ordinary British deciduous woodland there are three bird communities, consisting of those birds which roost or nest in a wood but feed outside, those

A pair of jays at their nest in a mixed wood in Norfolk. The female greets the arrival of the male by raising her crest

Eric Hosking

Eric Hosking

Long-eared owl in a Norfolk wood

which feed in the trees and shrubs, and those which feed on the ground. Examples of the first are the rook and wood-pigeon; of the second, all the tits, the spotted woodpeckers, and most of the migrants; and of the third, the thrush, blackbird, and, if the herbage is to be included with the ground, the wren. These distinctions are perhaps obvious, but need postulating; in the present state of ecological knowledge it would be quite impossible to define woodland bird communities more accurately. As it is, overlap occurs, as it does in all nature: even the flycatcher has been known to eat earthworms.

The number of species sheltering in a wood and feeding outside is small. It is obvious that the trees and shrubs produce more potential food than the ground and herbage, and the tree and shrub community therefore contains more species and more individuals than the other. The exact

number will depend on the type of wood; the presence of dense shrubs and nesting holes or boxes will encourage a high population of birds, and this highly varied habitat will also produce the maximum number of adaptations within a single community. The range of the habitat extends from the frailest twig to the largest bole, from a windswept leaf fifty feet above the ground to the humid leaf which hangs motionless above the herbage. Neither insects nor birds are distributed evenly throughout this space, although this is a subject on which very little is known as yet. By dividing a few woods into estimated vertical zones and recording the birds feeding in each, the writer has been able to show that different species in the community have different vertical distributions which, in spite of overlap, are fixed in the species, since they occur both in winter and summer and in varying woods. An easily observed example of this vertical distribution is that of the wren, a member of the ground community, which is never seen high up in a wood. The differences between the tree and shrub community are not so easy to perceive by ordinary observation, although one would expect to find the chiffchaff at a higher level than the willow-warbler. By simple statistics, however, it is possible to discover the relative vertical distribution of each species; this can be done either by recording all the individuals seen in the zones, or by estimating the height above the woodland floor of every bird seen feeding, finally taking an average for each species. The vertical distributions and relative abundance of four species are shown in the diagram, illustrating figures collected in an Oxfordshire wood. It will be seen that there is normally little overlap between the upper canopy community, represented by the wood-pigeon, and the ground community, represented by the wren; birds of the tree and shrub community feed in the intervening zone. The abundance of each species is in direct proportion to the size of its feeding habitat, being greatest in the wood-pigeon, which feeds over hundreds of acres, and least in the wren, feeding in the herbage.

This figure shows what can be confirmed by any naturalist in an hour or two, that the blue tit inhabits a higher level of the wood than the great tit; the first is, in fact, primarily a tree species and the second a shrub species. It is interesting to examine the two birds in the light of this knowledge. The blue tit is very light and extremely quick and agile, with a delicate bill; the great tit is (for a tit) relatively ponderous, with a stout bill. Here is another instance of adaptation, rather less obvious in character than some already described; the small species is suited for feeding in the constantly swaying trees, and the larger for the more sheltered shrubs, where seeds and berries are frequently found. To break down the community into its component parts, and to recognise the ruling adaptations of its members, is an occupation full of interest, and is certainly as instructive as the pursuit of the individual species.

It was natural that the blackbird and other species of the ground community should come into the woods, because the soil fauna is there very much greater and more varied than outside. It must be remembered that this fauna is not

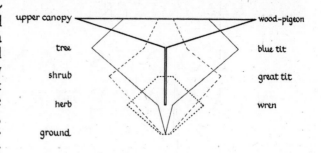

Showing vertical distribution (vertical scale) and relative abundance (horizontal scale) of four species common in oakwoods

spread uniformly over the woodland floor—it too inhabits vertical zones, just as much as the birds. In the leaf layer the mites predominate, in the loose humus the springtails are most abundant, while the topsoil and unstirred mineral soil has (like the bird community in the tree-tops) but few species. Only the ubiquitous earthworm, which may perhaps be likened to the squirrel, passes easily from one zone in the soil to another in response to conditions of drought, frost, or rainfall.

REFERENCES:

M. K. COLQUHOUN AND AVERIL MORLEY (1943) *Vertical Zonation in Woodland Bird Communities.* Journal of Animal Ecology, 12: 75-81.

M. K. COLQUHOUN (1940) *The Density of Woodland Birds determined by the Sample Count Method.* J. Anim. Ecol. 9: 53-67.

M. K. COLQUHOUN (1941) *Visual and Auditory Conspicuousness in a Woodland Bird Community: a quantitative analysis.* Proc. Zool. Soc. Lond. Ser. A, 110: 129-48.

M. K. COLQUHOUN (1942) *Notes on the Social Behaviour of Blue Tits.* Brit. Birds, 35: 234-40.

D. LACK AND L. S. V. VENABLES (1939) *The Habitat Distribution of British Woodland Birds.* J. Anim. Ecol. 8: 39-71.

C. ELTON (1935) *A Reconnaissance of Woodland Bird Communities in England and Wales.* J. Anim. Ecol. 4: 127-36.

D. LACK (1933) *Habitat Selection in Birds: with special reference to the effects of afforestation on the Breckland avifauna.* J. Anim. Ecol. 2: 239-62.

D. LACK (1939) *Further Changes in the Breckland Avifauna caused by Afforestation.* J. Anim. Ecol. 8: 277-85.

STEPHEN POTTER

BOOKS AND THE AMATEUR NATURALIST

THE editor of the NEW NATURALIST MAGAZINE has asked me a question. As an amateur naturalist do I consider that, so far as the literature of natural history is concerned, the amateur is well provided?

A generation ago, the easiest way to make sure of a sale of ten thousand copies was to write a book on a Literary Birthplace. England was divided up into Areas of Authorship: books on Lakeland, books on the Hardy Country, books on the Highways and Byways of Tennyson Land.

This wave of English Literary topography, linked to our own age by the Open Road school of anthologies and some very indoor essay-writing on very outdoor subjects, has been almost entirely superseded by books for the amateur naturalist. In place of the old Eng. Lit., as it has been called, comes the new Nat. Hist. Another kind of Ramble has been substituted for the old Literary Tour. Too many of our natural history books for amateurs take us over the beaten track; we are taken the rounds, as it were, of the "correct" species of birds, plants and butterflies. The excitement of discovery is gone. That is why we so often go back to the natural history books of the nineteenth century, to the great exploring naturalists, or to the Rev. Mr. Johns, collecting specimens so enthusiastically while he clambered about the cliffs of Cornwall in his top hat. Or we go back to Fabre. Or, for our flower book, we still stick to our old copy of Bentham and Hooker, a book planned expressly for amateurs yet combining, with its simplicity, great accuracy; with its completeness, beautifully exact observation.

One certain advantage, of course, our contemporary books for naturalists can provide: the blessing of illustration by modern photographic technique, which has made such dramatic advances since the pioneer work, fifty years ago, of men like O. A. J. Lee. But even here, the gain of the new art of photography seems to be counterbalanced by the loss of the old art of exact descriptive drawing. Where now is our Gosse, our Curtis, and our Syme? Because modern painting has emancipated itself from the chains of representational art, the modern illustrator of natural history books feels at liberty to be vaguely impressionist—so vaguely, that it is impossible to distinguish the impressionist from the slipshod. We must go back to the old books to find, in text and illustrations, the infectious enthusiasm of the pioneer and discoverer.

I have another criticism. To me it seems so often that the natural history writer believes, when he is arranging his material for general consumption, that there is some kind of necessity to "soften the blow", as if the art of presenting Natural History was the art of presenting it as something else. *Up Pops Mrs. Frog*-ism is fortunately on the wane; but Nature study for young amateurs is not yet free from pathetic and sometimes odious anthropomorphism. Again, a man may be a competent observer, yet find himself incapable of giving us the record of his observations "straight". He is under a compulsion to prove to us that he is something vaguely known as "nature lover", and it is just at this point that his power of observation dries up. "I walked to find my willow-warbler", he says, "through a wood carpeted with bluebells." Carpeted with sphagnum perhaps, pine needles, or (if he is lucky) the rosetted root leaves of *Primula elatior*. But "carpeted" is the least suitable of verbs to use for the bluebell, the flowers of which, however crowded the plants, always remain isolated and individual.

Sometimes, very understandably, the observer wants to tell us that for him the study of nature is a purification of the spirit—for him, and for all of us. But too often he forgets that the man who can write with real illumination on such matters only occurs once or twice in a generation. He forgets that no gloss he is likely to be able to put on the situation can have a hundredth part of the eloquence of the fact of the living object which he is describing. He forgets that most people prefer to work out their own stumbling realisation of beauty or mystery for themselves.

It is therefore that I find myself turning, more and more, even to the most scientifically tabulated documents of the professional naturalists, less and less to books of the Nature Ramble kind, which are aimed, presumably, at an exclusively amateur public. I turn less to a *Haunts of the Heron-lover*, more to a recent account of bird display in *British Birds*, or the section on the greenshank in Witherby, that masterpiece of professionalism. For my plants, I dig about in the pleasurably stiff and resistant Tansley. For my guide to evolution, Julian Huxley is the site of my excavation. Here there are no trimmings, no false starts, no last thoughts. Whatever can be got through quickly, is got through quickly. The tale is not embroidered, nor is it twice-told. Some measurable area, an acre or a square inch, is cleared for the first time. And, above all, to the professional writer, there is no thought, because the notion has never occurred to him, of "softening the blow".

Current specimen books for naturalist amateurs are before me. I note that two-thirds of them are about birds. Four-legged animals are not represented. Neither are there any plant books. There is one really admirable example, and it is specifically for amateurs. Sandars's *Insect Book for the Pocket* was completed just before his recent death. His method of arrangement should be made standard for all such works. The man who carried a pocket book of all the British species would need the strength of Hercules and the sports coat of Titan. Sandars has selected, not on the flat and boring principle of Common Only, nor, of course, on the Rare and Queer Only principle, that incitement to collector-maniacs. He very properly puts the amateur through the drill of classification, and teaches him to identify the families, describing typical genera in each, and describing them with such easy accuracy and wit and clarity that I, who know nothing about insects, could compare myself for once with the reviewer who so often finds himself in the fabulous position of being "unable to lay the book down".

After Sandars, the standard drops. In *Our Bird Book,* price one guinea, the illustrations are competent, but the text, written "for children and their parents", is not for this parent, nor for this parent's child. It is a pretty thought that the early morning song of birds is a salute to the rising sun. It is amusing to say that the blue tit "has a nicer character" than the great tit. But it is bad natural history, and it starts children, and their parents, unerringly off on the wrong foot, the anthropomorphic foot.

Haunts of British Divers illustrates perfectly the "contemporary contribution"—the art of bird photography. The photographs of the red-throated diver are particularly valuable, taken as they are to show the activities of the bird in series, and introduced by fully descriptive photographs of its Shetland habitat. The notes on bird behaviour are detailed and interesting. Yet occasionally even in this fine book, the startling effect of, for instance, certain gannet photographs is watered down by captions which tell us that "The wise and contented expression on the part of the old bird" suddenly changes "to open abuse". The gannet is neither wise nor irascible, but gannet-like, which is something much more worth observing, if it is much more difficult to understand.

Bird Life in Two Deltas illustrates a real weakness. The photographs, again, are excellent. And it is no doubt of some interest to explain the difficulties which beset the author who wishes to photograph the shy, tree-top-nesting night heron. But those diaries! The lighter the style, the heavier the going for the reader. This journal is written in the "we sallied forth" manner. The humorous passages stand out particularly, owing to the number of exclamation marks.

"Too much Me" will be the verdict on many current naturalists' books, no doubt. Yet it is difficult to generalise. The "I" in Leslie Brown's *Birds and I* is remarkably unegotistical. His kind of personal narrative makes for vividness, so that we seem to participate in his adventures, prospecting, with him, eyries in the Angus Highlands, or the sea caves of Trinidad.

Is there really an unwritten law which compels the naturalist photographer to stuff pads of redundant text between his photographs? The excellence even of S. Beaufoy's *Butterfly Lives* might reasonably be said to suffer from this practice.

The photographs are better than good natural history: they are a real achievement in the art of the camera as well. Mr. Beaufoy has been wonderfully successful with his illustrations: he has been less fortunate in his search for a text to go with them. Animal photographers often seem to insert their reading-matter as an afterthought. All the same Mr. Beaufoy's text is accurate and true, as anybody familiar with the standard text-books can perceive for himself!

The same excellence of illustration and the same atmosphere of boiled-down text-book in the reading matter, is to be found in C. A. Gibson-Hill's *British Sea Birds*.

Better than any of these books for amateurs is a book *by* amateurs, for professionals. We must blame the war, I suppose, for the present shortage of guides. In North Scotland, particularly, we have to fall back on a second-hand copy of an out-of-date book, which sandwiches a reference to a "difficult climb" or a "magnificent view" between the classification of a non-existent hotel and the fare of a ferry which has long ceased to operate. Natural History is scarcely mentioned. That is why I like so much the entirely factual *Ilfracombe Fauna and Flora*, edited by a professional, but embodying the researches of the Ilfracombe Field Club. That is why I envy visitors to the Ilfracombe district, who will have a guide that they can use.

Very often the brilliant amateur, when he comes to write his book, develops a hyper-professional eye for accuracy. E. A. Armstrong's *Bird Display and Bird Behaviour*, for instance, is a model of care. Lists of scientific names, bibliographies, and a monumental index take up the last eighty pages of the book. Perhaps, indeed, there is almost too much footnote and counter-checking. The reader determined to take in each valuable fact in the chapter on "The Psychological Basis of Nest-Building", will have to get used to being tripped up by references. (And who, by the way, ever does *refer*—to "Angier 1927" or "Dembo 1931"?) But it is a fault on the right side, in this small Golden Bough of bird ceremonial.

But best of all, still, for me, is the book by the professional for professionals. David Lack's book on *Darwin's Finches* makes exactly the right use of the opportunity for the study of the architecture of evolution which Darwin discovered in these birds and their history in the Galapagos Islands. The author believes in the beauty of fact. There is no tendency to insult the reader by suggesting, in an effort to make the subject palatable, that this beauty of fact means less to him than it does to the author. The method, and the style, is not unlike that of Darwin himself, who could say, with such provocative understatement, that "the natural history of these islands is eminently curious, and well deserves attention".

Perhaps, therefore, my plea is this: that publishers of natural history should have mercy on their public. Do not, please, try to make things nice for us. Do not tell us that nature is wonderful. Remember that the gap between amateur and professional is not of the kind which you suppose. We amateurs do not earn our living as naturalists, it is true. But if we are not full timers, we are at least tenth timers, and for that precious tenth of our time we are at least as ardent, at least as eager to get to the root of the matter, as our professional fellow students.

Books referred to in Stephen Potter's article are:

G. BENTHAM AND SIR J. D. HOOKER (1886) *Handbook of the British Flora*. 7th edition, 1945. London, L. Reeve & Co.

British Birds: a magazine published monthly by Messrs. H. F. & G. Witherby.

H. F. WITHERBY, F. C. R. JOURDAIN, N. F. TICEHURST AND B. W. TUCKER (1947) *The Handbook of British Birds*. 4th edition. London, Witherby.

A. G. TANSLEY (1939) *The British Islands and their Vegetation*. Cambridge, University Press.

JULIAN S. HUXLEY (1942) *Evolution: the Modern Synthesis*. London, Allen & Unwin.

EDMUND SANDARS (1946) *An Insect Book for the Pocket*. Oxford, University Press.

SIDNEY ROGERSON AND CHARLES F. TUNNICLIFFE (1947) *Our Bird Book*. London, Collins.

NIALL RANKIN (1947) *Haunts of British Divers*. London, Collins.

GEORGE K. YEATES (1947) *Bird Life in Two Deltas*. London, Faber & Faber.

LESLIE BROWN (1947) *Birds and I*. London, Michael Joseph.

S. BEAUFOY (1947) *Butterfly Lives*. London, Collins.

C. A. GIBSON-HILL (1947) *British Sea-birds*. London, Witherby.

ILFRACOMBE FIELD CLUB (1947) *Ilfracombe Fauna & Flora*. Ilfracombe.

E. A. ARMSTRONG (1948) *Bird Display and Behaviour*. London, Lindsay Drummond.

DAVID LACK (1947) *Darwin's Finches*. Cambridge, University Press.

The Sound of Harris: the sea-pass through the Outer Hebrides   *Violet Banks*

THE NEW NATURALIST

A JOURNAL OF BRITISH NATURAL HISTORY

SUMMER

THE WESTERN ISLES OF SCOTLAND

CONTENTS

THE WESTERN ISLES OF SCOTLAND 70

ARTHUR GEDDES: *The "Outer" Hebrides* 72

GORDON MANLEY: *The Climate of the Hebrides* 77

J. W. HESLOP HARRISON, F.R.S.: *The Passing of the Ice Age* 83

JAMES FISHER: *St. Kilda* 91

ROBERT ATKINSON: *Leach's Petrel* 110

H. G. VEVERS: *The Natural History of Ailsa Craig* 115

THE ATLANTIC SEAL 122

F. FRASER DARLING: *Science or Skins?* 128

EDITOR: JAMES FISHER • ASSISTANT EDITOR: ELISABETH ULLMANN

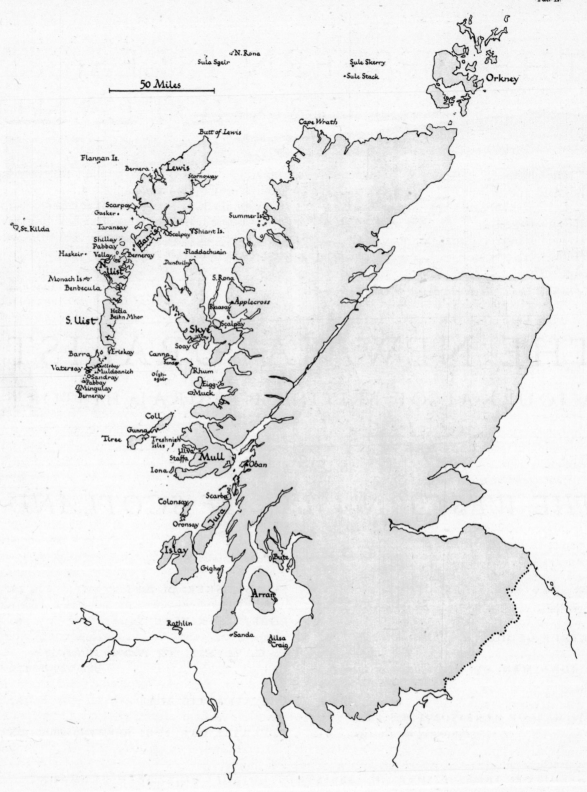

Fair Is.

Sula Sgeir   ◦N. Rona

Sule Skerry
•Sule Stack   Orkney

50 Miles

Butt of Lewis   Cape Wrath

Flannan Is.
Bernera   Lewis
Stornoway

Scarpay
Gasker•
◦St. Kilda   Taransay   Summer Is.
Shillay   Scalpay ◦Shiant Is.
Pabbay
Haskeir   Valley Berneray   Fladdachuain
Monach Is.◦   N. Uist   Duntulm
Benbecula   S. Rona
Applecross
Haela   Raasay
Beinn Mhor   Scalpay
S. Uist   Skye
Soay
Barra ◦Eriskay   Canna
Vatersay   Muldoanich Sanda
◦Sandray   Oigh-   Rhum
Pabbay   sgeir   Eigg
Mingulay   ◦Muck
Berneray

Coll
Gunna
Tiree   Treshnish
Isles   Ulva
Staffa   Mull
Iona◦   ◦Oban

Scarba
Colonsay   Jura
Oronsay

Islay   ◦Bute
Gigha◦
Arran
Rathlin
◦Sanda   Ailsa
Craig

THE WESTERN ISLES
OF SCOTLAND

THE chain of islands which stretches two hundred and seventy miles from Ailsa Craig to North Rona—the western isles of Scotland, the Clyde islands, and the Hebrides—is Britain's greatest *natural* treasure. Other regions of the British Isles have titles to such fame, but each has one or two only; the western isles have many. Their scenery defies description: the granite and gabbro cliffs of St. Kilda have no rival in the North Atlantic, and the gabbro ridge of the Skye Cuillins few rivals in the Alps. The shell-sand beaches, and the flowery *machairs*, are unique. The colours of sky and sea, of mountain and meadow gain intensity and at the same time subtlety from the peculiarities of the weather. The Hebrides, through their scenes, insidiously capture and enslave the subconscious minds, and sway the emotions, of those who dwell in them and of those who visit them.

The western isles' appeal, is, however, not purely to the emotions, or in the wide sense, only through the magnificence of their general scenery. It can soon be discovered that beneath the romance of nature in the isles is a strange reality, and many unexplored matters. Indeed, the western isles are, perhaps, also our greatest *biological* treasure. For here there are problems of human history, geology, geography, ecology and evolution which are unsolved. As a living museum, the isles are quite peculiar.

We are only at the beginning of a biological survey of the isles, and this part of the NEW NATURALIST does no more than bring together the views of several of the investigators who became attracted some years ago to these fascinating fields, and who have returned each year—as if under some kind of compulsion—ever since. It will be seen that these workers have different points of view, though it is our opinion that they are complementary and not conflicting.

A synthesis of recent scientific research in the western isles will soon be needed. Biologists have been exploring this region very much on their own, and without much linking or cross-criticism of each other's explorations. Nobody could depreciate the enterprise of these workers (and considerable enterprise is needed to get to some of the western isles), but everybody must hope that soon a new synthesis will be made, and new targets set by a united band of scientists, eager to do research in these glorious isles, where they are on the threshold of new discoveries.

As a step towards this objective, we must welcome the periodical, *Scottish Naturalist*, now revived after a long wartime lapse. This is a journal with a long history, extending back into the last century, and in its new form, and under the editorship of Professor V. C. Wynne-Edwards, it should be the most helpful single agency by which the new synthesis will be reached. But a medium of publication, alone, is not enough. We suggest that a new organisation is also needed. In these days of over-organisation, and of a multiplicity of initials, it is a rash writer that suggests a new body; but a new body there should be—a Hebrides and West Highland Biological Society, or at least a H. and W.H.B. Conference, which could be held most suitably in Glasgow, and which would do much to resolve misunderstandings, find new friendships, and create the conditions under which we can learn, from the stuff of our own islands, yet more about animals and plants, more about evolution, more about natural history—more, indeed, about the history of history.

ARTHUR GEDDES

THE "OUTER" HEBRIDES
HEART OF "THE NORTH AND WEST"
OF BRITAIN

IN the "Outer" Hebrides, commonly regarded as the most "outlying" inhabited lands of the British Isles, are found not only the most ancient of British rocks, the Archaean, but probably the oldest form of communal life in Britain. This life, in present and past, will interest some by characteristics which may seem unique, and others by the underlying universality of many of its features. A comparison may be found in the Archaean rock which underlies a succession of younger strata to the south-east.

The population of Lewis-and-Harris numbers only 30,000, and that of the entire Outer Hebrides barely 40,000; but this does not lessen the significance of the community. The strongly rooted island life is laid bare in the rocky environment, its rhythm responding intimately to the day's weather and the cycle of the year; while the flowering of its communal ways in song and spiritual tradition offers a new vision of regional, even of national, life to-day. Throughout Britain, and beyond, fresh need is felt for the practice of team work and for ideals of free community. But it is in characteristics common to the evolution of "the North and West" of the British Isles that island life is most suggestive, most revealing.

Rising in imagination to a point above the summits of the Harris hills, we gain a new perspective of the British Isles and beyond. The island below is now the nearest, and to us, as to the Isleman, a heartland of Britain. Looking to the lands across the Minch—each farther from the isles of home—are two regions, (1) Scotland, Northern England, Wales and Ireland, all sculptured in old rocks, and (2) the lowland or "Plain" of England beyond. Towards the horizon may be descried the coasts of Scandinavia, the Low Countries and France, and beyond the Alps and the Pyrenees, the Mediterranean.

From Harris, on one side, reaching to the Severn and Tees is "the North and West", with its isles and headlands, mountains and hills hewn in old rock, and its firthlands, straths and marginal, hill-foot lowlands, markedly sculptured by rivers and ice, and heaped with glacial drift. Beyond this line is the "Plain", with its low scarplands of younger rocks sloping smoothly down to river-sculptured vales, and bounded by the smoother coasts of south-eastern England, or simply "the South-east".

Although "the North and West" is divided from "the South-east", not by a single line, but rather by zones of transition, there can be no doubt of the contrasts between the extremes. How strikingly different from any view over the English plain is that from our Harris hill-top! It overlooks the ice-scraped rock of the fells, the ill-drained hollows studded with gleaming lochs and deeply overgrown with peat, and the indented insular coast-line with widely-spaced crofting townships looking seaward to where a few fishers' sails dot the vast expanse of ocean.

Men have long recognised the homogeneity of the English "Plain" with its recurring vale and wold, compact within its rounded coast-line. They have sensed the unity inherent in varying dialect, history and life, and all the rich heritage and charm centred on a single capital. But in the north and west the strongly contrasted diversities of the land have obscured the underlying unity in geographic origins and in historic and social evolution. To understand the civilisation of the British Isles, it is vital to perceive in a broad way the complementary qualities found in the two great regions, and to face their corresponding weaknesses or limitations.

From the evolutionary point of view, the revealing character of island life lies not only in static survivals in what Sir Arthur Mitchell so vividly described as "the Past in the Present": it lies still more in the dynamic strength of its continuity—

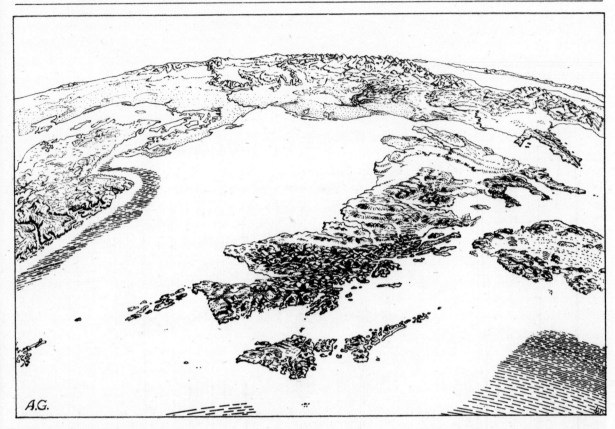

A.G.

The "Outer" Hebrides, seen as the Heart of NW. Britain. We look over Lewis-and-Harris south-eastwards to the Highlands and Lowlands of Scotland; the "highlands and firthlands" of England, Wales and Ireland; and the English "Plain" beyond, with its recurrent scarp-and-vale. Across the seas lie Scandinavia, the N. European Plain, the Paris Basin and Brittany. On the centre horizon rise the Alps, to right Iberia and the Atlas.
We see the unity in diversity of "the North and West" from the Scottish Isles to Brittany, by contrast with the homogeneity of the SE. English "Plain".

notably of early or primitive Christianity—and also in the late occurrence of changes.

The social consequences of these regional differences in land and evolution are profound. In the "Plain" to the south-east of the Severn-Tees line, large village communities with "common fields", forming the manor villages of medieval times, prevailed. To the north and west, the more varied, hillier lands encouraged the continuance of hamlets. These hamlets sheltered close-knit family groups, composed of four or five to a dozen relations or friends—in Scots even to-day (much as in Gaelic) "friend" frequently implies kinship. Each small group formed a team. Together the men ploughed their mingled rigs (or ridges) and herded their stock, in common, and on the coast they rowed their boat as its crew. The women, too, did much together, as when they spun their yarn, and fulled or "waulked" the cloth that one of them had woven, and helped by turn in child-birth and child-care.

In favourable circumstances several hamlet-teams were linked in a larger group, commonly pastoral, the germ (in the Hebrides) of the present township with its common grazing. These "sociable hamlets" or "little commonwealths", as understanding writers on the Highlands and on Harris called the units they found, lived on in the Hebrides until a hundred years ago. Features of their form and life survive; but we believe that these have not yet been envisaged in their full dynamic significance.

Robert Adam

A crofter hamlet in West Lewis, at the mouth of Loch Roag

The homesteads, informally grouped in these small hamlets, have been mistakenly described as solitary or "dispersed" by scholars accustomed to larger and more compact grouping. The mistake was made by geographers of the nineteenth century, such as Meitzen, with reference to the hamlets of Brittany. In the same way, the vital facts of team-work and joint-holding have been overlooked or mistakenly described as "individualistic". It is true that in Scotland, as elsewhere, such hamlets have been split up into farms and scattered cottages, at various dates, producing a fundamental regional cleavage within "the North and West".

Partly as a result of their small size, the tenure of farm-hamlets was frequently informal. In northern England, the hamlets and their lands were not entered in Domesday Book; still less are early entries complete in Scotland. For this and other reasons, jurists and historians may fail to notice the absorption or suppression of rights held in common in "the North and West", together with the abolition of the duties of fellow-workers to one another. They often failed to inquire into the former existence of common rights and fellowship-duties, the observances of which have so much to teach. The peasantry of the Gael, particularly in the Hebrides, were strictly equalitarian in sharing labour and rights—a fact testified by customs and rentals until after 1800. And to judge from the completeness of the Hebridean evidence, and from historic changes in the Norse Isles and the Lowlands, the suppression of common rights and duties, region by region, caused a profound social and moral revolution.

Now, although so fundamentally equalitarian within themselves, these hamlet-communities of the Gael were subjected to the lordship of a chief

Robert Atkinson   *Robert Atkinson*

Two St. Kildans (1938). The marked race-types in different islets and townships of the Hebrides show, as a rule, long deep-rooted continuity of settlement. In expression, the faces of the Islesfolk record long hours of quiet and "monotony", yet a capacity for swift response to emergency; they blend a sense of society with that of solitude; and sympathy for sorrow with lively humour

or laird, either directly or through an inter-mediate gentleman-tenant, a "tacksman". Pre-history suggests that such lordship goes back to early conquests of self-supporting agricultural and pastoral communities by well-armed raiders of many races, including the Celtic-speaking swords-men of the Iron Age. The last and most notable of these conquering raiders were the Norsemen. Their influence was profound, whether—sailing direct from the Scandinavian forest settlements and fjords—they raided and settled as heathen Viking crews; or, at a later stage from Normandy (that fertile province of France which they had made theirs, in fact and name) they invaded England under the panoply of civilisation and with Papal benediction. A generation after the Conquest they began the penetration of Scotland.

The paradox of loyalty to one's fellows with loyalty to a lord, of stoutly equalitarian thinking bound up with fervid admiration for an aristo-cracy, is nowhere more marked than among the Gael. They sought to reconcile these conflicting loyalties by claiming common ancestry for chief and people, as the children (*Clann*) of a hero of history or myth. The years 1945-7, which mark a centen-ary of the last of the desperate Jacobite Risings, stand at the close of the latest of many wars in which fame has been won for the symbol of clanship—the tartan, long proscribed (by the Act of 1747) "to every man and boy in the Highlands". At such a time, the Gael's loyalty to the death cannot be forgotten although old kings, old chiefs, have gone.

This paradox must not only be remembered but understood. Rooted in communal life and en-vironment, it supplies the key to important features of our own time, such as the failure of Lord Lever-hulme's seven years' endeavour in Lewis, and the present opportunity of Highland renewal.

Violet Banks

South-west Lewis; the ancient burial-ground at Uig

If an intensive study of a single isle and community can throw fresh light upon certain essential characteristics of the less understood region of the British Isles—that lying outside the south-eastern plain—it can contribute to more than economic reorientation. The significance of the island life—not so much for the past which cannot be changed, as for the future, which can—lies in the intensity of its communal traditions, extinguished elsewhere. It is this quality which makes the Hebrides less the "Outer" part of Britain, than—in the opposite perspective—the Innermost part, a Heart of Britain.

It is true that much has gone—many fishing crews have been disbanded and team-work has been weakened—but much lives on, and much has been learned. The Gael have still to make their full contribution to English-speaking civilisation. To do so they must find their own fulfilment, within the framework of the Highlands of Scotland and of "The North and West of Britain".

REFERENCES:

ARTHUR GEDDES (1948) *The Isle of Lewis-and-Harris and its Future: A Study in British Community*. Edinburgh University Press—forthcoming.
In this book the Hebridean evidence will be applied to principles of historical and communal geography in the North and West of Britain. It is hoped here to present what may be the completest chain of evidence available of the unity of primitive communal life in Scotland—geographic, economic, social, psychological and religious. This unity has long been obscured by the difficulties of research owing to language, distance, poverty and other factors.

In a second volume of ancillary essays wider applications of findings in Lewis will be developed to aspects of environment and community in the "North and West of Britain".

ARTHUR GEDDES (1936) *Lewis*. Scottish Geographical Magazine, 1936: 224-31, 300-13.

GORDON MANLEY

THE CLIMATE
OF THE HEBRIDES

AMONG all the environmental factors which make a lasting impression on the visitor to the Hebrides climate is of surpassing importance. It acts not only as a deterrent but (admittedly less directly) as an attraction. The Hebrides are remote, and lack modern transport; but these difficulties would quickly be overcome were it not for the fact that the population, without reserves of capital, continues to try to gain its living from the infertile rainy slopes or ill-drained peaty lowlands. The better-drained sandy margins of an emergent coast lend themselves well to cultivation; and many share the opinion that if the peat cover were removed, the opportunities for lowland pasturage and cultivation would be considerably enlarged. The flatter southern islands such as Islay and Tiree already show that the Hebridean climate is by no means lacking in advantages over that of the near-by mainland.

From many points of view the Hebrides compare with the Scottish Midlands much as these in turn compare with Eastern France; that is, they are more windy, damp and cloudy, the number of days with rain is greater; summer is cooler but winter, if anything, is a little milder.

The elements of climate of which we are most conscious inland are temperature; amount, frequency and character of precipitation; and humidity. But at the intermediate temperatures prevailing in the Hebrides exposure to wind is of major importance, from the point of view of comfort, to man or to his animals. In such a region windiness is in turn associated with the great frequency of rain and low cloud. Everywhere from Islay to the Butt of Lewis the essential factors governing the climate are the same and local differences principally arise from the varying sizes of the islands and the extent to which they are mountainous or otherwise.

Wind will, therefore, be considered first.

Throughout the year the Hebrides lie close to one of the principal tracks of the most vigorous Atlantic depressions. The centres of most of these pass from west to east a little to the northward, but in the autumn months many follow a track from south-west to north-east, or are held up off the Scottish coasts. Hence winds from between south and west are dominant, and in winter are often very strong. Records of the frequency of winds of various strengths are maintained at a number of exposed weather stations around the British coasts. According to these, the average annual number of hours with wind of gale force or more is greater at the Butt of Lewis than at any other station; and with regard to gusts the local record of 108 m.p.h. at Tiree has only been exceeded twice at any other British stations.

Southerly and south-west winds in particular appear often to become particularly strong off north-west Scotland, probably on account of the trend of the coasts and the slight hold-up of advancing depressions by the mountainous Highlands. Gales in the Outer Islands have, however, been recorded from every quarter. Throughout the autumn and winter quiet spells of more than a few hours' duration are rare. In summer the pressure gradient associated with passing depressions is generally less marked, but strong winds are still quite frequent.

Late spring and early summer (May–June) give the best chance of quiet sunny weather, associated as a rule with anticyclones approaching from the Atlantic. Sometimes the spring months are characterised by a prolonged spell of light or moderate north-easterly winds, when a persistent anticyclone develops over the Norwegian Sea or N. Scandinavia. Towards the fringes of such anticyclones, southern England in particular may experience unpleasantly fresh penetrating east to north-east winds, notably in March, April

Robert Atkinson

Rhum from the east (from the same direction as the photograph on the opposite page); a choppy sea in the Minch

and May, accompanied by extensive North Sea cloud. In such circumstances the Hebrides often enjoy prolonged brilliant sunshine. In May 1946 Tiree recorded the remarkable average of 10·6 hours of sun daily, whereas less than six were recorded on the east coast of Kent; high pressure was exceptionally dominant towards the north. Nevertheless, the fact that the Hebrides are surrounded by a sea with a laggard rise of temperature from a minimum in early March means that the April and May sunshine is still tempered by a cool breeze; this is, of course, more noticeable in the Outer Isles. On a fine hot May afternoon, with temperatures exceeding 70° in the Scottish midlands, 60° will scarcely be attained at Stornoway.

Further, within the air masses most commonly reaching the Hebrides the probability of formation of low cloud is high. Air originating in warmer latitudes and approaching over the ocean from south or south-west is not only humid; the surface layers are being gradually cooled as the air moves over cooler seas, and hence very extensive low stratus cloud is liable to develop. In addition to this the normal frontal belts of rainfall of the advancing depressions are also of frequent occurrence and passage. But even if the whole group of islands lies in the warm southerly current of air with its low cloud, such a humid air-stream meeting the mountains, e.g. the Cuillins of Skye, gives persistent orographic drizzle and rain resulting from forced ascent and further cooling due to expansion. Thus we find that on many dull, damp and mild winter days when the rainfall may be very small on a flat island such as Tiree, an inch or more will fall among the mountains.

But a great deal of air approaches the Hebrides from westerly points. Originating over a colder region such as Labrador or the Greenland seas, it

Robert Atkinson

Rhum from the east, with Eigg; seen from Morar on the mainland, showing the contrast between overcast and sunny weather in the Isles

flows eastward over a considerably warmer sea surface. The surface layers not only become more humid; the whole air mass becomes "unstable". That is, the surface layers are so much warmer than those overlying them that they tend to rise on the slightest provocation. This process is generally rather intermittent; it becomes particularly notice-able wherever hills or mountains encourage the unstable surface air to rise suddenly, forming vast piles of spreading cumulus and cumulo-nimbus cloud from which vigorous showers fall. No type of day is more common in the Hebrides than that with a fresh or strong cool westerly wind, with intermittent bright intervals of an hour or two's duration alternating with lashing showers of rain. Not infrequently hail falls in these showers in the colder months, or sleet if the air is a little colder (that is, when it follows a shorter track from its Arctic source-region).

Sometimes in the winter months the rapid ascent of the moist surface air into the colder environment above is so marked that lightning and thunder accompany the showers. On the average the Hebrides have thunder on about three days yearly, for the most part in the colder months when a stiff west to north wind is blowing.

We thus observe a high proportion of cloudy skies, though not so persistent as on the adjacent mainland of the mountainous West Highlands; and a high frequency of days with rain, although on the flatter islands the amount is not excessive. Bright intervals are more prolonged, too, away from the hills; and it will be seen that the flatter island of Tiree enjoys over 20 per cent more sun-shine compared with Stornoway, together with 9 per cent less rainfall.

The high proportion of cloud, the relative rarity of calm days, and the small size of the islands

A dark rain-cloud hangs over the deserted whaling station of Bunaveneadar in Harris, Outer Hebrides, and obscures the top of Gillaval Glas (1,544 ft.)

compared with the adjacent sea all tend to keep the temperature remarkably uniform. On the more exposed islands the diurnal range of temperature throughout the year is about half that which we expect inland. Seasonal range of temperature is also limited, as the figures show. But although the extremes are not great for so northerly a latitude, Stornoway on the large and rather hilly island of Lewis is considerably more liable to frost than Castlebay in the small island of Barra, or for that matter, Tiree. Duntuilm in Skye, lying on a relatively steep slope adjacent to the sea, resembles the milder islands in its freedom from great extremes. Very small distances inland however make a difference; no doubt the centre of Lewis is much more subject to frost than Stornoway, and even the station on Colonsay records in general greater extremes than Tiree. Statistics are chiefly derived from the stations just named, though a

number of additional short records exist here and there which enable judgments to be made.

FOR STORNOWAY we have the table on p. 81 from the published statistics of the Meteorological Office. In addition, snow-lying is observed on an average of six days; thunder on three; days with gales average twenty-four, and occur from September to April. Absolute extremes of temperature on record (52 years) are 78° and 11°. 49 per cent of observations give wind from S., SW. or W. Mean amount of cloud in tenths, 7·5 ranging from 7·1 in April to 7·8 in July.

FOR CASTLEBAY (BARRA) the means for each month are generally 1°–2° higher, and the mean daily range varies only between 6° and 8°. Snow-lying averages about three days; days with gales eleven, days with snow or sleet seventeen. Rainfall,

STORNOWAY	J	F	M	A	M	J	J	A	S	O	N	D	Year
Mean temperature, ° F. (15 years)	41·2	40·9	41·7	43·5	47·5	51·9	55·7	55·1	51·9	47·2	43·4	41·7	46·8
Mean daily range, nearest ° F.	7	8	10	11	11	10	10	10	10	9	8	6	9
Average extremes	51:26	51:26	53:25	58:29	64:33	69:39	69:41	67:40	64:37	60:32	54:29	52:26	72:21
Average rainfall, inches	5·2	4·5	4·1	3·0	2·6	2·4	3·0	4·0	3·9	5·2	5·8	6·3	50·0
Days with measurable rain	25	22	24	19	19	17	21	22	21	23	24	26	263
Average daily sunshine (hours)	0·9	1·9	3·5	5·0	5·8	5·5	4·7	4·1	3·7	2·5	1·5	0·7	3·3
Percentage of possible	12	21	30	35	35	31	27	27	29	24	19	11	27
Days with snow or sleet	5	5	5	3	1	0	0	0	0	1	2	4	25

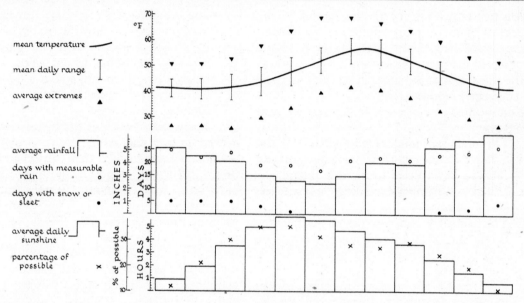

TIREE	J	F	M	A	M	J	J	A	S	O	N	D	Year
Mean temperature, °F. (10 years)	42·0	41·5	42·9	44·6	49·7	53·5	56·7	56·7	54·3	49·8	45·3	41·5	48·4
Average daily sunshine (hours)	1·3	2·4	3·9	5·8	7·6	7·7	5·3	4·9	4·2	2·7	1·5	1·0	4·0
Percentage of possible	17	25	33	41	47	40	31	32	32	26	18	14	33

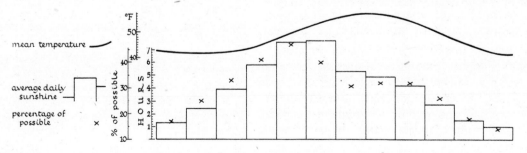

36.3 in. on 254 days; maximum in December. Extremes of temperature on record (19 years) are 75° and 21°; average extreme minima for each month are higher than at Stornoway. Castlebay is a relatively sheltered location and the decreased average frequency of days with gale by comparison with Stornoway must not be assumed to apply to the more exposed parts of these southern islands.

FOR TIREE

Snow-lying average about two days; days with gale (5 years only) 33. Rainfall averages 45·3 in., falling on 243 days. Extreme minima for the year are generally higher than Stornoway.

FOR DUNTUILM (SKYE) average rainfall 54 in.; average sunshine appears similar to Stornoway; average snow-lying about three days. It should be observed that with the exception of Stornoway all the above records are rather short; but the figures are adequately representative.

Commenting on the above figures we may summarise:

i. The mean daily range of temperature is slightly larger on the coasts of the bigger islands, and can be expected to increase inland.
ii. Hot days (maxima exceeding 70°) are very few in number.
iii. The frequency of occurrence of precipitation is very high, yet the total amount averages less than 40 in. in Barra, part of Islay, and at Butt of Lewis.
iv. Considering the relative mildness of the winter temperatures the number of days with snow or sleet observed is rather high in the northern islands, but near sea level it does not as a rule lie for long. In the smaller southern islands snow-cover rarely lasts more than a few hours. The higher hills of Lewis and Skye are, however, covered with snow for long periods.
v. The high relative humidity of the air. In Barra with a restricted daily range of temperature, the average at 1 p.m. for each of the twelve months lies between 80 and 86 per cent.
vi. The highest proportion of sunshine occurs in April, May and June; it falls off sharply in July. In spring and early summer the tendency for anticyclonic development is marked, and with relatively warm dry air flowing gently off Scotland stable conditions over the cool sea can be expected, with decreased chance of cloud formation especially nearer the mainland. The average percentage of possible sunshine at Tiree in May is about as high as anywhere in Britain.
vii. June is in general the driest month, followed by May. August is often persistently cloudy and rather wet; summer months such as August 1947 (average at Stornoway, 6.4 hours' sun daily, with a total of half an inch of rain) are rare, dry and settled weather being much more likely in the early summer.
viii. Although frost on the smaller islands is never severe and even in January the mean temperature is high enough for some growth of grass to begin, the very slow rise in spring followed by a cool summer means that growth and ripening are slow. Crops ripen very late, especially in the north, and at a season when humidity and rainfall are often high as the October figures show.

One noteworthy feature of the Hebridean climate is freedom from fog, which occurs at most coastal stations less frequently than anywhere else in Britain. But low cloud and hill-mist are, as we have seen, very common. Further, the winter temperatures are such that in spite of the relative freedom from frost the raw, damp wind has a peculiarly chilling quality; strong, moist winds between 35° and 40° are very prevalent, and cannot be said to give a favourable impression. By contrast, the brilliance of early summer can be extremely attractive. Rapidly varying skies and lights, with many windy and showery days and a prevailingly moist atmosphere, in winter often rainy, remain dominant in most visitors' minds.

REFERENCES

METEOROLOGICAL OFFICE. *Book of Normals. Averages of Temperature and Sunshine, 1906-1935. Monthly Weather Report* (since 1884). H.M.S.O.

EARLY DATA in J. Scot. Meteorol. Soc. and Bartholomew's *Atlas of Scotland.*

MANLEY, G. (1940, 1947). Meteorol. Mag. (Snowfall and snow-cover).

BILHAM, E. G. (1938) *The Climate of the British Isles.* London, Macmillan (the most useful summary).

GOLD, E. (1936). *Wind in Britain.* Quart. J. Roy. Meteorol. Soc. 62.

J. W. HESLOP HARRISON

THE PASSING OF THE ICE AGE
& ITS EFFECT UPON THE PLANT AND ANIMAL LIFE OF THE SCOTTISH WESTERN ISLES

THE idea of exploring the remoter parts of Scotland for the purpose of studying their natural history has always had a great attraction for me, which occasional visits to its northern counties have done but little to satisfy. Hence, when in 1934 the opportunity of examining the Isle of Raasay, lying between Skye and Ross-shire, presented itself, it was seized with enthusiasm. The results of that reconnaissance proved so stimulating that, in the winter of 1934-35, far-reaching plans were made by the Department of Botany, King's College, Newcastle upon Tyne, for a complete survey of the Inner and Outer Hebrides.

Originally, our investigations were undertaken with the increasing of our knowledge of the distribution of the plants and animals of the area as our primary aim, but to this was added immediately, as a natural corollary, an attempt to determine their relationships with the flora and fauna of the rest of the British Isles.

Almost simultaneously with the inauguration of our researches, the discovery of unexpected species and well-marked island races demonstrated conclusively that discrepancies existed between the plants and animals of the Western Isles and those of the mainland of Scotland. So striking were these in some respects, that we were forced to the opinion that certain sections of the two populations differed in origin and history. In fact, it became clear that biogeographical problems of major importance had been encountered. Furthermore, some of these were obviously identical with those recognised by students of the Irish flora and fauna. Representing this section amongst the plants appeared the Irish Lady's Tresses Orchid (*Spiranthes stricta*) on the Isles of Coll and Colonsay; the Pipewort (*Eriocaulon septangulare*) on Skye, Coll and Scalpay; the American Pondweed (*Potamogeton epihydrus*) on South Uist; and the Slender Naiad (*Naias flexilis*) on North Uist, South Uist

and Colonsay; amongst animals, the freshwater sponge (*Heteromeyenia ryderi*) on most of the Outer Isles. At this point, it should be emphasised that the Hebridean headquarters of this, the so-called American element of the British flora and fauna, is located on the Isle of Coll.

From these remarks it follows that the solutions to our problems, like those tackled by Irish botanists, and by ourselves in Upper Teesdale, depend, in part, at least, upon the possibility of living organisms' having survived the great Ice Age on ice-free areas. This we had demonstrated was almost certainly the explanation in the cases of plants like the Spring Gentian (*Gentiana verna*) and the Shrubby Cinquefoil (*Potentilla fruticosa*) in Teesdale. The problems thus propounded, difficult as they are, are rendered more complex inasmuch as they have just as much to do with the far-reaching changes in geographical configuration, which these islands have experienced during the Ice Age, as with the climatic vicissitudes themselves.

That the Hebrides were islands at the onset of the Glacial Period has ready proof in the form of preglacial raised beaches, marking former sea levels, along the Irish coast and on the Treshnish Isles, Mull, Colonsay and elsewhere. Clearly, too, the Hebrides in all probability possessed a temperate flora and fauna, resembling that of the British area of the time. However, nothing is more certain than that the islands, Inner and Outer alike, were overwhelmed at the time of maximum glaciation by ice advancing from the mainland. If this involved a complete blanket of ice, then any survival of life was impossible. It is at this stage that biological evidence, in general stressed so feebly, becomes of paramount importance.

Amongst the most characteristic of present-day Hebridean plants is the beautiful moss, *Myurium Hebridarum,* known throughout the Outer Isles and from Coll, Tiree, Rhum and Canna in the Inner

J. W. Heslop Harrison

The Bheinn Mhor–Hecla–Feaveallach mountain massif, South Uist, with Loch Ollay in the foreground, a habitat for the Slender Naiad, Naias flexilis. The new British Pondweed, Potamogeton epihydrus, occurs in a lochan in this area

group, but now restricted outside Britain to the Canary Islands, Madeira and the Azores. Thus it exhibits discontinuous distribution of a remarkable type, explicable only on the basis of a dispersal in Tertiary times. Of a similar kind of distribution are several liverworts and the water beetle, *Deronectes canariensis*, captured by us in a loch on the Isle of Barra. That being so, more especially as the moss does not fruit, it seems incredible that anyone should appeal to postglacial and recent dispersal of an accidental nature to account for their present British distributions. Almost certainly, these species, remnants of old and formerly widely spread Tertiary floras and faunas, have survived the Glacial Period in localities not far removed from their present stations.

This view, of necessity, implies the presence of areas, on at least some of the islands, free from ice action—and these exist. The upper ridges of the

Beinn Mhor massif on the Isle of South Uist show no signs of glaciation. There, at an elevation of 1,500 feet at the head of Liadale, significantly enough associated with such plants as the Roseroot (*Sedum roseum*), the Mountain Sorrel (*Oxyria digyna*), and the Starry Saxifrage (*Saxifraga stellaris*), *Myurium* flourishes. Similarly, on the seaward cliffs of Ben na Hoe, the moss abounds. If *Myurium Hebridarum*, with its southern predilections, could survive, then it is reasonable to infer that some, at least, of the Arctic-Alpines accompanied it.

Of this there is further proof. The Alpine Foxtail Grass (*Alopecurus alpinus*), limited as far as its European range is concerned to Scotland, also occurs on Beinn Mhor. Whence could this grass be derived had it not maintained its position since the early stages of the Ice Age?

Areas likewise free from ice at the period of

maximum glaciation have also been detected at many points on Harris, as well as on Rhum. Further, the evidence supplied by the Cushion Pink (*Silene acaulis*) and other plants on Rhum, Canna, Eigg, Pabbay, Berneray, Mingulay and elsewhere, points to their persistence on the ice-free ledges of mountain and sea cliffs.

Thus on scattered nunataks,* and on cliff ledges, it is pictured that most of the Arctic and Alpine plants, exemplified by the sedges *Carex capitata, C. bicolor* and *C. glacialis,* the woodrush, *Luzula spicata,* the grass *Poa alpina,* the Arctic Scurvy Grass (*Cochlearia arctica*), the Fleabane (*Erigeron uniflorus*), the Alpine Saw-wort (*Saussurea alpina*) and the Norwegian Sandwort (*Arenaria norvegica*) amongst the flowering plants, and *Andreaea Blyttii, A. Hartmani* and *Ditrichum vaginans* amongst the mosses, survived the rigours of the Ice Age.

Let us now pause to consider the changes in configuration the islands have undergone as a result of the coming of the ice and of its temporary fluctuations. Undoubtedly, one of the first effects of the abstraction of water from the sea during the build-up of the ice-fields would be a lowering of the sea level of the type known as eustatic,† with a consequent westward extension of the Outer Isles, and a possible development of a continuous Hebridean land mass. In addition, this amplification would be exaggerated by the pressure of the ice load elsewhere producing an isostatic† depression on the land beneath it with a consequent outflow of the earth's plastic subcrust to the periphery. If these new land areas were ice-free, wholly or in part, as is rendered probable in the Outer Hebrides (when the comparatively slight development of glacial drift to the west of some of the mountains and their presumably oceanic climate are taken into account), then conditions would arise approximating those of Herschell

---

* Ice-free peaks and ridges projecting through the ice-shee are called "nunataks".

† A fall or rise in sea level brought about by the abstraction of water from the sea, or its return thereto, is called "eustatic". On the other hand, the pressure of an ice load not only depresses the land beneath it, but, by means of the accompanying outflow of the subcrust, provokes compensating rises in land surfaces elsewhere. Such movements, and the return to normal levels when the loads disappear, are termed "isostatic".

J. W. Heslop Harrison

The characteristic Hebridean moss, Myurium Hebridarum, *Ceann a'Mhara, Tiree*

J. W. Heslop Harrison

The arctic-alpine Fleabane, Erigeron uniflorus, *from its only British station, Isle of Rhum*

J. W. Heslop Harrison

The Pipewort, Eriocaulon septangulare, *Loch a Mhill Aird, Isle of Coll*

Island in the Canadian Arctic. There the flora and fauna, as revealed by the Canadian expedition, resembles, even to the inclusion of identical species, those living in the Scottish Western Isles. In that category, under such circumstances, the humble bee, *Bombus smithianus,* the gall-making sawflies of the genus *Pontania* attached to willows, the Eriophyid mites of similar food habit, the various Dytiscid water-beetles, and spiders of the genera *Xysticus, Lycosa,* and *Erigone,* would occupy prominent places. Over and above this, every one of these organisms implies the existence of members of other groups for its sustenance.

Having thus put forward deductions concerning particular species which have, in all probability, persisted throughout the Glacial Period, let us look at the evidence in favour of possible further survivals, employing the word "survival" now in a more limited sense.

No one studying the flora and fauna of the Hebrides would fail to be impressed by the fact that so many of the indigenous plants and animals are racially separable from the corresponding forms occurring on the Scottish mainland. Amongst these, the plants are represented by the Hebridean Spotted Orchid (*Orchis Fuchsii* var. *hebridensis*), the Hebridean Pyramidal Orchid (*Anacamptis pyramidalis* var. *fudayensis*), the Honeysuckle (*Lonicera Periclymenum* var. *Clarkii*) and almost all the wild rose forms of which *Rosa Sherardi* var. *Cookei* provides an outstanding case. Of the animals, amongst the birds are the Hebridean Thrush and Wren, and amongst the mammals the Hebridean Long-tailed Field-mouse, *Apodemus hebridensis,* with its numerous subspecies. The various insect groups supply their quota of examples; of these the butterflies are represented by special races of the Dark Green Fritillary (*Argynnis aglaia*), the Meadow Brown (*Maniola jurtina*), the Grayling (*Eumenis semele*) and the Common Blue (*Polyommatus icarus*), the moths by the Belted Beauty (*Nyssia zonaria* var. *atlantica*), the Foxglove Pug (*Eupithecia pulchellata* var. *hebudium*) and the Yellow Shell (*Euphyia bilineata* var. *atlantica*), the bumble bees by *Bombus jonellus* var. *hebridensis,* the Psyllids by the speckled forms of *Livia juncorum,* the Coccids by strange races of *Lecanium capreae* and *Chionaspis salicis,* the beetles by the ladybird, *Coccinella 11-punctata* var. *boreolitoralis* and the dragonflies by *Sympetrum striolatum* race *nigrofemur*. In what way, where and when did these forms evolve are questions that demand an answer at once.

Here an appeal must be made again to the geological evidence. As is well known, the Quaternary Ice Age was interrupted by a series of interglacial periods of varying lengths, during which the ice sheets waned under an ameliorating climate. Of these only the last need concern us, for it seems profitless to speculate about the earlier ones, so difficult would it be to interpret events masked so effectively by later phases of ice action.

Clearly, owing to the release of water by the melting ice, the last interglacial period would be ushered in by a eustatic rise in sea level leading to a marine transgression and thereby to a diminution in Hebridean land areas. As far as the Outer Hebridean zone was concerned, this occurrence would be less intense owing to the peripheral bulge originated and maintained by the ice load elsewhere. Moreover, as the ice vanished, or reached a minimum, a general isostatic recovery would set in. When finally equilibrium between eustatic and isostatic movements was attained, with the development of a continuous land mass to the west of Scotland, the favourable climatic conditions then prevailing would permit of the inrush of plants and animals of diverse affinities, long penned up in milder southern climes. Whilst the immigration could have taken place in the last interglacial period, it is not inconceivable that it occurred during one or other of the periods of temporary amelioration known to have interrupted the last or Upper Pleistocene Glaciation. In any event, short or protracted, such milder phases were only temporary, yielding in the end to a more rigorous state of affairs. To such an extent were the Scottish mainland and some of the islands icebound that the remainder of the Hebridean land

area, with such populations as could withstand the conditions, was cut off by an ice-barrier.

But what about the Hebrides themselves, or what then represented them? Were they covered by ice sheets of local development or were they more or less clear of ice? Almost certainly, if one judges from field evidence in the Outer Isles, at the maximum of the last glacial period they were practically ice-free, whilst the uninterrupted condition of the hundred-foot late-glacial beach on the Isle of Rhum, lying between the sea and any ice passing southward from the Barkeval-Hallival-Askival mountain group, suggests that Rhum and its neighbours were also able to support animal and plant life.

On such areas, in the Inner and Outer Hebrides, but especially in the more western and oceanic stretches, isolated populations of animals and plants were left not only to survive, but also to evolve along paths quite independent of those traversed by the parent stocks. In this manner, the endemic Eu-Hebridean* races, enumerated previously, came into being; these must be regarded as a second contingent of glacial survivors.

Such conditions, however, did not last. The ice sheets vanished, and the water locked up as ice was restored to the parent ocean. In consequence, once again a eustatic rise in sea level took place, and as its influence made itself felt, the newly evolved species and races fell back before the rising sea to reach the stations they now hold on Inner and Outer Isles alike.

Here the problem of the plants and animals peculiar, as far as the British Isles are concerned, to Ireland and the Hebrides must be attacked. If these can be imagined as surviving on a more extensive "Long" Island, there appears no reason for regarding their history as separable from that of the Eu-Hebridean group. Manifestly, species like the moss, *Campylopus shawii* and the bramble, *Rubus iricus,* and, possibly, the Slender Naiad (*Naias flexilis*) moved with the Eu-Hebridean forms and survived with them. But what, we ask, is the situation of the entire American element, of the Irish Orchid, *Orchis majalis,* detected on the isles of Coll and Tiree, of the Irish form of the Greasy Fritillary Butterfly (*Euphydryas aurinia*)

---

* A form which has been evolved in the Hebrides is described as "Eu-Hebridean".

The two raised beaches of SW. Jura. The upper (100 ft.) makes a plateau-like skyline, capped with gravel. From the lower (25 ft.) project what must have been rock islets when the sea was at this higher level

found on Tiree and Gunna, of the Irish Burnet moth (*Zygaena purpuralis*) recorded from Gunna, Eigg, and Rhum and of similar species? Their absence from ideal habitats in the Outer Isles suggests that they survived elsewhere. To put it plainly, the available evidence points strongly to their having passed at least the last period of glaciation on lands free of ice stretching to the west of the Ireland of to-day. From that haven of refuge, they seem to have migrated to their present habitats, a view which receives support from the occurrence of the Pipewort in western Irish interglacial deposits.

The answer to the question of the date of this event is not obtained so simply. The well-developed, late glacial or post-glacial hundred-foot raised beach, so patent on the Treshnish Islands and on Rhum, coupled with the contemporaneous marine deposits marking the extent of marine

transgression on Coll, demonstrates that, in late glacial and early post-glacial times, the Coll-Tiree group was just awash, except for scattered skerries representing Ben Hogh, Ben Hynish and similar elevated points. This, most emphatically, renders it difficult to press any view that the populations of Coll, Tiree and Gunna have been continuous from the last Interglacial period, or any interstadial phase, to the present day.

Isostatic recovery in early post-glacial times, although delayed and masked by the eustatic movement expressed in the hundred-foot beaches and rock notches, finally made itself felt and thereby raised land levels high enough to produce, even if precariously, the necessary union with Scotland and Ireland. In this way, forms marooned on the Outer Isles and in Ireland, or advancing from the south-east, could colonise the formerly submerged areas. Thus Coll obtained the contingent of

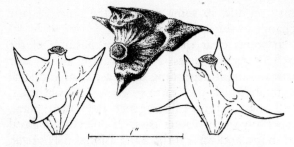

Nut of Trapa natans *L., Loch Ceann a' Baigh, S. Uist*

plants of diverse origin it now possesses. This event, on the basis of evidence supplied by the study of Hebridean peats, by the discovery of a subfossil nut of the Water Chestnut, *Trapa natans*, on South Uist and from the history of the formerly extensive Hebridean woodlands as worked out by us, must have taken place during the warm dry "Boreal" Period more than 8,000 years ago.

Farther away, where the ice load had been greatest and lasted longest, isostatic recovery, although delayed, could not be postponed indefinitely, and land at last freed from its icy mantle began to rise, accompanied by an inflow of the semifluid subcrust from the marginal regions, thus causing a sinking of land level there which reached its maximum extent in the extreme west. Accordingly, the sea was enabled to cut off, firstly, the Outer Isles, then Coll and Tiree and, finally, Rhum, Eigg, Canna and Muck. Hence the last-named islands would continue to receive forms of southern tendencies for a somewhat prolonged period, and so would be explained the presence on Rhum of such species as the Large Blue Butterfly (*Maculinea arion*), the Small Fan-footed Wave (*Sterrha biselata*), the Peach Blossom moth (*Thyatira batis*), the Silver Hook (*Eustrotia uncula*), the Narrow-bordered Bee Hawk (*Hemaris tityus*), the

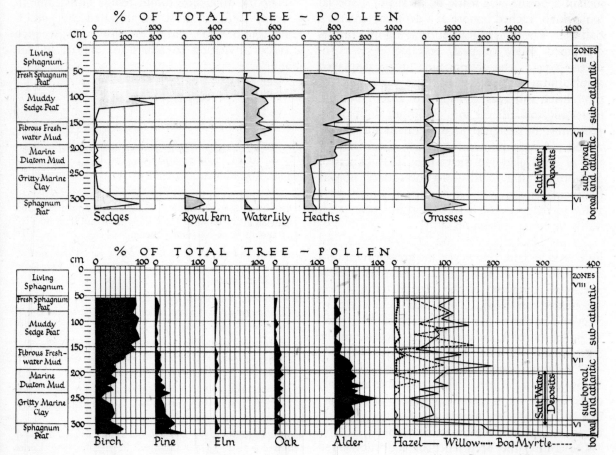

By courtesy of Dr. K. B. Blackburn

Pollen diagrams from the freshwater Loch Mòr, Soay (Skye); showing a marine phase of the 25-ft. beach period

Carder Bee (*Bombus agrorum*), the Palmate and Smooth Newts, and the rush, *Juncus capitatus*; on Muck of the Toad and on Coll of the Small Pearl-bordered Fritillary (*Argynnis selene*), the Straw-berry Clover (*Trifolium fragiferum*) and the Vivi-parous Lizard. The same circumstances, too, would allow some of the Eu-Hebridean forms, not only to reach the Scottish mainland, but in some instances to cross the Border into England, in this way giving rise to mixed colonies in which over-lapping and interbreeding of two distinct races could take place.

Of the date of the last marine transgression, which carved out the configuration of the islands much as we see it to-day, we have obtained evidence of the greatest value. The Isle of Soay, separated from Skye by a narrow sound, consists of two halves linked by an isthmus, a little to the north-east of which lies Loch Mor. At the edge of this lochan a boring was made by means of a special tool which reached bottom at a depth of ten and a half feet. The tool, instead of bringing up samples composed solely of peat, revealed deposits of diverse types. The bottom nine inches displayed a sphagnum peat containing high percentages of pine, birch and hazel pollen, with alder gradually increasing towards the top. Without doubt, this peat must be assigned to the end of the Boreal period. Above it succeeded, first, a foot and a half of gritty clay and then a similar thickness of grey-brown mud. Still nearer the surface, fibrous freshwater muds were encountered which gave place to sedgy peats, fresh sphagnum peats and, lastly, to living sphagnum.

Of the latter deposits, and the gritty clay, but little need be said. However, the grey-brown mud contained innumerable saltwater diatoms indica-tive, with certainty, of the marine transgression represented on Soay, Rhum and elsewhere in Scotland by the 25-foot raised beaches. Moreover, its pollen content, by the striking increase in the representation of alder and oak, proves that it is of "Atlantic" age, the moister period which followed Boreal times. Thus we have not only dates for the transgression, but have also shown that it attained its maximum during Atlantic times and persisted almost to their close.

Obviously, the occurrence of still submerged forests and peats lying off the shores of the Isle of Pabbay (Harris), Vallay, South Uist and Barra

may be due, in some cases, to the same eustatic change in sea level.

It seems clear that the present position of the 25-foot beach gives an indication of a later isostatic uplift depending upon a partial and local restoration of the earth's shape. Nevertheless, still more recent submergence has taken place, especially in the Outer Isles. If one climbs Eaval on Barra and surveys the Barra Isles as they stretch out at one's feet, or ascends the South Lee on North Uist and looks at the surrounding landscape, an impression is gained of lands drowned a very short time ago. How short may be gleaned from a consideration of Lochs Scadavay and Blashaval on North Uist, Loch Bee on South Uist and Loch Obe on Barra, all in the process of transformation into sea lochs. This submergence almost certainly takes its origin as a compensatory effect for isostatic uplifts, still in action, in other parts of Europe.

Here the discussion of our results must come to an end. Still, it must be admitted that much remains to be done, and by many workers; we give a hearty invitation to others to join us in our labours.

REFERENCES

A short list of papers about the subjects of the article.

B. P. BEIRNE (1943) *The Relationships and Origin of the Lepi-doptera of the Outer Hebrides, Shetlands, Faroes, and Iceland.* Proc. Roy. Irish Acad. 49 (B): 91-101.

MEMBERS OF KING'S COLLEGE, UNIVERSITY OF DURHAM, BIOLOGICAL EXPEDITIONS. Many papers on the flora and fauna of the Hebrides in Proc. Univ. Durham Phil. Soc. 10, 11 and 12 Scot. Nat. and J. Botany.

J. W. HESLOP HARRISON (1938-48) Many papers and notes on the entomology of the Hebrides in Entomologist, Ent. Rec., Ent. Mon. Mag.

J. W. HESLOP HARRISON and K. B. BLACKBURN (1946) *The Occurrence of a Nut of* Trapa natans *L. in the Outer Hebrides,...* New Phytol. 45:124-31.

J. W. HESLOP HARRISON and E. BOLTON (1939) *The Rose Flora of the Inner and Outer Hebrides and of Other Scottish Islands.* Trans. Bot. Soc. Edin. 32: 424-31.

T. H. JEHU and R. M. CRAIG (1923-34 *Geology of the Outer Hebrides:* Trans. Roy. Soc. Edin. 53: 419-41, 615-41; 54: 467-89; 55: 457-88; 57: 839-74.

R. Ll. PRAEGER (1939) *The Relations of the Flora and Fauna of Ireland to those of Other Countries.* Proc. Linn. Soc. Lond. 151: 192-213.

W. B. WRIGHT (1937) *The Quaternary Ice Age.* London, 2nd ed.

JAMES FISHER

ST. KILDA
A NATURAL EXPERIMENT

THE visitor to the Hebrides, if he stands upon the island of Muck or upon the lighthouse skerry of Oigh-Sgeir, or in some other central spot, is confronted with a view of fantastic crags and mountains. These are the Black Cuillins of Skye, whose knife-ridge few climbers can traverse in a day; the hills of Rhum—Sgurr nan Gillean, Ainshval, Trallval, Askival, Hallival; and the Sgurr of Eigg. It was probably the movements of the crust of Western Europe, which produced the Alps, that also produced these unique mountains. The line of Tertiary igneous intrusions, and volcanic lava sheets, that makes the Inner Hebrides so peculiar, runs from the Giant's Causeway in Northern Ireland as far as the Shiant Islands, in the Minch, north of Skye. The cliffs of Ailsa Craig, the hills of Mull, Fingal's Cave of Staffa, the curious sombrero-like shapes of Bac Mor and Lunga in the Treshnishs, all belong to this arrangement and compel the curious traveller, and the inquiring naturalist, to look up their geology books, and to wonder how such scenery came to be made. But the Tertiary volcanic disturbances did not intrude, through the most ancient lands of Western Scotland, upon this line alone. One such intrusion is an outlier: St. Kilda.

The islands of St. Kilda are the remotest British islands. They have the highest sheer sea-cliffs and the highest stacks in Britain. (Several great "cliffs" of Ireland, which are higher, slope so markedly that they cannot rank in the same category.) They had up to 1930 a unique human colony with peculiar skills and peculiar habits. They are the home of at least four unique animals,* and another† of great rarity. More than a fifth of the world's gannets and a third of Britain's fulmars live on them, and their puffins number millions. They form the most perfect natural sanctuary for wild life in the North Atlantic.

St. Kilda is 110 miles west of the mainland of Scotland, and 45 miles west of the Outer Hebrides. It is so remote, precipitous and inaccessible that it has never been mapped by the Ordnance Survey. Instead, it was surveyed privately in 1927 by John Mathieson and A. M. Cockburn. Though the total acreage is only 2,112 the work took them five months. Their map, six inches to the mile, is a remarkable work. Hirta, the main island, with its village and two bays, has nearly nine miles of coast. Its great hill, Conachair, is 1,396.8 feet (over a quarter of a mile) high; it has two other great cliffs, Oiseval and Mullach Bì; it is about 2½ miles long, and nearly 2 miles across. Soay, the sheep isle, is about a mile long and 1,225 feet high, the westernmost island of Scotland. Boreray, the gannets' isle, is also a mile long, and 1,245 feet high, and about four miles NE. of Hirta. The village bay of Hirta is guarded by Dùn, a craggy breakwater nearly a mile long, and 576 feet at its highest point.

The great cone of Stac an Armin, by Boreray, is the highest stack in Britain, 627 feet high. Also by Boreray, like a tooth, is Stac Lee, 544 feet. A stack called Levenish stands at the entrance of the village bay of Hirta, some way out. In the rough channel between Soay and Hirta is the long mass of Soay Stac, the pyramid of Stac Dona, and the 236-foot needle of Stac Biorach. Under the cliff of Conachair are Bradastac and Mina Stac; and, round the islands, many lesser stacks and rocks. Conachair of Hirta and the western precipices of Boreray and Soay are the three highest sheer sea-cliffs in Britain—the least of them, Soay, at 1,225 feet, is five feet higher than its nearest competitor, the famous and awful Kame of Foula, in Shetland.

St. Kilda has been visited by a succession of

---

* St. Kilda wren, Soay sheep, St. Kilda field-mouse and (probably extinct) St. Kilda house-mouse.
† Leach's fork-tailed petrel.

naturalists. It is one of the most highly docu-
mented islands in Britain, as Malcolm Stewart's
excellent bibliography demonstrates. The first, and
certainly one of the best, of naturalists to visit St.
Kilda was a Skye man called Martin Martin, who
was governor (tutor) to the children of the McLeod
of McLeod, the owner of St. Kilda. Martin
Martin's account, *A Late Voyage to St. Kilda*, is a
minor classic. He arrived there, after a somewhat
eventful voyage, in June 1697. He observed the
habits and life of the people, and the habits and
life of the animals. He noticed the wren, described
most accurately the fulmar (which was then
practically unknown to the civilised world),
described the great auk with considerable veri-
similitude, and wrote a most interesting, amusing
and, indeed, moving account of the gannet.

Martin said of Hirta, "the hills are often covered

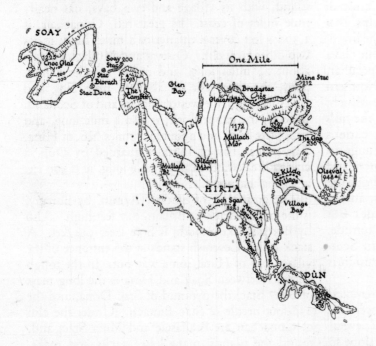

Based on the Ordnance Survey map. By permission of H.M. Stationery Office

with ambient white mists". He was right. St.
Kilda is a home of clouds: it is a cloud-maker, in
a part of the Atlantic where there is plenty of
material to make clouds from. Soay and Hirta
and Boreray comb and rake the sky with their
rugged fangs, and the weather spills out of it. On
a fine day they have crowns of cloud, blowing
away with the wind, and making as they blow.
Gusts and dark clouds and showers come out of

nothing. When Boreray makes black clouds it
looks like a smoking anvil.

The village, in 1697, had 180 souls, Gaelic-
speaking Outer Hebrideans. Later the population
fluctuated and after 35 people had left for Australia
in 1855, it fell to 78. From then until 1921 it was
never less than 70, or more than 80. Then it
declined again. By 1930 it had fallen to 43, and
these 43 gave up: they took work on the mainland,

*St. Kilda, 30 July 1947. A day of exceptional calm. The Village Bay gives safe anchorage
unless it blows from south or east*

Air photograph by Eric Hosking

Robert Atkinson

Village Bay, Hirta. The rocky, long island of Dùn, 576 ft., protects it from the south

and on 28 August 1930 a ship took them there. St. Kilda has been uninhabited since, save by a few old St. Kildans and visitors in the summer months.

The St. Kildans lived very largely on birds, and exploited most wild things on the islands. The sudden evacuation of the islands provided a natural experiment. What changes in the wild-life followed the departure of man? Less than a year after the evacuation, in the summer of 1931, an expedition of six scientists from Oxford and Cambridge (Buchan, Harrisson, Lack, Moy-Thomas, Petch and Stewart) stayed for over three weeks on Hirta, and studied the plants and animals. Among other things, they made a census of the numbers of the land-birds, and nearly all the sea-birds breeding there. Eight years after this, in 1939, another expedition (Huxley, Nicholson, Blacker, Robertson and Fisher) went there, to study

birds. We repeated the 1931 census. After another eight years, in June 1947, I went back again, this time with Robert Atkinson (who had been on St. Kilda before) and John Naish.

Martin Martin sailed for St. Kilda from the Sound of Harris on 29 May 1697, by the calendar of the day. If we allow for the eleven days' difference, this was 9 June by the modern calendar. Sailing as we did, on the evening of 9 June 1947 from the Sound of Harris, we began our voyage on the 250th anniversary certainly to the day and possibly to the hour, of Martin's voyage. We sailed twice to St. Kilda in 1947, by night. On the second voyage it was clear and calm, and in the morning twilight the islands hove up more than twenty miles ahead. I watched, for hours, the rocks and stacks slowly get bigger, and change their relative positions. They looked like huge and terrible animals, watching each other. The village

Robert Atkinson

THE CLETT: THE ST. KILDAN DRYING-CHAMBER

Cletts are usually between twelve and eighteen feet long. They are stone cells; their doors and curious wooden locks have nearly all rotted away now. Their inside height is six or seven feet; they are entirely of dry-stone. Their walls, four feet or more apart at the bottom, converge to the top with cleverly laid courses, until they are a foot or eighteen inches apart, and can be bridged by flat slabs. Upon these slabs the St. Kildans piled earth, and turf; and let the turf grow. There are cletts over the hill in Glen Mor, and on the edges of most of the cliffs, and on Soay and Boreray. In all, there are between six or seven hundred; most of them long and tall, of the shape of a tall potato clamp. A few are conical, like the so-called Amazon's House in Glen Mor on Hirta, and Calum Mor's house in the village.

The clett is a stone age drying machine. It was the only possible invention for keeping things dry in a place like St. Kilda which is humid, which makes weather, which is windy and rainy. The rain cannot get through the turf roof. Through the thick dry-stone sides the wind can whistle easily, but it cannot carry the rain with it; the rain is left behind on the stones, and trickles away. Inside, the wind, now dry, dries whatever lies inside very easily. In these cletts the St. Kildans dried everything; turf and peat for burning, clothes, fishing nets, bird nets, and eggs and birds. The sea-birds (gannets, fulmars and puffins especially) on which they so largely lived, were split up the back and partly cleaned, and then just packed, feathers and all, in cletts. They were eaten at any time in the following year. Under these dry conditions, there was a race between desiccation and decay, which was sufficiently won by the powers of desiccation to make the result tolerable to the St. Kildan palate.

The cletts provide nesting-places for three sorts of birds: starlings, twites and wrens. Other birds, particularly rock- and meadow-pipits, and sometimes snipe, like to perch on them. Soay sheep, the ancient brown St. Kilda breed, take refuge in them, and go into them to die.

became visible round the dome of Oiseval. The inland slopes of Hirta, steep though they were, appeared smooth and green: singularly smooth and rolling, in comparison with the rugged cliffs.

As our anchor rattled down to a good bottom, a wren echoed the rattle from a clett (see p. 95) in the dead village—a St. Kilda wren, with a St. Kilda wren's song. Only about seventy wrens in the world sing this song. Martin Martin, who appears to have missed little, found wrens on St. Kilda in 1697. In 1758 the minister Kenneth MacAulay found them too; and speculated as to "how these little birds could have flown thither". For many years after this the St. Kilda wren went unnoticed and unrecorded. But the minister who came in 1829, Neil MacKenzie, knew of it, and so did the visiting naturalist G. C. Atkinson, in 1831. It was in about 1881 that the ornithologist A. G. More, who never went to St. Kilda, but who made a special study of the geographical distribution of birds, suspected that the St. Kilda wren might prove to be different from the mainland wren. His friend Richard Barrington, the botanist, went to St. Kilda for three weeks in June 1883. For some reason Barrington found the wren very elusive, and obtained no specimens.

Next year, Charles Dixon went to St. Kilda. He landed on 5 June 1884, and found the wren common. He noted many things about it, the loudness of its song, its disposition to nest in cletts and walls. He obtained some specimens from which Henry Seebohm described a new species, *Troglodytes hirtensis,* the St. Kilda wren. Since Seebohm's day it has been reduced to its proper rank, a geographical subspecies.

Seebohm's description had its result. In June 1894, ten years later, the wren's eggs had become known to the St. Kildans as of value, and were taken and sold to dealers. Steele-Elliott, who visited St. Kilda then, thought that the wrens had been reduced to fifteen pairs. In the same year W. H. Hudson, who had become the victim of his own (considerably justified) pessimism and propaganda about the fate of rare birds, said, of St. Kilda collectors, "the result of their invasion is that the St. Kilda wren no longer exists".

Hudson's report of the St. Kilda wren's end was, like the report of Mark Twain's death, greatly exaggerated. There were quite a lot of St. Kilda wrens about on the islands in June 1896, when Richard Kearton explored them. In 1902 Dr. Wiglesworth found them without difficulty. All the same, collectors did visit St. Kilda, and did bribe the St. Kildans to take wrens' eggs, and did not, of course, publish accounts of their transactions. There was a real justification for the successful sponsorship, by Sir Herbert Maxwell and others in 1904, of the Wild Birds Protection (St. Kilda) Amendment Bill. As well as protecting the wren, this Bill protected Leach's fork-tailed petrel, which only breeds on four other islands in Britain. Nevertheless, one or two collectors still went on raiding St. Kilda. Harry Brazenor, the dealer, took birds and eggs of both these species in 1907, and advertised another collecting trip in 1908, soliciting subscribers in advance for a collection of birds and eggs of which many, as he put it, were "likely to greatly increase in value owing to their growing scarcity and to the increasing stringency of the Wild Bird Protection Laws".

There is no doubt that until well into the present century, the wrens were raided, and became rare in the accessible parts of the islands, particularly round the village of Hirta. But when W. Eagle Clarke visited St. Kilda in 1910 and 1911, he found the wrens living in the village, in the cletts and walls, in broken ground up the hills, and down the sheer cliffs and on the undercliffs; in the same places, in fact, where they are found to-day. In 1931, just after the evacuation, Harrisson and Buchan of the Oxford-Cambridge expedition studied its distribution and habits most thoroughly. They found 45 pairs on Hirta, of which 12 were in the village, 11 pairs on Dùn, 9 on Soay and at least 3 on Boreray, 68 pairs in all. By 1938 there seems to have been some increase, at least in the village, for in a thorough search of every building and wall (over 130 houses, byres and cletts) Atkinson found 12 nests with young or eggs, or from which young had flown, 4 nests which were probably those made by the cocks, and 2 which were probably of the previous season.

In the next year, 1939, Huxley, Nicholson, Blacker and I hunted the village and all the islands (except Soay) from 31 May to 2 June. We found exactly the same population in the village—12 pairs—as was there in 1931 and 1938. Our conclusion was obvious—the wren was quite unaffected by the evacuation of the human beings,

Air photograph by Eric Hosking

St. Kilda from the east; Hirta's highest cliff, Conachair, 1,397 ft., is supported by a prominent granite buttress. In the right distance is the blunt gabbro pyramid of Soay, 1,225 ft., the westernmost island of Scotland

and had a remarkably constant population. In 1947 as I worked through the village in June, the wrens sang loudly from the old graveyard, and from the old houses, now ruined cow-byres, and from the newer cottages, built in 1861-62, now also ruins. I found ten pairs of wrens occupying the deserted village. It is striking, indeed, how constant the numbers of the St. Kilda wren in the village seem to be.

The wrens nest among the steepest cliffs, at the bottoms and at the tops of precipices and slopes. In this steep ground they are not easy to find, and census work was difficult and not so accurate as in the village and round the cletts and walls.

One of the most exciting things about cliff exploring is the moment of unveiling you get as you overcome the last few feet of the backslope of a cliff. Suddenly your eyes explore the new, marvellous landscape, and seek something to focus

on. At the top of Conachair it does not take a second to find this focal point. It lies, not on the vast precipice below, or on the massive buttresses to each side, but on the horizon. It is Boreray and the stacks, four miles away across the sea. That distance does not dwarf them. Below, after a very steep short slope, and then an awful vertical precipice, is the Atlantic ocean, beating on the granite of Conachair, and the gabbro of the Glacan Mor, fourteen hundred feet below. The cliff is over a quarter of a mile high. It is possible to get a better view of the cliff itself from a narrow shoulder, or buttress-top, 350 feet lower. "The entire slope", said Julian Huxley here, "is dotted with white specks. The impression is of strange cliff flowers; but they are in reality fulmars."

As you come to St. Kilda, or go from it, fulmars are your companions. Between Boreray and Hirta, on calm days, they sit on the oily

St. Kilda, 23 April 1942, from SW. at about 1,200 ft. In the foreground is Hirta; beyond (about 6 miles from the camera) Boreray and the Stacks. The cliff facing the camera is Na h-Eagan, which rises to 828 ft. The table-land on top of it is Mullach Sgar, 715 ft., on which the golden plover was found breeding, for the first time, in 1947. Low down, on the right edge, a tiny triangle of sea, part of the Village Bay, is visible, and by it is the Manse. The hill above the Manse is Oiseval, 948 ft., whose skyline descends to the Gap, 536 ft., in the centre of the photograph. From the Gap, the slopes, studded with cletts, rise towards the top of Conachair, 1,397 ft. The Gap frames Boreray, 1,245 ft., and the Stacks, all of gabbro. Stac an Armin, 627 ft., is to the left of and beyond Stac Lee, 544 ft.

Atlantic swell and cackle to each other. Between twenty and thirty thousand pairs of fulmars nest on St. Kilda, on the steep slopes, and on the edges and ledges of rock, but not on the sheerest cliff-faces. There are many nests on the gendarmes of rock on the summit ridge, the sea-edge ridge, of the gabbro cliff. They make nothing of a nest save a scrape, lined with a few flaky pebbles or a stem or two of sorrel. Some of the nests, in June, are quite surrounded by primroses, or clumps of red sorrel. I have seen one sitting under a great rosette of rose-root, midsummer-men, overflowing from a crack in the rock.

The fulmar was, once, *entirely* St. Kilda's bird, for until 1878 it nested nowhere else in Britain. To-day it has two hundred and fifty colonies, or more, elsewhere in Britain, and it is still spreading and colonising round the coasts of Scotland, Ireland, Wales and England in an extraordinary way.

Until they left St. Kilda, the St. Kildans used birds as their primary source of meat all the year round. Though in Martin's time they seem to have liked gannets best, by the time of MacAulay in 1758 the fulmar began to replace the gannet more in their staple diet. N. MacKenzie, who was minister from 1829 to 1843, thought that about twenty thousand young fulmars were hatched on the islands, of which twelve thousand were taken for food. His figure of twenty thousand was remarkably close to modern census results. In 1875 nearly 600 gallons of oil extracted from fulmars*—representing nearly ten thousand birds —were exported, and from then, until as late as 1910, usually seven and a half thousand fulmars, and often up to nearly ten thousand, were taken every year. After this the number taken decreased. Some people have suggested that the spread of the fulmar to the rest of Britain, which started in 1878, was due to an overflow of birds from St. Kilda; and that they overflowed because the inhabitants stopped eating them when they could get preserved food. They suggest this happened when the *Dunara Castle* started the first regular service to the islands in 1877. This is not so: as long as the human beings flourished, they took and ate 125 fulmars per man per year; and they flourished and did this until long after the fulmar had become established in the rest of Britain.

---

* Used for lighting and cooking, and sometimes medicinally.

I believe that the fulmars in the rest of Britain came from the Faeroes and Iceland, where there were big spreads and increases in population early in the nineteenth century.

The gannet was nearly as important in the economy of the St. Kildans as the fulmar. Martin in 1697, and MacAulay in 1758 both surely exaggerated when they said twenty thousand young were taken every year, and it was Neil MacKenzie who put things in their right proportion. He wrote that up to 1829 never more than 5,000 young were taken, and that while he was minister it was never more than 2,000, and often considerably less. Gannets went on being taken, in varying numbers, not usually over 2,000, through the eighteenth and nineteenth centuries. In 1895 an exceptional number of birds—3,200—was taken in all. In 1902 Dr. Wiglesworth climbed Boreray and the Stacks on 10 June. He gave a most admirable account of the gannets, and made the first effort at anything like an accurate census— estimating nearly fifteen thousand nests. Raids were beginning to stop now, the St. Kildans concentrating on the more accessible fulmars, and only three *hundred* gannets were taken in 1900. In 1910 six hundred adults were taken but no young were caught, and after 1910 gannet-taking seems to have petered out altogether.

In 1931 the Oxford-Cambridge expedition estimated about 16,500 pairs nesting, and in 1939 we estimated 16,900. Since then there has been a definite increase. Of the seventeen thousand-odd nests, in 1939, about 9,500 were on Boreray, 2,500 on Stac an Armin, and 5,000 on Stac Lee.

Landing on Boreray is difficult. There are two possible places, at the south end, and at a very slight indentation on the east side where in a rowing-boat we waited our moment, in 1939, to step ashore on a foot-ledge of rock, and scramble up some steep slabs. The name of the place was Sunadal. The steep slabs gave way soon to a green slope, at the very steep angle of sixty degrees. This slope was full of puffin burrows. On both sides of Sunadal were walls of rock, and on the ledges of these walls were rows and rows of gannets on their nests. All up the 1,245 feet of Boreray gannets nested on ledges on the buttresses and cliffs. There were few on the sheer western precipice just because it was sheer and smooth, and lacked ledges. Looking down from the slope of Sunadal,

Robert Atkinson

Stac Lee, 544 ft., from the east (sea-level). This remarkable gabbro rock, whose east and west ends both overhang, was climbed by the St. Kildans to collect young gannets in August and September. Over 5,000 pairs nest on it

James Fisher

Stac an Armin, 627 ft., from SSE. (observer 1,200 ft. near top of Boreray). On this, the highest stack in Britain, over 2,500 pairs of gannets nest. On its base, in or about 1840, the last British great auk was killed

About half the five thousand pairs of gannets on Stac Lee nest on its bevelled top, which faces away from the 1,245-foot western precipice of Boreray

gannets in the sun shone with the utmost resplendence, very bright white. There was an incessant harsh, raucous, coughing, rattling, roaring, rising noise of gannets.

This huge gannet colony, on Boreray, Stac Lee and Stac an Armin, had one-fifth of all the 167,000 breeding adult gannets in the world, in 1939. It was nearly twice as big as any other gannet colony. It was then, and is now, more magnificent and wonderful than any other, remote and steep and romantic as many of the others are, Stac Lee, though less high than Stac an Armin, is the more remarkable of the two stacks. It is 544 feet high, and was climbed by the St. Kildans as a routine every season, to obtain young gannets. To get on, a rope must be cast from a boat round an

Finlay MacQueen, last of the St. Kildan wildfowlers. At the end of the long tapering rod is a horsehair noose, which he guides under the feet of the puffins. Seabirds often regard the noose with curiosity, until the fowler strikes

iron peg on a blind ledge. At least two ornithologists, Dr. Wiglesworth, and Mr. Oliver Pike, the well-known photographer, have climbed it, and the two enterprising naturalists, the late Norman Heathcote and his sister, Miss Evelyn Heathcote, climbed it in July 1898. Miss Heathcote is the only woman to have done so.

The bevelled top of Stac Lee is seen at its best only from an aeroplane, for it is turned away from the cliff of Boreray across the way, and faces upwards and out to sea. From the air Eric Hosking and some R.A.F. photographers have taken photographs straight down on to this top face, where the gannets are crowded solidly at beak-range. Each nest occupies almost exactly a square yard. Off the north end of Boreray the other stack—

Stac an Armin—higher and bigger, and more conical, has a sheer face to sea. The rest of it is less spectacular than Stac Lee. At Stac an Armin the last British great auk was found.

The great auk, or garefowl, was about 30 inches long—very like a double-length razorbill with an ordinary razorbill's wings; it was quite incapable of flight but a magnificent swimmer. The last great auks ever seen by man were killed in Iceland on 4 June 1844. St. Kilda was one of its last breeding-places in Britain. Martin in 1697 talked to St. Kildans who certainly had seen it breeding; but it is doubtful whether it was still breeding then. By 1758 it was only an occasional visitor. One was taken on Hirta in 1821. The last of all the British great auks was caught on Stac an Armin in July of 1840 or a neighbouring year, and beaten to death by the St. Kildans, McKinnon and MacQueen, as they thought it was a witch.

Another St. Kilda animal that has now become extinct, or most probably so, is the St. Kilda house-mouse. Though this animal must have been on St. Kilda for hundreds of years, the earlier writers do not mention it. In August 1844 James Wilson was ashore on Hirta for a week, and mentions mice in his account. He did not say whether they were house- or field-mice. In June 1894 J. Steele Elliott found two sorts of mice on St. Kilda—a house-mouse, which was "fairly numerous among the dwellings", and a specimen of *Apodemus,* the long-tailed field-mouse, much greyer than the normal *Apodemus.* These two animals were described as new species by G. E. H. Barrett-Hamilton in the *Proceedings of the Zoological Society of London* for 1899. There are two coloured lithographs of the mice in this paper, by the artist J. Smit. Most people nowadays regard these creatures as geographical races of the mainland forms, and not as full species. James Waterston, on St. Kilda in 1905, gave serious study to them. He found that the field-mouse fed largely on grass and various seeds, and was distributed fairly commonly round Village Bay and in Glen Mor. On Dùn it was abundant, and the men who sometimes slept in a semi-underground house there said that at night the mice ran over their bodies in numbers. There was none on Boreray. The house-mouse he found swarming in all the houses, and in cletts within the cultivated area. It varied greatly in size and coloration of the belly, which

was sometimes smoky and sometimes "a lovely creamy yellow".

In 1910 and 1911 W. Eagle Clarke spent nearly 12 weeks on St. Kilda, and prepared sixty skins of the field-mouse, and forty of the house-mouse. He found the field-mouse almost everywhere on Hirta, Soay and Dùn, in the crofted area, near the houses, in the warehouses, on cliff-faces, hillsides, hilltops, and in cletts and walls. In the cletts and walls, it overlapped with the house-mouse, which was very abundant in the houses.

The house-mouse continued abundant in the houses, especially in Cottage No. 16, up to the evacuation in 1930. In 1931 the Oxford-Cambridge expedition set traps in every house and clett in the village, with six catch-alive traps for six days. They caught one house-mouse in No. 8, found ten house-mice in No. 16, and caught one other house-mouse in a clett. All the rest caught were field-mice. They concluded that the dozen house-mice encountered were not far short of the entire population. Their researches showed that the *field-mouse* continued to thrive and was abundant. They may be the last people to have seen the St. Kilda house-mouse alive.

Our party found only field-mice in 1939. In 1947 we could find no trace of the house-mouse; we searched every house. I believe that *Mus musculus muralis*—or *Mus muralis*—the St. Kilda house-mouse, became extinct after 1931, probably not long after. Now it is the *Apodemus* that haunts the ruins of the old village.

This history illustrates the theory, now widely held among biologists, that two closely allied species cannot live in the same place and share the same home and habits. As long as there were men to provide the house-mice with a commensal life indoors, the house-mice could survive. They overlapped with the field-mice in the cletts and walls and barns, but their staple was fundamentally different. When the men went, the house-mice had to live on the same food as the field-mice, and enter into direct, open competition with them. They failed, against a species better adapted. If there had been no field-mice on St. Kilda, the house-mice would probably have survived and have adapted themselves to a field-mouse type of existence. That house-mice can do this, in the absence of *Apodemus,* has been abundantly proved. In the Faeroes, where there is no *Apodemus,* the

Fulmars on their nests on a cliff-buttress of Hirta, St. Kilda, the headquarters of the breeding distribution of this species in Britain

Robert Atkinson

The St. Kilda field-mouse, photographed in captivity. This is greyer and larger than the Apodemus *of the rest of the Hebrides, or that of the British mainland. It is found on Hirta, Soay and Dùn, but not on Boreray*

house-mice (which have been on many of the islands for at least 250 years) live an outdoor life, and though their headquarters are in the villages, some live quite happily on bird-cliffs, as Vevers and Evans have found. Also, on Lunga, in the Treshnish Isles (Inner Hebrides) Darling caught seventy-five house-mice in his camp in four months in 1937. Lunga had been uninhabited by human beings for about eighty years, and has no *Apodemus*. Conversely, in many parts of the Highlands where there are no house-mice, *Apodemus* comes into the houses in winter. But there is no proved case, from anywhere, of field-mice and house-mice living *together* in the open country without the house-mice being in some way dependent on man (e.g. living on, or in, corn-stacks). The only possible case of this kind, reported by Oldfield Thomas from Portugal in 1896, lacks circumstantial detail and is open to doubt.

Though it is difficult to prove the absence of a secretive animal, there is little doubt that the St. Kilda house-mouse is extinct.

The other St. Kilda mammal which was brought there by man is by no means extinct. Nobody knows when St. Kilda was first colonised, or by whom, though the native tradition was that their ancestors came from North Uist, the nearest part of the Outer Hebrides. But very early in the history of St. Kilda a little brown sheep was brought there by the Norsemen who were masters of the Hebrides at that time. This sheep is unique. It resembles the wild mouflon more than does any other domestic sheep, though it is smaller. It is a relic, a living fossil, of the domestic sheep of a millennium ago. In the days when St. Kilda was inhabited, it was established purely on Soay; the herd belonged to the laird, who was for many years the McLeod of McLeod.

Robert Atkinson

1947

On Hirta various breeds of sheep were tried by the natives, changing as new types came along in the Hebrides and were imported. Most of the Hirta sheep had a good deal of blackface in them, and by the time of the evacuation blackface predominated. At the evacuation on 28 August 1930 a few blackface were left on Hirta, and quite a lot on Boreray. By about 1937 the last Hirta blackface had been removed and the new laird, the present Marquis of Bute, had successfully established a herd of Soay sheep on Hirta. Now Soay and Hirta are both full of fine Soay sheep. Boreray still has half-wild blackface—blackface untouched and untended since 1939. There are at least three hundred on the steep green southern pastures. In 1939 there were, according to Lord Bute, 500 to 600 Soay sheep on Hirta (many more than there were in 1931): in 1947 there were at least 400. The sheep were now grazing the village

meadows. Where, in 1939, there was a marsh with rushes, in 1947 there was short turf, well-trodden. This has affected the snipe. When the people went away, snipe took over the village. In 1939 we found a great change from 1931; about twenty pairs were actually nesting in or near the village, and snipe were standing on the roofs of the ruins and singing. But by 1947 the sheep had grazed their cover right down, and there were only *two* pairs breeding in the village. The increase of sheep has also been the probable cause of the change among the starlings on Hirta. In 1931 there were nine pairs, in 1939 at least twenty-six, and in 1947 at least fifty. The starlings nest all over the place, in cletts and walls and holes in the ground and rocks. While we were there the harsh cry of hungry young was heard from the nests, and I found eleven nests in an hour.

The changes in the breeding animal population

of St. Kilda since the evacuation, as shown by the censuses in 1931, 1939 and 1947, are interesting. A large number of animals have been apparently unaffected; in their numbers we can detect no change: such are the raven, hooded crow, twite, meadow- and rock-pipits, wheatear, wren, peregrine, great black-backed gull, kittiwake and guillemot. Some burrowing species defy census work, and we do not know what has happened to the populations of storm- and Leach's petrels, the Manx shearwater, and the amazingly numerous puffin, except that they exist, and are substantial. We know that the field-mice have invaded the houses and barns in the deserted village, but whether they have increased elsewhere we cannot tell.

Two animals have markedly increased throughout the sixteen-year period—the starling and the eider duck (the St. Kildans used to take eider eggs). The shag, the razorbill and the Soay sheep increased between 1931 and 1939, and have stayed constant since. The numbers of the gannet, oystercatcher, herring- and lesser black-backed gulls were roughly the same in 1931 and 1939, but increased markedly between 1939 and 1947. The fulmar also increased between these years. The snipe on Hirta increased remarkably in the first half of the period, but partly regressed in the second. The domestic sheep on Boreray have fluctuated, and were probably more numerous in 1939 than in 1931 or 1947. The black guillemot, in 1939, looked as if it was on the way to extinction. Only one bird was then seen; but two pairs at least were present in 1947. Two species *have* become extinct, the house-mouse (probably between 1931 and 1939) and the rock-dove (between 1939 and 1947). In most parts of its range the rock-dove breeds on sea-cliffs but feeds in cultivated fields. One new breeding species has arrived; the golden plover, found breeding for the first time in 1947 by John Naish, on the table-land of Mullach Sgar.

Grey seals are about the cliffs of Hirta all summer. On 29 September 1947, which is in the breeding-time of the seals, from an aeroplane over St. Kilda we looked hard in all likely places for cows hauled out, and for new-born calves. We saw none, though many seals were swimming in the bay. Now that it is quite deserted, St. Kilda would be a safe place for seals to breed. Seal calves could lie happily, as they do on Rona, upon the little fields that man once ploughed.

St. Kilda *is* a safe place for life. It *is* a sanctuary. The Marquis of Bute, who has been laird since 1934, himself a naturalist, keeps it so. He allows nothing to be taken, no human souvenir or relic, no stone or plant or animal. He wishes it to be left as a perfect sanctuary, where wild animals and plants may go the ways of nature, without any trace of the influence of man. There can be no other great place in Britain where such a natural experiment is possible.

Man's future on St. Kilda is in one role only—the role of *observer*. He is miscast, now, in any other part. As observer, he may see new things, such as the first breeding of the golden plover which we saw in 1947: he may follow the increases, as of eider duck, and gannet, and lesser black-back: he may, one day, determine the exact nesting-grounds and numbers of the petrels and shearwaters: he may find a method of counting the puffins: he may watch the spring and autumn bird migrations, which have only been closely studied for two seasons in St. Kilda's history: he may study the insects, of which there are now little more than lists, and plot the succession of the plants. Whatever he studies, the future observer of St. Kilda will be haunted the rest of his life by the place, and tantalised by the impossibility of describing it, to those who have not seen it.

REFERENCES

A selection of sources from which facts about St. Kilda may be derived is as follows:

G. E. H. BARRETT-HAMILTON (1899) *On the species of the genus Mus inhabiting St. Kilda.* Proc. Zool. Soc. Lond. 1899: 77-88.

A. M. COCKBURN (1935) *The geology of St. Kilda.* Trans. Roy. Soc. Edinb. 58: 511-147.

T. H. HARRISSON AND DAVID LACK (1934) *The breeding birds of St. Kilda.* Scot. Nat. 1934: 59-69.

NORMAN HEATHCOTE (1900) *St. Kilda.* London.

RICHARD KEARTON (1899) *With nature and a camera.* London.

KENNETH MACAULAY (1764) *The history of St. Kilda, etc.* London.

MARTIN MARTIN (1698) *A late voyage to St. Kilda . . .* London.

E. M. NICHOLSON AND JAMES FISHER (1940) *A bird census of St. Kilda, 1939.* Brit. Birds 34: 29-35.

HENRY SEEBOHM (1884) *On a new species of British wren.* Zoologist. 1884: 333-5.

GEORGE SETON (1878) *St. Kilda past and present.* Edinburgh.

MALCOLM STEWART (1937) *A bibliography of the island of St. Kilda in St. Kilda Papers* (collection), Oxford.

J. WIGLESWORTH (1903) *St. Kilda and its birds . . .* Liverpool.

Troglodytes troglodytes hirtensis, *the St. Kilda wren, at its nest in a clett behind the Manse on Hirta*

Robert Atkinson

ROBERT ATKINSON

LEACH'S PETREL

"I THINK it would hardly be possible to name a bird which apparently could have less to do with distribution than a petrel." Thus Charles Darwin, in a letter of 2 March 1859. He had in mind, no doubt, the vast ocean range of pelagic petrels, as against the narrow landward territories of many common residents; the breadth of the Atlantic being no particularly wide range for a petrel. One homogeneous race (*Oceanodroma l. leucorrhoa*) of our own Leach's petrel—the rarest and most pelagic of the petrels and shearwaters which breed at British coasts—nests from the fringe of Britain, by North Atlantic islands to the east coast of America, and, in the next ocean, to the Aleutian and Kurile Islands of the North Pacific. This is not any haphazard distribution. A plankton map of the Atlantic shows a band of greatest plankton density spreading right across the ocean, from Britain and Norway to Labrador, Newfoundland and Maine on the American side, belling up in between to the northward, to within the arctic circle. All the

Atlantic breeding stations of Leach's petrels lie neatly within this comparatively narrow band of thickest plankton: the petrels come ashore to breed to Britain in about latitude 58°N., north and west to the Faeroes and islands off Iceland, to Greenland, and to the American east coast, down as far south as Maine in about latitude 45°. Leach's petrel—it explains itself—is a planktonic feeder.

The British colonies are confined to the extreme north-west periphery of Britain, to the smallest and outermost isles of the Outer Hebrides—the species but brushes a wing-tip at the British Isles. The birds come ashore only at night and there burrow underground: no doubt if they could, they would never come ashore at all and would hatch upon the face of the waters. This is the only British breeding bird now exclusive to the Outer Hebrides (if some Hebridean subspecies or races such as wrens, starling and song-thrush be excepted), so it has a special place in the natural history of those Western Isles.

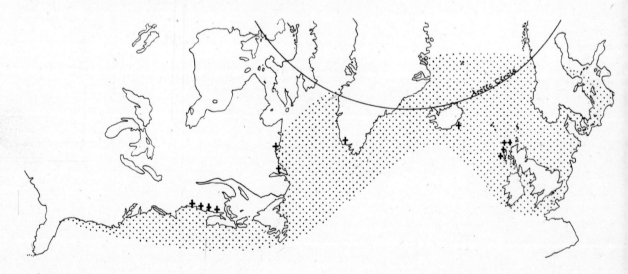

The greatest density of plankton (dotted area) and breeding stations of Leach's petrel (crosses) in the North Atlantic

Robert Atkinson

North Rona: entrance to the burrow of a Leach's petrel among the ruins of the deserted village.

At present Leach's petrels are known in two islands—North Rona and Sula Sgeir, and in two groups of islands—the Flannans (only Eilean Mòr so far) and the St. Kilda group. The population contained in these islands may be something of the order of 2,000 pairs, so that as a native speciality the species is rare by distribution and difficulty of access rather than by numbers. Human affairs have had little to do with it and though in the era cf collectors it suffered some interference in St. Kilda, Rona and the Flannans, this was never enough to do permanent harm. At the Flannans the birds still breed in ground swept by stray beams from the lighthouse; you walk a few yards from the lighthouse compound and come into the midst of their strange night flighting. Small petrels were negligible to old-time St. Kilda natives, among the myriad other sea-fowls, but in the Faeroes storm petrels and probably also Leach's—both being equally oily—used to be threaded with a wick and used as lamps: *Alata flamma*, as an old woodcut of such a lamp is titled.

The birds' peculiar habits make a naturalist's inquiry unusually difficult. Even in the Flannan Islands, where probably at least 200 pairs nest within a surface area of only some 40 acres, there is in day-time literally no sign or sound of petrel habitation. The burrow entrances are tiny in the broken ground, are usually overgrown with chickweed, mayweed or thrift, and even when discovered commonly show no signs of use. When John Ainslie and I at last got a landing on Sula Sgeir, on 3 August 1939, we started prising up the boulders lying scattered among the thick mayweed on the southern crown of the rock. But after heaving up—or attempting to—an exhausting number of boulders, most of which were immovable, we found just three Leach's petrel nestlings.

Drawing by "Fish-Hawk"

Yet as soon as darkness fell, the night air was alive with petrels: we guessed that here was a population of some 400 pairs, as many as in the relatively well-known colony on North Rona, where the green walls of the old half-underground village are riddled with petrels' burrows; and where, by contrast, burrow entrances are often quite obvious, drilled through the turf and thrift, and with sometimes a trickle of excavated earth outside so that they look like miniature rabbit burrows.

Sula Sgeir is probably an ancient nesting ground for these birds, but it is such a difficult place first to get to and then to land upon that the existence of the petrels was not suspected until

Malcolm Stewart spent a night on the island in the summer of 1932. He was the first naturalist to do so and he heard noises reminiscent of Rona nights. The one or two nineteenth-century naturalists who managed to land had been content with an hour or two ashore in daylight; it is not the sort of place to be liked by a skipper, particularly when he has put a party ashore. Our own night on the rock seven years after Stewart well confirmed his suspicions.

Many of the birds were nesting in and below the walls of the few dry-stone bothies on the rock. These ancient bothies are still lived in by the men who make the forty-mile voyage each autumn in an open boat from Ness in Lewis, to kill and salt down a thousand or two young gannets—local delicacy amongst the Lewismen. The gannetry has been slowly declining: as the gannets have retreated away from the area of the bothies they have left a soft debris, at once overgrown with thrift and very suitable for petrels' burrowings. The fact that we found Leach's petrels right up to the edge of the gannetry—flying out over the heads of the sleeping gannets at night—suggested that they might be ready for further expansion; it was a small pointer. There are two others. There was the record, not since confirmed, of a single pair breeding in 1933 at Sule Skerry between North Rona and Orkney; and in the summer of 1939 R. B. Freeman found a single bird, no egg, in a hole on Haskeir, a rocky island off the coast of North Uist. Leach's petrels *may* have been found-ing new colonies in the remoter Western Isles, un-visited by naturalists since before the war, but there may yet be long-established colonies still unknown simply because there are plenty of apparently suitable islands on which no naturalist has yet spent a night. There would be nothing obvious about a change in population, one way or the other, unlike the case of the fulmar; change could go unnoticed for years.

The night ashore is the difficulty! The most competent naturalist could easily miss a colony in a day-time visit. Dùn, for instance, at St. Kilda, has long been known as a breeding place; in fact the very first British specimen of a Leach's petrel was found at St. Kilda in 1818. But John MacGillivray in 1840, and H. J. Elwes, who included St. Kilda in a tour of some of the better-known Hebridean bird islands and cliffs in 1868, both tried Dùn and both were "disappointed in finding them". They must have been there. In a brief landing on Dùn in June 1947 I could see no burrow entrances but after heaving up a few boulders did uncover one Leach's petrel sitting on its egg—a pleasant reunion with the species I had last seen on Sula Sgeir in 1939. The strength of the Dùn colony remains quite unknown.

In the hand Leach's petrels are at once distin-guished from storm petrels by size, colour and the forked tail; their nestlings are similar but Leach's lack the bald spot on the crown noticeable in storm petrels' chicks; Leach's eggs are larger but otherwise the same. Occupied burrows of both species have a strong musky smell. However, once the watcher has been given a night on a possible petrel island he can be in no doubt about it: if the birds are present at all the commotion of cries and flying which they keep up all night above the nesting area will be unmistakable and the noises from underground soon reveal burrows. Certainly some petrel peculiarities are shared by Leach's, storm and fulmar petrels—the shyness of land, the laying of a solitary white egg each year, the in-tentional neglect of the grossly fat young as soon as they are fledged so that they are starved into flying condition—are common to all three; and young and adults of all three have the habit of

Drawing by "Fish-Hawk"

squirting oil when alarmed. But the night flight-ing of Leach's petrel is peculiar. And from the observer's point of view it is the spectacular part of the birds' life ashore.

The first birds begin to arrive soon after dark—a shadowy brushing of wings. They fly in silence. When a company has gathered the staccato calling begins, and soon works up to a pitch. The cries are loud and outlandish; the flight is headlong, at breakneck speed in the darkness. There are collisions—birds tumble to the ground. They plump down and shuffle underground to visit their young, and there feed them with oily regurgi-tation. Others are digging at their burrows—this continues even late in the season. They scuffle and call from underground as loudly as from the air and the excited peeping of the chicks adds to the noise. The impression of the night flying—for which no particular reason has been suggested—is of unbounded excitement and urgency, energy unleashed. It goes on without flagging all night until with the first sign of dawn, the activity gradually runs down; the birds go back to sea or, if they have eggs or newly-hatched chicks, remain quietly below ground all day.

The whole breeding economy appears to be con-ducted in a remarkably casual manner: a sitting bird not relieved by its mate may go off to sea and leave the egg to incubate itself; nestlings may be neglected for days together, quite apart from nights of storm when hardly a bird may be able to get ashore. Nor is this irregularity in feeding the nest-lings consistent throughout the colony, for one chick may be fed twice on a night when its next-door neighbour is not visited at all; this makes the problem of their parents' ocean feeding far from simple. How far they may forage during the day-time is quite unknown; in various trips about the islands I have not yet certainly seen a Leach's petrel at sea, though storm petrels, fulmars and shear-waters are comparatively frequent. The food is planktonic; probably individuals or small parties spread widely over the ocean rather than forage in flocks, though it is known that a flock soon fore-gathers at any rich spoil of food. Leach's petrels have been gathered off the American coast by boats trolling cod livers. The Atlantic food supply is probably variable, according to such factors as weather and the intermittent surface-breeding swarms of some of the constituents of plankton.

Petrels' ocean days are beyond the reach of private naturalists; only their nights are just within.

And the islands where unknown colonies of Leach's petrels may be awaiting a night of dis-covery? The likeliest islands for continued search will be small, oceanic and as near as possible to existing colonies. There are several suitable-look-ing islands westward of the main range of the Outer Hebrides, though far within the outermost line of St. Kilda–Flannans–Rona, so difficult to reach. The most promising of these seem to be the various Haskeir islands off North Uist, particularly after R. B. Freeman's find, and the solitary, little-known islet of Gasker, eight miles off the coast of Harris—I have a particular fancy for this one. There are also innumerable islets within the main range, and it does seem that in the past Leach's petrels may not have been so strictly confined to the extreme fringe of the Hebrides as they now are (so far as is known). H. J. Elwes, who failed to find the birds at St. Kilda in 1868, did find in Mingu-lay "a few pairs in holes and cracks in the peat". They have never since been found there. In 1871 Robert Gray told of having "instituted inquiries which resulted in the discovery of . . . an additional nursery . . . a more extensive breeding place in the island of Rum"; nor has this ever been found again. Some of the islands of Orkney might be considered, and colonies used to nest off the Irish coast, so any off-lying islands there are a proposi-tion. The birds are in their burrows from May to September.

REFERENCES

J. A. AINSLIE AND R. ATKINSON (1937) *On the Breeding Habits of Leach's Fork-tailed Petrel.* Brit. Birds 30: 234-48, 276-77.

R. ATKINSON AND J. A. AINSLIE (1940) *The British Breeding Status of Leach's Fork-tailed Petrel.* Brit. Birds 34: 50-55.

H. J. ELWES (1869) *The Bird-Stations of the Outer Hebrides.* Ibis ser. 2, vol. 5: 20-37.

R. B. FREEMAN (1940) *On the Birds of the Islands Oigh-Sgeir and Causamul, North Uist.* Brit. Birds 33: 330-32.

ROBERT GRAY (1871) *Birds of the West of Scotland.* Glasgow.

D. R. GRIFFIN (1940) *Homing Experiments with Leach's Petrels.* Auk 57: 61-74.

MALCOLM STEWART (1933) *Ronay.* Oxford, University Press.

H. G. VEVERS

THE NATURAL HISTORY OF AILSA CRAIG

SITUATED in the Firth of Clyde, 10 miles to the west of Girvan in Ayrshire, and 12 miles from the nearest part of Arran, Ailsa Craig is perhaps the most striking single feature of the landscape in this part of Scotland. It rises to a height of 1,114 feet, covers an area of 225 acres and is a little more than 2¼ miles in circumference at the base. During the Middle Ages the rock belonged for a time to the Earls of Carrick, the family of Robert the Bruce. From them it passed in 1404 to the Abbey of Crossraguel by whom it was granted in 1548 along with other lands to the Kennedy family, in whose possession it still remains, being part of the Marquisate of Ailsa. With the exception of a few acres sold to the Northern Lighthouse Commissioners, the Craig is rented to a tenant as a farm, whose principal products are at present curling stones and rabbits. At one time numbers of sea-birds were exported to the mainland as food, but this practice has now ceased.

To the naturalist Ailsa Craig presents many interesting features. Geologically the Craig appeared in the Coal Measure period as the plug to a volcano which had pierced the surrounding strata of the older Silurian and Ordovician periods. The material of this plug is a fine-grained granite made up principally of felspar and quartz, but also containing dark blue crystals of riebeckite, a rare variety of hornblende, found in very few other places in the world. On the south and west sides of the rock the granite forms tall perpendicular cliffs which are occupied by bird colonies. At intervals the granite is traversed by thin dolerite dykes which were forced to the surface during the Tertiary era as intrusions. Being relatively softer the dolerite has been weathered away at a faster rate than the granite and where this has occurred, caves and ravines have been formed. And so at the present time Ailsa Craig is a huge block of rock, with almost perpendicular cliffs to the south

and west, rising anything up to 600 feet (the Barestack, at this height, is probably the highest overhanging cliff in Britain) and with steep but not perpendicular slopes on the north and east sides for the first 400 feet. Above this level the gradient decreases until the summit is reached. This, then, is the structure on which the plant and animal communities of Ailsa live.

The plant communities are fairly well defined, and they play a large part in determining the character of the land animal communities. From the summit down to about the 400-foot level are what may be termed the main slopes, where the gradient is low, drainage good without being excessive, and where the soil layer is relatively thick. Here we find a large area covered with grasses, of which the most abundant are bent grass (*Agrostis canina*), and sheep's fescue (*Festuca ovina*) interspersed with sheep's sorrel (*Rumex acetosella*), heath bedstraw (*Galium saxatile*) and a number of mosses and lichens. This is the main feeding ground of the rabbits which abound on the island, and which keep the turf well nibbled and compact. The most abundant land bird on the grassland is the meadow-pipit which gives place in the more rocky, but not necessarily lower-lying, parts of the island to the rock-pipit. In places where there have been large falls of rock one finds screes made up of huge angular granite boulders covered with mosses and lichens, and affording excellent shelter to rabbits, and to a few pairs of blackbirds. In one sheltered area of the main slopes, on the east side between 400 and 500 feet, the ground is a little more level, so that more soil has accumulated. Here the grasses are replaced by a community in which the dominant plant is bracken interspersed with blue-bells (*Scilla nonscripta*) and red campion (*Lychnis dioica*). In this habitat a study of the soil profile with its contained plants shows some interesting

James Fisher

Ailsa Craig; the Main Craigs. Gannets nest on the flat ledges where a dolerite dyke splits the cliff

Ailsa Craig from WNW., the coast of Ayrshire beyond. The cliffs are white with the bodies and guano of about five thousand pairs of gannets

points: the bluebell roots and bulbs are found at a depth of 8 inches, and the plant grows up and flowers in spring. The bracken rootstock, on the other hand, grows only 4 inches below the surface, and its fronds grow up in the late summer and shed their spores in early autumn. Here therefore is an example of two plants living in the same area and yet being, as far as is known, relatively independent of each other.

On the sides of the rock clefts and caves there is good shelter from the wind, and an abundant water supply, but there is very little soil to provide anchorage for plants. The only plants which occur commonly in these conditions (and in luxuriant form) are navelwort (*Cotyledon umbilicus*) and a fern, the sea spleenwort (*Asplenium marinum*), together with one or two mosses and a liverwort. These sheltered places provide excellent cover for the smaller land-birds, especially the rock-pipits, of which each pair takes up a breeding territory

Eric Hosking

Navelwort, Cotyledon umbilicus

Robert Atkinson

Rock-pipit

which is vigorously defended against intruders of the same species. There are also about ten pairs of wrens on the island, most of which are seen in these clefts and caves above highwater level. Both these birds are resident the whole year round: in spring, however, a few pairs of migrating willow-warblers and robins also appear in the same sheltered spots.

On the east side of the rock from 20 feet up to the 400-feet level the angle of slope is steep although never perpendicular, and the soil layer is much reduced in thickness. These factors combined with the acidity of the soil and the drying power of the wind have resulted in a heather association with bell heather (*Erica cinerea*) as the dominant plant, accompanied by sheep's fescue (*Festuca ovina*) and occasional plants of dog violet (*Viola canina*) and wild strawberry (*Fragaria vesca*).

This brief survey of the vegetation of all parts of the rock except the bird cliffs shows how the plant communities vary strikingly according to the physical and chemical factors in their environment, such as angle of slope, exposure, drainage, thickness of soil layer and acidity. We have also seen how the smaller land birds and rabbits fit into the scheme and how each keeps to its own type of habitat. But there are other mammals, besides the rabbits, which roam all over the island looking for food and shelter. Perhaps the most important of these from the biological viewpoint is the brown rat which appeared on the island after a nearby shipwreck in the latter part of the last century. It occurs everywhere, but mainly around the bird cliffs in summer and near the lighthouse buildings in winter when other sources of food are lacking. Next come the goats, which are kept by the tenant and lightkeepers for their milk, and finally the Soay sheep,* a rich brown variety of mountain sheep which has also been introduced by Man and which thrives exceedingly well on the grassland of the main slopes.

All the species of plants and animals so far mentioned are closely bound up with each other. The rock and soil provide anchorage for the plants, which supply food for the birds and mammals, which in their turn enrich the soil by their droppings. Now, however, we come to the other part of the island, the bird cliffs, where the inter-

---

* See p. 106 of this issue.

James Fisher

The battle between these gannets started 400 feet above on a cliff-ledge of Ailsa Craig over some nest-material. The gannets fell to the rounded, sea-worn boulders below, their beaks still interlocked, and continued their struggle among the seaweed

Kittiwakes

John Ainslie

Guillemots

John Markham

Razorbills

John Ainslie

relationships are somewhat different and where the vegetation plays a very minor part.

Along almost the whole stretch of the west and south sides of the rock are cliffs occupied in spring and summer by many thousand pairs of breeding sea-birds. In most cases each species nests in well-defined groups with others of its own kind. The gannets nest on the tops of the granite pillars and in other places where there is a fair amount of room, for they build an untidy nest of seaweed and grass which occupies an area of about one yard square. The adults arrive at the rock in early spring (in recent years a few birds have stayed near the Craig right through the winter), and lay their single egg in April-May. The young hatch out 40 to 45 days later and do not leave the rock until August-September. During 1939 a census was taken of the twenty-odd colonies of this species of gannet which skirt the North Atlantic seaboard and we now know, with reasonable accuracy, the actual breeding population on each rock and cliff. The grand total was 83,000 breeding pairs, of which 5,400 pairs bred on Ailsa Craig.

The other sea-birds on Ailsa have not been studied in such detail, but even so quite a lot is known of their habits and disposition during the breeding season. Of these the members of the auk family are among the most numerous. The guillemots nest in long rows on the narrower ledges which are unsuitable for the gannets, and lay a pear-shaped egg straight on to the bare rock. This shape is of some significance as it allows the eggs to spin round on the blunt axis when disturbed, without falling over the edge of the rock. Similar in general appearance but having a thicker bill with white markings is the razorbill. It nests in rather small numbers in rock crevices and under the shelter of boulders. The third auk species, the puffin, lives an even more secluded life, for it nests in holes and disused rabbit burrows, dug into the soil itself. It is, therefore, not found on the main cliffs, but either above them on the edges of the grassy slopes or below them in the talus which accumulates at their foot. Nowadays, however, the puffin is not so abundant on the Craig as it used to be, as its nesting habits leave it wide open to the depredations of the brown rats which take the eggs and young.

Of the gulls the most socially minded is the kittiwake, an attractive, delicately built species which nests on the very smallest ledges where one would scarcely expect a bird of its size could land let alone build its nest. The other species of the gull family, the herring- and lesser black-backed gulls, nest in small, scattered groups on the rocky ground above the main cliffs. During the breed-ing season they feed largely on the young of the kittiwake and guillemot, on the offal which sur-rounds the gannets' nests, and even on grain picked up on the fields of the mainland.

This completes the survey of the sea-birds, but there are two other important bird species, of each of which there is usually one nest on the rock. These are the raven and peregrine falcon, which together with the larger gulls form the predatory group of the island.

If one considers the bird colonies from the ecological standpoint it is at once apparent how differently they are orientated to their environment when compared with the land birds and mammals. The sea-birds use the rock as a resting and nesting place but they are quite independent of its plant cover and (with the exception of the impact of the man-introduced rats on the puffin), of its land mammals. Their main food is marine in origin and they derive nothing essential from the vegeta-tion—the grass used in the gannets' nests is probably only taken because it is at hand, for on more isolated, grass-free rocks the gannet breeds just as well on a purely seaweed nest. On the other hand the sea-birds contribute something to the land side of the picture, by reason of the manure which is dropped all over the rock.

A study of the natural history of Ailsa Craig therefore shows quite clearly that there are really two main habitats, one land and one marine. Within each habitat the species are closely inter-related ecologically, but between each habitat there is only a very slender link.

REFERENCES

J. FISHER and H. G. VEVERS (1943) *The breeding distribution, history and population of the North Atlantic gannet* (Sula bassana) *Part I. A history of the gannet's colonies, and the census in 1939.* J. Anim. Ecol. 12: 173-213.

R. LAWSON (1895) *Ailsa Craig: its history and natural history.* Paisley. (J. and R. Parlane.)

H. G. VEVERS (1936) *The land vegetation of Ailsa Craig.* J. Ecol. 24: 424-45.

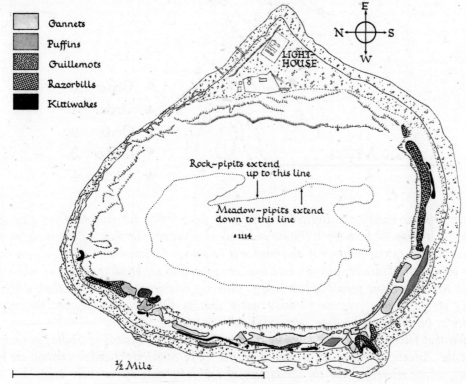

Legend:
- Gannets
- Puffins
- Guillemots
- Razorbills
- Kittiwakes

LIGHT-HOUSE

Rock-pipits extend up to this line

Meadow-pipits extend down to this line

▲ 1114

½ Mile

Based on the Ordnance Survey Map.   By permission of H.M. Stationery Office

Bird Map of Ailsa Craig

THE ATLANTIC SEAL

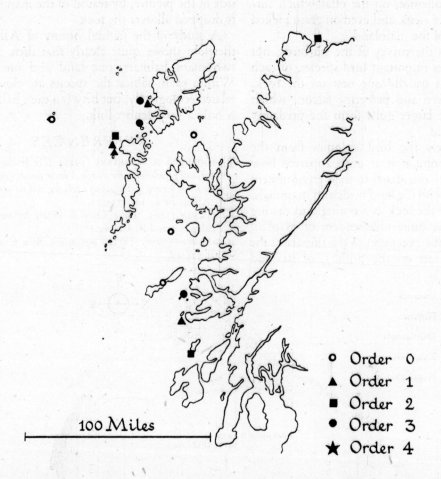

○ Order 0
▲ Order 1
■ Order 2
● Order 3
★ Order 4

100 Miles

The map shows what is known or suspected at present of the breeding distribution of the grey seal in the Western Isles. It is compiled from the literature and from observations taken on a flight made on 29 and 30 September 1947 for the special purpose of observing seal colonies. Colonies in Order "o" are represented on the map by open dots. These are places where seals are present in the breeding season, or where they have bred in the past, but are not now proved to be breeding. Breeding colonies in Order 1 are those where probably under 10 young are produced a year: in Order 2 under 100: in Order 3 under 1,000: the only breeding colony in Order 4, North Rona, produces over 1,000 calves a year.

The photographs that follow were mostly taken by Robert Atkinson on the island of Shillay in October 1947. Shillay lies at the Atlantic mouth of the Sound of Harris. The commentary and description are by Dr. F. Fraser Darling, whose researches into the life-history of this interesting animal have taken him to North Rona and the Treshnish Isles. Two of the black-and-white photographs are also by Dr. Fraser Darling.

F. Fraser Darling

Here is an Atlantic seal bull newly come from the sea. He is in magnificent fat condition and probably weighs 8–9 cwt. His coat is still wet and shiny. The bulls haul out a few days before the cows and take up territories ashore, possibly three hundred yards inland, but often within a few yards of the sea. By the end of the breeding season this bull will be thin and decrepit-looking, rheumy-eyed and with a bad breath. Meantime, he is on top of his form.

Robert Atkinson

The seals are now well ashore and the cows have their calves of about a week old. The bull on the left is in repose, on his own territory, with a harem of a few cows. The area shown by the photograph is just about the size of a bull's territory. At the moment all is peace, but if the calves wander about they cause a great deal of bickering among the mothers who are very jealous. The bull takes no notice of the calves.

Robert Atkinson

*Here are two calves on the shell-sand beach among the sea-worn boulders. The marks in the sand show the move-
ments of the seals. The calf in the foreground is newly born. Note how thin it looks in comparison with the other,
which is already a week old, and has been fed on the very rich milk of the seal cow. On the seal's first day of life its
limbs look larger and more conspicuous than at any other time, and on this day alone it may use its hind flippers as a
means of progression on land. Ever afterwards the flippers are quite useless for that purpose.*

Robert Atkinson

How different is this seal calf from the newly-born one! It is about 12 days old, nearing the time when, at a fortnight, it will be left by the mother entirely to its own resources. Even now, the long white coat in which the calf is born is beginning to shed from the front of its hands, and henceforth a fortnight or more will be spent rubbing off this baby coat.

Robert Atkinson

Here is the young seal at three weeks to a month old, with all the white coat rubbed off its back, but a good deal left on the flanks. Although it is starving, the youngster is still very fat, having gained weight at such a prodigious rate in that first fortnight—from 30 lb. to 84 lb. (which is nearly 4 lb. a day). This seal should get rid of the rest of its baby coat in another week, and will then shuffle down to the ocean, but it will have to learn to feed of its own accord. There is no "further education".

F. Fraser Darling

The Atlantic seal is an inquisitive animal, but none the less wary. One may come up to take a look at you in a boat or walking on the shore, but if you should turn your head directly towards the animal or make some sudden movement, the reaction will be characteristic: the seal rises slightly out of the water in an upright position, at the same time turning over to one side with its head thrown back, so that by the time it is coming down on to its belly it is able to give the surface of the water a tremendous smack with the outstretched hand. The pistol-like crack can be heard half a mile away if the weather is calm. All neighbouring seals are warned. These animals in the picture had grown accustomed to me and if I went to the sea's edge of an evening and called to them, they would come romping through the sea to within a few yards.

ATLANTIC SEALS ON THE SHORES OF SHILLAY

The beauty of this picture is in its quality of wholeness. First, there is the Atlantic Ocean beating on the shores of Shillay, a small, uninhabited islet at the western end of the Sound of Harris in the Outer Hebrides. Secondly, there is a glimpse of shell-sand beach, another characteristic feature of the west side of the Outer Isles. We see masses of bedded rock, the Archaean gneiss, which is the oldest rock in the world and that of which the Outer Isles are composed. Then there are sea-worn boulders in the foreground, as smooth as the bodies of the seals themselves and not unlike them. Most striking of all are the seals, hauled out of the ocean for the autumnal breeding season. The Atlantic seal is a mammal which has not yet arrived at a point in evolution when it can assume a totally marine existence. The animals come ashore on these remote islets in various parts of the Hebrides in August, September and October, have their calves, suckle them for a fortnight, mate again and go back to the sea, all in a month or six weeks. The adults come ashore in very fat condition and, as far as we can see, do not feed again until they return to the ocean. This photograph shows the animals in the sea, and newly ashore, and one upon the grass about to suckle a calf. The little pool in the foreground shows a calf playing in the water (which they like to do), and it may well be the place where the calf's mother will mate again 11-14 days after its birth. The rare autumn sun gives an idyllic quality to the whole scene.

Robert Atkinson

F. FRASER DARLING

SCIENCE OR SKINS?

THE articles appearing in this number which are devoted to the natural history of islands have perforce mentioned the sub-speciation which has taken place among the isolated stocks of animals—examples are the field mice of St. Kilda, the wren of St. Kilda, the starling of Shetland and the Hebrides, the Hebridean song-thrush and hedge-sparrow. This fact of sub-speciation within the confines of our own small country is exciting to eager minds, for we have before us a living array of evolution. Interest cannot help being intense when we discover that it is not only disposition of land and sea which creates biological islands, but that the habits of animals and their social systems may also produce quite rigid insulation of stocks until some new, and again interesting, factor works change. The Atlantic grey seal, for example, has a wide range about the northern, western and island coasts during spring and summer, but the breeding stations are few. It is almost certain that the summer ranging stocks of these seals intermix, because their areas of diffusion overlap, yet the indications are that the individuals return to their own place for breeding so that each stock is genetically closed. The careful observer can note differences between the several stocks, mostly of colour and the pattern of the coat, but I have also noticed a difference of external ear development in the male sex of one stock. We may remark that these small differences are of inessentials, so to speak, and not in major structure; nature can withstand some sorting-out and expression of small differences without imposing the rigorous sieves of natural selection—but, of course, we cannot be sure about this.

Another interest was given to this aspect of natural history when Julian Huxley crystallized the idea of the *cline*, i.e. a more or less orderly trend of variation or varied numerical expression of a character between two different points of the earth's surface. The creation of biological islands by physical or psychological factors causes breaks in clines, and if the breaks are large enough to make the animal sufficiently different from its fellows at the next place along the cline, it is given sub-specific rank. The subject is, to use advisedly a much misused word, fascinating; especially when a cline is found to encircle the world, and at its point of meeting the individuals of the two ends of the cline are so different as to keep apart, and to all intents and purposes to be different species. Britain happens to be in the area where the herring-gull and the lesser black-backed gull occur together, so these are regarded as distinct species, but a study of individuals round the Palaearctic zone shows that a cline exists of intergrades between the two. The great tit also follows a cline round the hemisphere and the region of overlap appears to be in eastern Siberia. The great land masses tend to give us the evenly-graded cline; islands break it and favour that apparent discontinuity of variation which orderliness demands shall be called sub-speciation.

The general facts and ideas concerning this state of affairs in natural populations can be understood in a few minutes, but they took many years to elucidate. We have come through observation, speculation, postulation and determination to knowledge, which is science. All well and good, but do not let us forget the toll on wild life which this work has involved. Thousands of skins of once-living birds have had to be compared and measured to give us the story of the gulls and the great tit. Fortunately, they are both very numerous species.

Mankind is a species given to collecting series of objects, from tram tickets at four years old to porcelain at forty. The variety of things considered worthy of collection by adults in years is quite bewildering. Collecting can become a mania, though for the most part it is a harmless one providing a safety valve for a certain kind of temperament, and it has been responsible for preserving much that is beautiful in this world. Few of us could call ourselves free of this human specific characteristic. The trouble comes when the object fastened on for collection is a living thing which must be killed in order that it may take its place in the collector's array. A big-game hunter collects "heads" as he calls them (and a few tails as fly whisks) and makes no excuses. He shot the animals for what he thought was sport and he wanted the heads to adorn his staircase. You may not agree with that man but at least he is simple in that he shot the animals because he wanted them and is ready to say so. Years ago men shot little birds in this country and stuffed them for a collection; the rarer a little bird might be, the greater it became as a prize. Public opinion turned against these men and some of them saw that it was not a good form of collecting and gave it up voluntarily. A few may even now pursue this hobby but they place themselves outside the close friendship of their fellow men.

You may wonder what all this has to do with islands, clines and what appear to be sharp jumps of variation on certain islands. Briefly, it is this—that these natural phenomena excite the mania for killing and collection of living things, and now it is not necessary to pursue the hobby clandestinely because of public opinion and the law, poor as it is. The collector can piously clothe himself in the mantle of science and go forth shooting where he will. The idea of insular sub-species has given a new collecting value to the commonest birds and what is more, if a collector manages to establish some variant as a sub-species, he may have a fellow collector's name tacked on to it in the genitive as the third trinomial, and next time his friend will do the same for him. Not only is the urge to collect satisfied but the desire some people have to perpetuate their names in some way or other.

These collectors are frequently people of little scientific qualification and the quality of their minds appears to be such that sustained thinking and the formulation of ideas is not congenial. But they can observe closely, have great patience and can continue a hum-drum course of investigation for an indefinite period. The hunt for sub-species is therefore exactly suited to their temperaments

and the glittering prizes are their friends' and their own latinized names in the trinomial. Even the latinity gives a superficial impression that the business is scholarly. Actually, the kind of work they are doing under the cloak of science is that which would be relegated to a painstaking lab. boy anywhere else, except that the lab. boy would tire of killing long before these collectors do. It should be emphasized that a sub-species is not a real thing that can be found; it is a convenient figment of the human mind, a mental pigeon-hole into which a certain set of observations can be sorted. It is a useful mental file which must not be overfilled or it loses its value entirely. The idea of the cline should have distinct humane as well as taxonomic consequences, for it clears the mental filing cabinet of separate and complicating folders. A species remains intact as well as the idea of species; variation within it is accepted and explained by the cline.

But the collector of sub-species arranged on minute differences of plumage and measurement of certain external structures cannot be satisfied with the cline. He wants his hobby to be arranged with the virtuosity of Stanley Gibbons' astounding stamp catalogue. It would not matter if birds were not living things, but as such they are part of the earth's heritage. They are also beautiful things which the nation has the right to ask shall be left alone. The skylarks of Salisbury Plain have a right to existence, surely, without being penalized for some slight or imaginary difference from the skylarks of elsewhere. Chaffinches and crested tits have been slaughtered in the same way, and in the early summer of 1947 two ornithologists landed in South Uist and shot wheatears in an attempt to establish the existence of a distinct type or subspecies. These collectors are causing the word ornithologist (a bad word anyway) to stink. The inhabitants of South Uist were deeply offended at these men shooting wheatears with folding guns. Such practice is not within their code.

The uninitiated may ask, does not the law prevent this kind of thing? Not at all. One would imagine that the law had been fashioned for the immunity of the collectors. For example, if one reads that a number of skins of crested tits of the Scottish race have been prepared for research purposes, it would seem perfectly straightforward to bring a prosecution. But the tits may have been taken in Inverness-shire, Nairnshire or Banffshire, and that is a point one does not know. To bring a prosecution the case must first be placed before the Procurator-Fiscal of the county in which the alleged offence took place. The fact of the preparation of the skins of the tits may be stated, but the county of origin is not, so no action is possible. Wheatears are protected in Inverness-shire, of which South Uist is a part, but the protection did not protect the birds against the sub-species hunters professing research. Wrens are another species inclined to differ from island to island and though protected are nevertheless a quarry for the collectors. These people do not seem to care that the small-bird populations of small islands are strictly finite and will not stand being shot up for a series of skins. For example, the wrens on Priest Island, Ross and Cromarty, number about half a dozen pairs. If they are a very slightly separate race from the wrens of the mainland, I contend that we are not justified in establishing the fact if we endanger the existence of the stock. Ever so many museums at home and in America would like a series of male, female and immature of the St. Kilda wren. Doubtless it would be scientifically useful to provide the museums with specimens, but with a total stock in existence of less than 100 pairs, it cannot be done.

We should not forget that few of these collectors are even collecting for museums, and their so-called scientific work can be of very little value when the material (the euphemism for a bird's skin) is not available to others for study and verification. The skins are closely kept by the collectors as private property and we know nothing of how the individual specimens were selected. Some of the collectors salve their consciences by bequeathing their collections to a museum, but that is just sophistry. As it is, series of birds' skins are

property of monetary value. Some collecting of bird skins is obviously necessary from time to time, but surely it should not be at the whim of anyone who interests himself in the subject. A worker desiring to undertake a study involving the killing of a series of legally protected birds should have to state his case before a Wild Life Commission who ought to be extremely sparing in their grant of licences. All the skins obtained should be the property of the nation and placed in the national museums. This argument of law, state and property, however, is not the one on which I should wish to base a case for the suppression of collecting series of bird skins by unauthorized individuals for establishment of doubtful or non-existent sub-species. It must be on the principles of morality, humaneness and responsibility to those who follow us.

Failing the imposition of heavy sentences of penal servitude, it is probably better that cases of bird-killing should not come before the courts. Piffling fines do not deter collectors. Social ostracism could be the stronger weapon if public opinion were to express itself much more firmly than at present. Such bodies as the British Ornithologists' Union and the British Ornithologists' Club should investigate alleged offences in a stricter manner and expel proved offenders. It is the duty of societies of this kind to respect the law of the country. The editors of journals devoted to birds should refuse to consider papers dealing with attempts to establish sub-speciation by means of measurements and assessments of colour of series of skins obtained without authority and scientific check. Ultimately, we may hope that new and clearer laws will help to prevent this pseudo-scientific despoliation of limited stocks of living creatures, but law must be backed by firm public opinion if it is to be effective.

Whooper swans   *Wash drawing by Keith Shackleton*

THE NEW NATURALIST
A JOURNAL OF BRITISH NATURAL HISTORY

AUTUMN

MIGRATION

CONTENTS

C. B. WILLIAMS: *Some Problems of Animal Migration* 133

C. B. WILLIAMS: *Notes on British Immigrant Butterflies* 141

G. V. T. MATTHEWS: *Bird Navigation* 146

PETER SCOTT: *The Migration of Wild Geese* 156

K. B. ASHTON: *The Problem of the Corn-crake* 161

R. M. LOCKLEY: *Bird Migration Stations in Britain* 165

A. LANDSBOROUGH THOMSON: *The Value of Bird-Ringing in the Study of Migration* 172

JAMES FISHER: *The Last Hundred Bird Books* 177

EDITOR: JAMES FISHER • ASSISTANT EDITOR: ELISABETH ULLMANN

C. B. WILLIAMS

SOME PROBLEMS OF
ANIMAL MIGRATION

IN the fifth century B.C., Anacreon, a Greek poet, welcomed the return of the swallows in the spring from their winter quarters in the Nile valley: but in A.D. 1555 Olaus Magnus in Sweden described how rolled-up lumps of hibernating swallows had been dredged from water by fishermen.

In the Book of Exodus there is described how "the locusts went up all over the land of Egypt and rested in all the borders of Egypt": but within the last fifty years naturalists have scoffed at the idea of an insect crossing the twenty to fifty miles that separate the shores of England from those of France.

So the problems of migration have engaged the mind of man for well over two thousand years, and progress has been by no means steadily forward. Let us make a brief survey of the subject and try to get in perspective what we know, what we guess, and what we do not know.

Within the Animal Kingdom there is great variation in powers of movement. Some lowly animals, like plants, are fixed for most of their life. Some float in the sea and drift hither and thither at the mercy of currents. Some can swim and so are able to a certain extent to control the direction of their movement. Some can walk or run on dry land; and some can fly.

Among the flyers (which include the insects, the birds and the bats) many of the smaller insects are so weak that they cannot overcome even a light wind current, and so, when in the air, they drift like the floating plankton in the sea: others have a more powerful flight and can make headway against winds of varying strength. Some of the strongest insects can make airspeeds of twenty miles an hour or more, and birds may reach forty to sixty miles, possibly occasionally higher.

These flying animals, with which we are largely but not entirely concerned in the study of migration, normally continue to fly for many hours in a

day, but their flight is backward and forward, here and there, between nest and food, between flower and flower, as often in one direction as another, so that at the end of the day they are not far from where they started at the beginning—often indeed at the same spot. They keep within a limited territory, which is their home and their feeding ground.

If, for some reason or other, the normal day's flight of an insect or bird were to be straightened out so that it was all in one direction we would get a movement right out of the previous territory, and we would probably be impressed by the distance that had been covered, although in air-miles it was no greater than before. This is the basis of "migration"—a change of location in a uniform direction which is controlled by the animal itself and not by currents of air or water.

Approaching the problem from a different angle —not all parts of the world are equally suitable for animal life, and few parts are equally suitable at all seasons, particularly as to temperature, water supply and food supply. There are large areas in the cold temperate zone where for half the year or more conditions are so severe that active life is almost impossible, but in the summer period there is abundant light, moisture and vegetation. If the animal life in such an environment is to make the best of the seasonal stores of food, and not die out in the period of scarcity, it can do so either by going into a state of rest, such as hibernation or aestivation, or by leaving the area as conditions become unbearable, to return again at the commencement of the new period of abundance.

In some way which we do not understand, and in certain groups of animals but not in others, by the interplay of these two factors of movement and the seasonal distribution of food supply, the habit of migration has arisen. The animals concerned could not get moved in the right direction at the

Swallows assembling for their autumn departure

right time of the year by trusting to "drift", as the physical laws of the varying winds and sea currents were not developed to suit them.

Let us then define "migration" in such a way that we will, to the best of our ability, neither exclude relevant information, nor bring in irrelevant facts. It is not easy, and many different opinions have been expressed.

My own definition is that "migration" is a continued movement, in a direction over which the animals exert a control, and usually in one definite direction, which results in the animals concerned leaving their old territory and occupying for a shorter or longer period a new territory.

It will be noted that this definition rules out all passive distribution of insects or other animals by wind or water currents. Most naturalists will agree to this limitation, although some may consider movements as involuntary which others consider are determined by the animal itself.

It will also be noted that I have not insisted on a return flight, at a different season, back to the point of origin, as a criterion of migration. This is my own opinion, and is supported by many naturalists, but strongly objected to by others. It will be discussed more fully later; in the meantime we can only note that without difference of opinion there would be little progress in Biology.

There are three kinds of question that we can ask in a study of this nature: questions of fact—what? when? where? questions of method—how? and questions of reason—why?

In the first group come, for example, what animals migrate? when do they move? from where do they start? what route do they take? when and where do they stop? Do all individuals of a population move or do some stay behind (and if so, do the non-migrants differ in any way from the migrants)? What is the relation of the migration to length of life, sexual development and breeding season? does the same individual migrate more than once in its life? and so on. To answer these questions thousands of observations must be made both in the field and in the laboratory, and recorded without fear or favour, without exaggeration, minimisation, or selection to prove a preconceived theory.

The questions in the second group are more difficult to answer, and there is more room for personal opinion. How, for example, do the internal or external conditions determine the start of the movement? how do the migrants keep to their path? how do they know when to stop?

The questions of the third group are most difficult of all to answer, and are usually the first to be asked. Why do certain animals migrate, and others do not? is it an advantage? is it a necessity? and why and how has the habit originated in the course of evolution? It must in this connection be noted that there are two questions that can be asked about the reason for migration in any animal—first, why that species migrates, and secondly, why these particular individuals of the species have chosen this particular moment to move in this particular direction.

To return to the problems of fact—migration, as defined above, exists in certain insects, birds and bats by flight; in fishes and marine reptiles and mammals and in some birds by swimming; and in certain land mammals and possibly in land-crabs and some Amphibia by walking and running.

In the birds it is found chiefly among the insect-eating species and the distance covered may reach several thousand miles. The chief long movements are away from cool temperate climates in the autumn towards or across the equator to avoid the winter; but there are many other types, including some quite short-distance seasonal movements up and down the slopes of mountains. No bird is known to hibernate. The possibility of marking birds with reasonable prospect of recovery has enabled the movements of single individuals to be traced. The close study of sub-specific and racial differences has also helped considerably.

Of the bats the movements are very little known or understood, in spite of the modern development of marking. Most species of bats in cool temperate areas hibernate in the winter, but others migrate many hundred miles, and some appear both to migrate and to hibernate.

Among the insects the best-known migrants are the locusts, of which there are, however, barely a dozen different species; but several hundred species of butterflies and moths regularly cover great distances. Migration is also known in beetles, dragonflies and some other orders. The flight may be up to two thousand miles, and in several cases we have evidence of a return flight in the opposite direction at a different time of the year. As in the

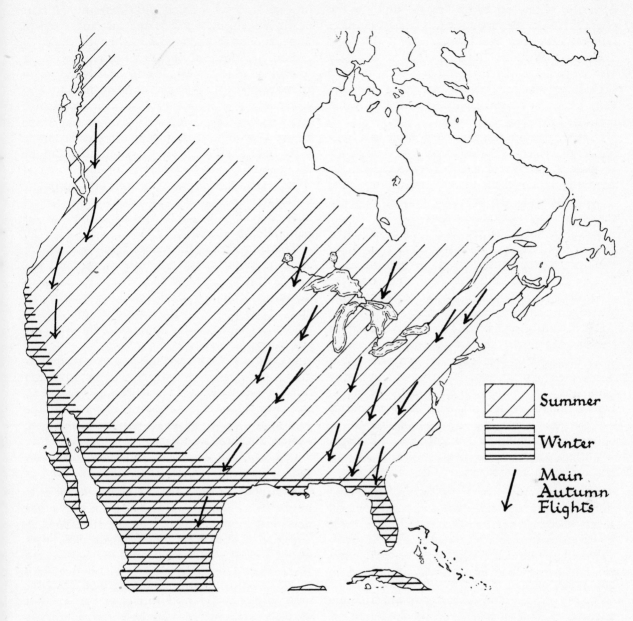

Summer and winter disrtibution of the Monarch butterfly in North America and its main autumn flights to the south

case of birds the movements in temperate climates are usually towards the equator in the autumn and away from it in the spring; but there are exceptions to this rule, and also many migrants in the tropics where seasons are more confused. Owing to the short life of most insects (the longest seldom if ever more than one year as adults) it is very rare that the flight in both directions is made by the same individual; in the Monarch Butterfly, in North America, however, this does occur.

Owing to the rapid fluctuations of numbers insect migrations vary in intensity in different years; often the flight in one direction is large and in the other direction small. In some insects, particularly locusts, the migrant individuals differ in shape, colour, physiology and behaviour from the non-migrants (Uvarov's Phase Theory). It has not yet been found possible to trace the movements of individuals by marking, although experiments along these lines are now being carried out in many parts of the world.

Migration by means of swimming is found among many kinds of fish and is usually connected with the breeding season. Some species, such as the salmon, breed in fresh water, but spend most of their life in the sea. Others, such as the eel, spend most of their life in fresh water, but breed in the sea. Still other migrations are entirely in fresh water or in salt water. In some cases, particularly in the last class, the movement of the very young fish from the breeding area appears to be more of a drift with the current than a deliberate movement, but the return of the mature fish is deliberate and usually against the current.

There is some evidence that salmon, and possibly other species, having hatched from the egg in a particular stream will return, after a period of several years in the sea, to the same stream and even, it is said, to the same branch of it. Much interesting work has been done on the migration of fishes by marking and recapturing, and also by the possibility of telling the age of fishes by their scales. The great economic importance of the world fisheries and their dependance on migration has made possible research on a scale not found in other groups.

Marine mammals such as whales, seals and dolphins carry out extensive and regular movements often covering thousands of miles, and some penguins make long-distance migrations at sea by swimming. Sea-snakes also make regular movements out to sea and then back again to land for breeding purposes.

The migratory movements of land mammals have not been well studied in the past, and are now being rapidly destroyed by the development of agriculture and civilisation. In the early days of the United States great movements of bison took place on which many Indian tribes depended for their food: to-day the few remaining bison are protected in reserves. In Northern Europe there are at intervals great movements of lemmings which appear to be of a migratory nature: and in Africa there is evidence of irregular or regular mass-movements in some of the Ungulates.

Even frogs have been reported as making regular short-distance movements to and from breeding pools.

So we see that there are few groups of animals in which some form of migration has not developed on a larger or smaller scale. It is most obvious and has attracted most attention in the birds, and it is probably in this group that most progress has been made in the study.

The second group of problems that we mentioned above are those concerned with ways and means.

For example, how do the external conditions determine the start of a migration? There is no doubt that most migrations are related to seasonal changes, and particularly but by no means entirely to winter and summer, in which cases the main movements are in autumn and in spring. For certain birds it has been shown that the changing length of daylight, and hence of activity, is an important factor, and the advent of the urge to move can be delayed or even reversed, by artificially altering hours of activity for birds in captivity. It would appear that the immediate effect is on the development of the sexual organs, and through that on the migratory instinct. It is however important to point out that this discovery does not in any way explain the directional nature of the movement.

In tropical countries, where temperature changes are not great, migration may be related to wet and dry seasons; for example in Ceylon, the peak of migration in butterflies is just after the start of the north-east monsoon rains. On the other hand in Trinidad in the West Indies, where there is no seasonal change of temperature, the Scissors-tail Flycatcher (*Milvulus tyrannus*), which is a non-breeding migrant, arrives about the end of May or in June and leaves during October. These dates do not correspond with seasonal changes of rainfall in Trinidad, but may possibly do so with those in its breeding area. However this is the place to discuss general rules rather than exceptions.

Once the migration has started there is no doubt that the most fundamental—and completely unsolved—problem is that of orientation. Young eels swim across the Atlantic from west to east; old eels cross it ten years or more later in the reverse direction. A migrant swallow flies from a particular garden in England to somewhere (perhaps a particular spot) in Southern Africa; and then six

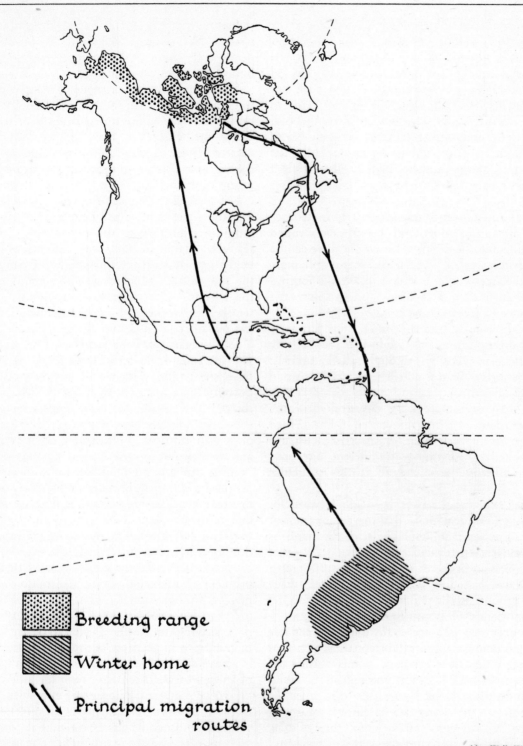

Breeding range

Winter home

Principal migration routes

After Wells W. Cooke

Distribution and migration of the golden plover, Charadrius dominicus. In the autumn it flies over the ocean from Nova Scotia to South America—2,400 miles—the longest known flight of any bird. In the spring it returns by way of the Mississippi Valley. Thus the migration routes form a great ellipse, with a minor axis of 2,000 miles and a major axis stretching 8,000 miles from Arctic America to Argentina

months later returns, in spite of cross winds, to the same garden to occupy perhaps the same nest. Among birds the same individual makes the journey a number of times during its life, so memory might be thought to play a part; but unfortunately for this idea the young birds in many cases fly quite independently of the old. With some birds which migrate between North and South America, it has been proved that the route taken on the southern flight is quite different from that used on the return to the north (see page 137).

And if the power of orientation and route finding is difficult to understand in birds, how much more difficult is it in fishes, for whom there can be little in the way of "land-marks": and still more so in the insects which seldom make the journey more than once in a lifetime—and in some cases only once in several generations.

The directional instinct of some butterflies is so strong during a migratory flight that they will fly through open windows, through railway tunnels, beat themselves against obstructions, and fly up to the top of narrow trees and down the other side rather than deviate from the direction in which they are impelled to go. I have seen in East Africa at one moment three species of insects, a locust and two butterflies, migrating in different directions and each keeping absolutely to its own particular route.

Many explanations have been put forward for this power of orientation—that they move into, or with, or at some constant angle to, the wind or water current—that there is a magnetic sense—that it is a question of the direction of the sun's rays— or it is determined by the movement of the image of the ground on the retina of the eye. But in my opinion none even begins to explain the facts.

It is extremely doubtful if any animal is capable of appreciating a uniform current in which it is floating, unless there are fixed points outside the current by which it can estimate its drift. And even if an insect or bird were able to estimate the direction of the wind from the variations in velocity, such as gusts (about which there is some doubt in the minds of meteorologists), there is still no evidence in the field that butterflies—with the migrations of which I am personally most familiar —do keep any fixed angle to the wind. On the contrary I have seen Cabbage White Butterflies

migrating steadily to the South in England for sixteen days, during which the wind was from nearly every point of the compass—but the direction of the flight never altered.

Fishes undoubtedly orientate to a rapid current in comparatively shallow water, usually by facing up-stream, when the ground beneath or the trees above are visible as fixed points outside the current. But I have still to see any evidence which shows how a fish swimming fifty fathoms down in the Gulf Stream (or even near its surface) and out of sight of the bottom can tell in which direction the water is moving. Before the discovery of radio direction finding the captain of a ship at sea was unable to allow for currents unless he could get, at frequent intervals, observations on the sun or stars which were fixed points outside his current. Otherwise in continuously cloudy weather he worked by "dead reckoning", which has put many a good ship on the rocks.

With regard to a magnetic sense we can only say that small-scale experiments in the laboratory have shown no evidence of any response to a powerful magnetic field by locusts and some other insects; and small-scale field experiments have shown no effect by attaching magnets to the heads of migrating storks. Furthermore no one has been able to discover in any animal an organ which from its structure might appear to be affected by a magnetic field. It is, of course, notoriously difficult to prove a negative case, but at least we can say that at the moment there is no positive evidence in favour of orientation during migration being determined by the earth's magnetic field.

Acworth in a recent book explains the whole problem of orientation by an assumption that the migrant bird or animal always knows instinctively the exact direction in space of the locality which it is striving to reach. I prefer the mystery of migration to the mystery of this explanation.

I have dwelt rather a long time on this problem of orientation because I consider it the fundamental difference between directional migratory movements and normal wandering in all directions.

Another fundamental aspect is that concerned with the existence of a return flight. The migrations of most birds, fishes and mammals take the form of definite movements of all or nearly all of the adult population from locality A at one season to locality B, and back again at the next change of

Arthur Brook

Salmon leaping a fall on its way up to the spawning beds

season to A. But there are other cases in which the return of the migrants to the original habitat does not appear to be established. One of the best-known cases is that of the lemming, which at irregular intervals moves in some numbers in a westerly direction in northern Europe, and at times the beasts go out to sea and are drowned rather than divert their movements to another direction. There is at present no evidence of a return of any of the lemmings to their original habitat. Something similar is stated to happen to many insects. In fact until a few years ago all movements of Lepidoptera were considered to be "overflows" from areas which had become over-crowded by breeding under favourable circum-stances. The departure of the large numbers of migrants from the normal breeding area was con-sidered to be to the advantage of the species by reducing overcrowding. All the overflow "emi-

grants" either died without returning or produced offspring in some other areas which then also died.

This idea, if correct, raises great evolutionary difficulties. How can a habit arise and persist over thousands of generations if every individual which develops the habit is lost to the species, and its offspring—if any—die out in adverse conditions elsewhere?

The difficulty is so serious that we have paid special attention recently to the question of a return flight of migrant insects. Twenty-five years ago there was only one butterfly, the Monarch, in which a return flight was believed to take place, though even this was denied by some naturalists. To-day evidence of a return flight at a different season exists for over twenty species and each year adds to their numbers. While writing these lines I have received records from the British Isles of definite flights to the south, in the autumn of 1947, of the Red Admiral and the Clouded Yellow Butterfly, for both of which species the existence of any such movement had been persistently denied.

What we find is that in nearly every case the movement in one direction is in large numbers and conspicuous, while the movement in the other direction is in smaller numbers and inconspicuous. Frequently in one movement the insects are gregarious and in the other solitary. Thus so long as the evidence for migration was based on chance observation of large swarms it was biased in favour of movements in one direction. Only half the facts were being brought to light.

Since we have had observers watching for even the thinnest migrations of butterflies the whole aspect has changed—and now one doubts whether there are really any butterflies which move in one direction only. There may be some such species, but at the present moment we must not mistake absence of evidence for evidence of absence.

Even in the well-known case of the lemming, I doubt if any close watch has ever been kept in periods of scarcity to see if there is any evidence of a return. It will not be easy. The movement, if it occurs, will almost certainly be at night, and in numbers very small indeed compared with the striking masses that get recorded in newspapers.

One last problem—and the most difficult of all—what are the causes, reasons and advantages of migration? and, incidentally, is finding an advantage the same as finding an explanation?

Some years ago Heape, in a book entitled "Emigration, Migration and Nomadism" attempted a classification of the different types of movement that I have dealt with briefly above. Starting from the point of view of a Physiologist he divided the movements into what he considered two fundamentally different types. First those *with* a return flight, which he calls "Migration", and secondly, those *without* a return, which he calls "Emigration". The first are due, he says, to a "gametic" urge for reproduction, and the second to an "alimental" need for food. In the first class he puts most birds, turtles, most fishes, some crabs, and a few insects including only one butterfly, the Monarch. In the second class are the lemming, the springbok of South Africa, the moose, a few birds including Pallas's sand grouse, most insects including locusts, dragonflies, and all "migrant" butterflies except the Monarch.

His classification appears at first to be simple, but almost immediately he himself gets into difficulties and has to recognise several other causes. In fact he finally admits that the causes of emigration may be (1) food; (2) climatic or (3) the result of over-population: while in migration the movement towards the breeding area is gametic, but the movement away from it is either climatic or alimental—in fact the same as the causes for "emigration". Since he cannot have a gametic "migration" without an alternating "emigration", I fail to see that a fundamental difference of origin has been established between the two.

And nowhere does his theory touch the problem of orientation. How do the animals move steadily in one direction over long distances at one time of the year, and steadily in the opposite direction at another season? Until we can get at this the real problem of migration has not been approached.

What we need now are far more critical observations over the whole of the animal kingdom. It is comparatively easy to make theories to suit one small section of experience, and so much more difficult as the field widens. Not only must the regular movements be observed but also the occasional departures or exceptions, which must have reasons for their occurrence, and which may throw light on the working of the rules. More experimental work is required both in the field and in the laboratory. There is plenty of scope for the Amateur and the Professional Zoologist, provided only that the most critical attitude is taken to all observations, not merely as to their truth and correct interpretation, but also to see if the observed facts are indeed a real unbiased sample of the facts of nature.

REFERENCES

W. HEAPE (1931) *Emigration, Migration and Nomadism*. Cambridge, Heffer.

A. MEEK (1916) *The Migrations of Fish*. London, Arnold.

E. S. RUSSELL (1917) *Fish Migrations*. Biological Reviews, 12: 320-337.

A. L. THOMSON (1926) *Problems of Bird Migration*. London, Witherby.

B. UVAROV (1928) *Locusts and Grasshoppers*. London (Imperial Bureau of Entomology).

C. B. WILLIAMS (1930) *Migrations of Butterflies*. Edinburgh, Oliver and Boyd.

C. B. WILLIAMS, G. F. COCKBILL, M. E. GIBBS and J. A. DOWNES (1942) *Studies in the Migration of Lepidoptera*. Trans. Ent. Soc. Lond. 92: 101-283.

C. B. WILLIAMS

NOTES ON BRITISH IMMIGRANT BUTTERFLIES

WE have in the British Isles about 68 species of Butterflies of which 17, or one quarter, are immigrants at times, or are known to take part in migrations in other parts of Europe.

These can be classified as follows:

(1) Rare immigrants which seldom or never breed:—
    1. The Bath White.
    2. The Queen of Spain Fritillary.
    3. The Camberwell Beauty.
    4. The Monarch.
    5. The Long-tailed Blue.
    6. The Short-tailed Blue.
    7. The Mazarine Blue.

(2) Immigrants which frequently breed here in the summer, but seldom if ever survive the winter:—
    8. The Painted Lady.
    9. The Clouded Yellow.
    10. The Pale Clouded Yellow.
    11. The Red Admiral.

(3) Residents in England, sometimes reinforced by immigration:—
    12. The Large White.
    13. The Small White.
    14. The Green-veined White.

(4) Resident in England, but occasional immigration of individuals of a distinct Continental race:—
    15. The Swallowtail.

(5) Recorded migrating on the Continent but not, so far, in England:—
    16. The Peacock.
    17. The Small Tortoiseshell.

The following are very brief notes on each species.

1. THE BATH WHITE is fairly common in France; but a rare immigrant in the south of England. In the 100 years up to 1944 only about 100 individuals were captured. In 1945, however, an extraordinary immigration occurred all along the south coast from Cornwall to Kent; and a few in South Wales. Over 500 captures were recorded, along with eggs, larvae and chrysalides.

2. THE QUEEN OF SPAIN FRITILLARY is a rare immigrant, found chiefly along the south coast. About 300 individuals have been recorded in the last 100 years.

3. THE CAMBERWELL BEAUTY is an autumn immigrant which comes to us from the east, possibly from Scandinavia. It is most often found along the east coast from Kent to Aberdeen, but is rare in the west and very rare in Ireland. Just over 1,000 specimens have been recorded in the past 100 years, the highest record being 436 in 1872. No caterpillar has ever been found wild in Britain.

4. THE MONARCH is a big, powerful-flying North American butterfly, which in its own home makes very long autumn and spring migrations. Since 1876 about 160 specimens have been seen or caught in Britain, mostly near the south coast, and it is a problem to decide whether they have been carried across by ships, or have flown across by their own efforts, assisted by the prevailing strong westerly winds.

5. THE LONG-TAILED BLUE is a rare immigrant on the south coast, of which only about 30 specimens were captured between 1824 and 1939.

6. THE SHORT-TAILED BLUE is a very rare immigrant of which only about a dozen have

been taken in the southern counties in the past 100 years.

7. THE MAZARINE BLUE is another rare immigrant of which about 100 have been captured in the last 125 years. It was commoner in the early days and the maximum recorded in one year was 20 in 1825.

The Painted Lady

S. Beaufoy

The Red Admiral

S. Beaufoy

8. THE PAINTED LADY is a regular immigrant, which comes to us chiefly from North Africa in the spring, breeds in the summer, and disappears in the autumn, possibly going

The Clouded Yellow

S. Beaufoy

back to the south. In some years it is rare and only found in the southern counties, in other years it is very abundant and reaches the extreme north of Scotland.

9. THE CLOUDED YELLOW is another spring immigrant which comes in from the south about June, lays eggs which provide a generation in August, and very rarely a second generation late in September or October. There was in 1947 an exceptionally large influx reaching to the north of Scotland, and equalling or exceeding in numbers 1877 which was also an outstanding year of immigration.

10. THE PALE CLOUDED YELLOW is similar in habits to the Clouded Yellow but generally rarer. It seldom reaches beyond the Midlands of England and has only been recorded once or twice in Scotland.

11. THE RED ADMIRAL comes to us from the south in the spring and breeds in the summer. There appears to be a small number which survives the winter as adult butterflies, but the majority die out or return to the south in the autumn.

Left:
The Small White
S. Beaufoy

Right:
The Green-veined White
S. Beaufoy

12 THE LARGE WHITE and THE SMALL
& WHITE migrate in large numbers southwards
13. from Scandinavia to central Europe about the
end of July. Offshoots of this migration
frequently cross the North Sea and the
Channel and enter our east and south-east

counties, sometimes in millions. There is as
yet no evidence of a return flight.
14. THE GREEN-VEINED WHITE is occasionally found accompanying the other "Whites"
on their flights but it is doubtful if it sets out
on a migration of its own.

The Large White   S. Beaufoy

The Small Tortoiseshell   S. Beaufoy

S. Beaufoy

The Swallowtail

S. Beaufoy

The Peacock

15. THE BRITISH SWALLOWTAIL is confined to the Cambridge and Norfolk fens. Occasional specimens found in the south, from Kent to the Isle of Wight, appear to belong to a continental form which can be distinguished by the markings. Our English race does not seem to wander.

16 THE PEACOCK BUTTERFLY has been
& recorded migrating in France and the SMALL
17. TORTOISESHELL in Corsica. They have not been observed on the move in Britain but on several occasions have been captured in lightships off our south-east coasts.

A group of naturalists, both amateur and professional, are trying to make a study of the immigration of butterflies and moths into this country. We want as many people as possible to watch out for the occurrence of the migrant species, and particularly for their sudden appearance in numbers, or for actual movement either across country or coming in from the sea.

The information we want is (1) the locality, (2) the date, (3) the direction of movement if definite and (4) the name of the butterfly—or better still, some specimens. After these four basic facts, there are many other observations that can be usefully recorded, the weather, the direction of the wind, the height of the flight above the ground, the approximate number of insects taking part, and the duration of any flight.

If the flight is definite the best numerical estimate is the number of individuals passing a line of known length (say 25 yards or 50 yards) across the flight in a definite number of minutes.

The information should be sent to Capt. Dannreuther, Windycroft, Hastings; or to the Keeper of Entomology at the Natural History Museum, London, S.W.7; or to Dr. C. B. Williams, Rothamsted Experimental Station, Harpenden.

The Natural History Museum has published for 6d. a small pamphlet on British Immigrant Butterflies, with five coloured postcard illustrations at 2d. each.

Residents in foreign lands are also invited to send in records of movements of butterflies in numbers, and travellers at sea are asked to send in any butterflies or other flying insects caught away from land, giving the date, and position of the ship at the time.

Camberwell Beauty on Buddleia

S. Beaufoy

G. V. T. MATTHEWS

BIRD NAVIGATION

"Doth the hawk fly by thy wisdom and stretch her wings toward the South"

MORE than 2,500 years have passed since that question was asked, yet a modern ornithologist, asked to "explain" bird navigation, might well echo "What shall I answer thee, I will lay my hand upon my mouth". Only in the last forty years has the problem been investigated experimentally, and the facts ascertained so far can only indicate some probable answers.

One of the main problems is to discover how young birds, a few weeks old, can reach a goal they have never seen before. Some birds, of course, travel with their parents. A young cuckoo, however, has never seen its parents. The adults of many species migrate at a different time, even by a different route from the young. Yet the winter quarters may be very small and distant—plovers from Alaska fly over 2,000 miles of open sea to Hawaii—and a slight deviation from track would be fatal.

These facts suggest that some hereditary guiding factor may be concerned. To examine this possibility, large numbers of storks and ducks have been reared artificially in their home area or after transplantation. When free to associate with wild members of the species they have migrated with them and generally returned to the rearing-place for breeding—never, in the case of the transplants, to the place where the eggs were laid. Such behaviour was observed even when the birds were of a non-migratory stock, as when English mallard were reared in Finland and East Prussia. A more

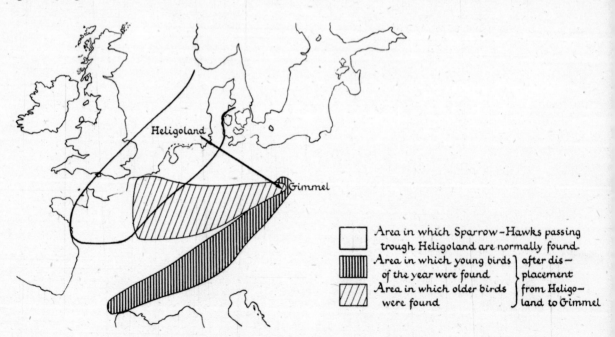

Fig. 1: *Effect of artificial displacement of sparrow-hawks during autumn migration*
Note: (1) *Young birds remained near release point or continued on original course; (2) Older birds attempted to regain normal area*

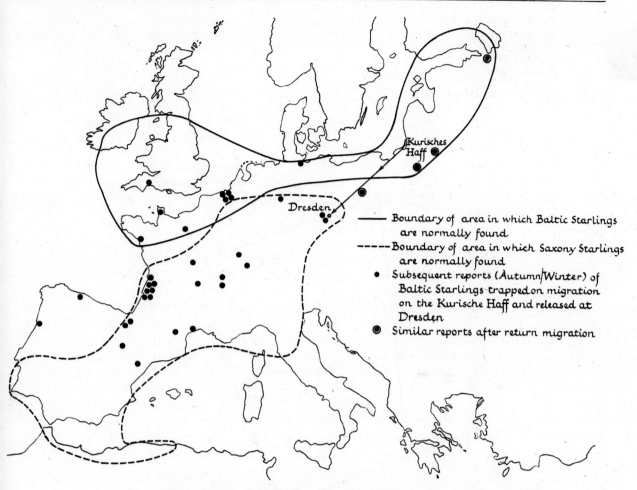

Fig. 2: Effect of artificial displacement of starlings during autumn migration
Note: *Some birds regained their normal area, others can be considered to have maintained their original line of flight or to have joined forces with Saxony migrants*

critical test is to rear birds in strict isolation and allow them to migrate only when local birds, if any, have already left and cannot act as guides. White storks have been so reared in western Germany and in England, after being hatched in East Prussia. Reports of the routes taken by such birds have unfortunately been scarce, and do not give a clear or consistent picture. Some followed what might be considered their hereditary track; others appeared to take the routes of local birds or wandered at random.

Another experiment is to trap large numbers of migrating birds and displace them geographically to an area through which they would not normally pass. Subsequent recoveries then indicate whether the birds have compensated for their enforced deviation and regained their normal seasonal area,

or have continued blindly on a predetermined course. Several such interceptions have been carried out, involving nearly five thousand birds. The results of two of the experiments are given in Figs. 1 and 2. These show that older birds have tended to regain their normal areas, but that first-year migrants possibly fly on a fixed compass course. However since migration trends all over the Continent are in a general SW. direction, similar results would have been obtained if the young birds merely followed migrants passing through the point of release. The direction "sense" if it exists, then, is readily modifiable by experience and example.

While it is returning to the breeding quarters, and on subsequent migrations, the bird has at least had experience of the goal to which it is

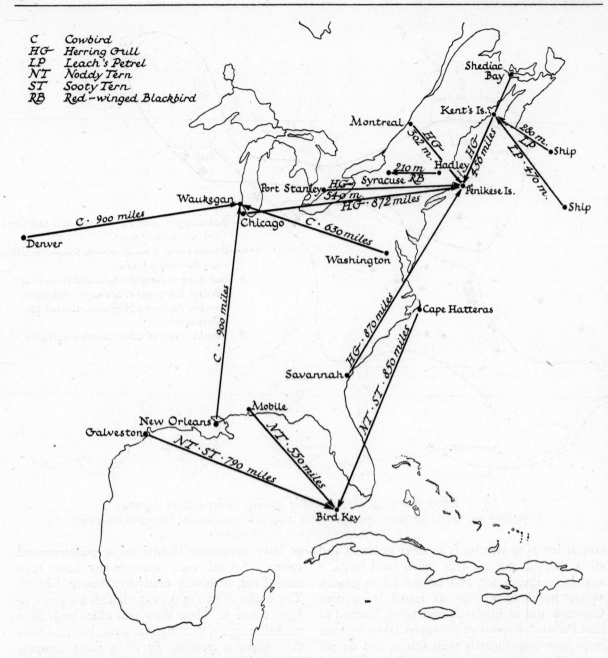

C   Cowbird
HG   Herring Gull
LP   Leach's Petrel
NT   Noddy Tern
ST   Sooty Tern
RB   Red-winged Blackbird

Fig. 3: Some of the remarkable homing flights successfully accomplished by North American birds

flying. It is the precision with which the return is made that is so astounding. Swallows return to the same nest year after year, making round trips of ten thousand miles in the intervals. Nor are they exceptions, for 80 per cent of birds from over 100 species were found breeding less than six miles from the place where they were hatched or where they had previously bred. The small amount of spread shown was largely due to the returning young being unable to take up territories next to those of their parents. This is clearly seen if ringing returns like the above are confined to birds ringed as breeding adults, when as many as 85 per cent are recovered within a thousand yards after subsequent migrations.

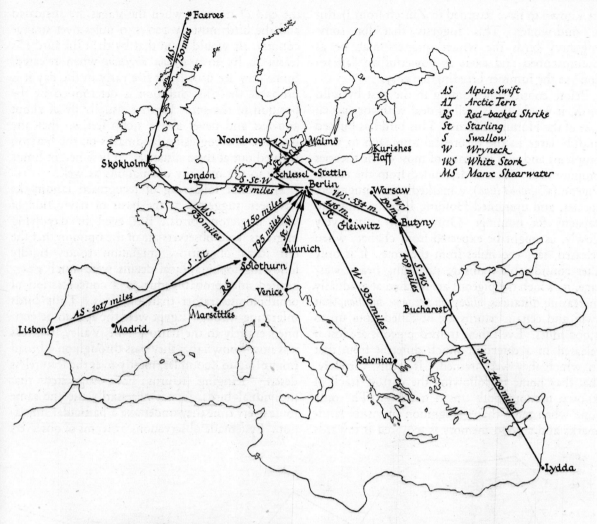

Fig. 4: Some of the remarkable homing flights successfully accomplished by European birds

A return to a known goal is also a feature of the remarkable series of "homing" experiments, and these may therefore be used to throw some light on the more general problems of non-hereditary navigation. In these experiments some 2,200 breeding birds of twenty-six species have been trapped, made identifiable as individuals by patterns of paint marks or by coloured leg bands, and released at distances of up to 1,670 miles from their nests. Those returning, in all just under a half, were identified by sight, confirmed where possible by retrapping and reading the usual numbered leg band. If large numbers of birds can be used the results have much greater significance, since chance variation is "averaged out". For this reason the most important, though not always the most spectacular, work has been that done on swallows and starlings by Rüppell and other workers on the Continent, and on colonial sea-birds by Griffin in America. Some of the longer flights successfully accomplished are shown in Figs. 3 and 4.

In addition nearly 3,000 birds have been trapped in *winter* quarters and released up to 435 miles away. "Homing" in these cases only amounted to 7 per cent, mostly from short distances, and the results are thus little use for the present purpose. However this may be largely due to the difficulties of identifying or retrapping individual birds in the winter. When conditions were particularly favourable for observing returns, five coots out of sixteen are known to have returned to Zurich from Berlin in mid-winter. This suggests that for some migratory birds the winter quarters may be as circumscribed and exert as powerful an "attraction" as the summer breeding territory.

Before considering homing to the nest by wild birds, it would be as well to deal with the special case of the Homing Pigeon. This bird has bulked unduly large in the theoretical approach to such problems and was the basis of most of the theories propounded. But it is descended from the Rock-Pigeon (*Columba livia*), a markedly non-migratory species, and untrained Homing Pigeons show no capacity for homing. Only a few return very slowly, as might be expected from chance, when released, say, 100 miles from the cote. It is only after considerable training, involving heavy wastage, in which the pigeons are released at gradually increasing distances, *always in the same direction,* that swift and certain returns are obtained from up to 1,000 miles. Even these trained pigeons are lost if released in a direction much different from that in which they were trained. It seems, therefore, that they home by following the narrow track of known territory built up in training. The only time when more than recognition of visual landmarks and a good memory is required is towards

the end of training when the stages are increased and the bird must fly 100–150 miles over strange country. It would seem that by then the bird has learnt to fly in a *certain direction* when released. Since they are usually set free early in the day it is probable that this direction is determined by the position of the sun. Pigeons usually fly at about 300 feet and never above 3,000 feet, so that any question of recognising landmarks on the horizon is ruled out at these distances. These height limits apply to the majority of migrants as well.

A similar following of recognised landmarks has been suggested as the basis of navigation of wild migratory birds. But even in day-flying migrants, field observers are of the opinion that the old ideas of narrow migration routes rigidly following topographical details were much exaggerated and probably due to a concentration of ornithologists rather than of birds. Thus birds migrating through Egypt were thought to be confined entirely to the narrow Nile Valley, whereas it is now known that they pass through on a broad front of up to 600 miles, mostly over the featureless desert. Ringing returns have suggested that individual birds do not necessarily use the same route every time they undertake a particular migration. Systematic observations by teams of observers

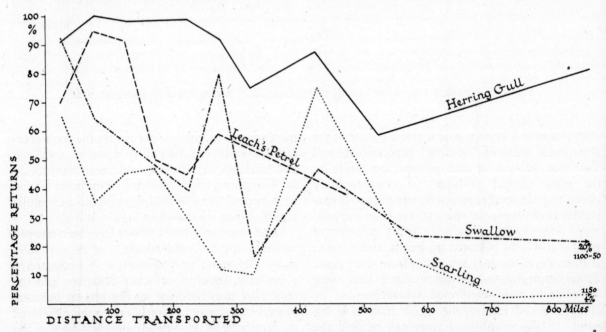

Fig. 5: Transportation of four species: percentage returns plotted against distance transported

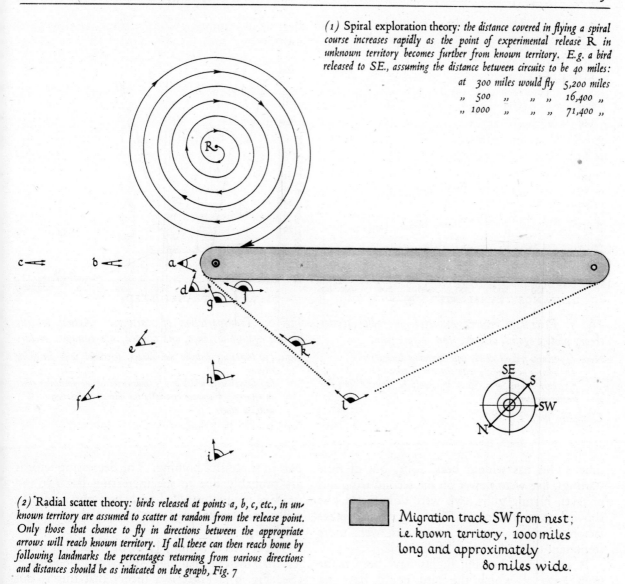

(1) Spiral exploration theory: the distance covered in flying a spiral course increases rapidly as the point of experimental release R in unknown territory becomes further from known territory. E.g. a bird released to SE., assuming the distance between circuits to be 40 miles:

at	300 miles would fly	5,200 miles
,,	500 ,,	,, ,,	16,400 ,,
,,	1000 ,,	,, ,,	71,400 ,,

(2) Radial scatter theory: birds released at points a, b, c, etc., in unknown territory are assumed to scatter at random from the release point. Only those that chance to fly in directions between the appropriate arrows will reach known territory. If all these can then reach home by following landmarks the percentages returning from various directions and distances should be as indicated on the graph, Fig. 7

Migration track SW from nest; i.e. known territory, 1000 miles long and approximately 80 miles wide.

Fig. 6: Two theories of homing shown in diagram form

indicate that migrating passerines fly in a "preferred direction", usually SW. or WSW. on the Continent, which is maintained over uniform country but is subject to modification, within limits, by birds avoiding unfavourable areas and keeping to those most resembling their usual habitats, or providing other advantages.

An experience of migration is necessary if birds are to "home" successfully. Some young, breeding starlings, reared over their first autumn and winter in a large cage, all failed to return to their nests, or

indeed to move far from the release point seventy miles away. The apparent lack of ability to "home" from any great distance in non-migratory species may be a related phenomenon. In both cases the birds have never made any long flights (no more than ten yards in the captive starlings) and this is probably more important than their lack of knowledge of the ground to be covered.

If recognition of landmarks was the basis of their navigation, birds should always return much faster when transported to the same place a second

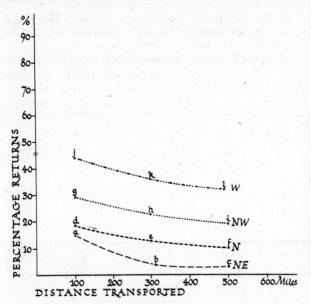

Fig. 7: Percentage returns expected on radial scatter theory plotted against distance from release point

Note: *(1) returns fall off slowly with increasing distance;*
(2) returns vary greatly with direction of release;
(3) only returns of 50% or less could be expected from un-known territory

Compare with Fig. 8

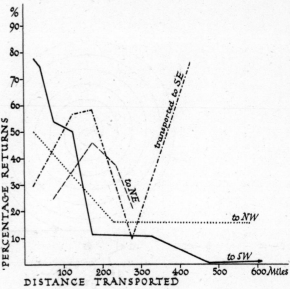

Fig. 8: Transportation of starlings. Actual returns plotted against distance, and divided into compass sectors

Note: *(1) Increasing distance not always associated with decreasing returns;*
(2) Direction in which bird is transported has no particular effect on returns. Compare especially the migration direction (SW.) with the others

time. This has seldom been done, but of nine starlings, five were slower on the second trip, and of seven herring gulls, two were slower and one showed no improvement. This suggests that other factors, such as weather conditions, were more important than experience of the route.

A number of homing flights have been made from areas of which the bird could have no previous knowledge, such as the Manx Shear-waters released outside their geographical range, at Venice and in the Alps.

The general falling off in percentages of success-ful homings with increasing distances (Fig. 5) has led to the suggestion that birds released in strange areas scatter radially from the release point. The only birds returning would be those acci-dentally reaching known territory. The area known to the individual bird is difficult to estimate, but the hypothetical one given in Fig. 6 is quite pos-sible. This diagram, when compared with some actual results obtained (Figs. 7 and 8), indicates the unlikelihood of chance playing an important

part in successful homing. The decreasing returns are probably due to the increasing hazards and strain of long journeys. Large, powerful birds like gulls and storks have not shown the trend so markedly.

The speeds of homing birds are invariably much less than their normal flight speeds of 20–60 m.p.h. (See Fig. 9). There is a theory that this is due to the birds undertaking a more or less systematic exploration, such as flying a spiral path as shown in Fig. 6. However it is certain that no bird could maintain so complicated a track, and the distance to be flown increases so rapidly in comparison with distance of objective that on the longer hom-ing flights it becomes fantastic. Unsystematic exploration would be of little use. In any case the homing speeds are often higher on the longer trips, whereas exploration would make them lower. The bird must forage, rest and keep itself in condition on the way home so the speeds achieved on migra-tion should be comparable. These are difficult to ascertain, being dependent on the lucky chance of

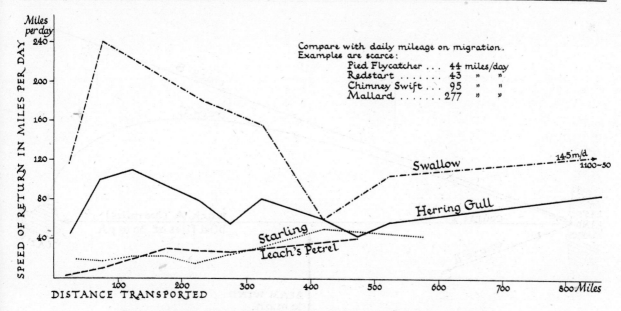

Fig. 9: Transportation of four species: speed of return plotted against distance
Note: *The speed of return does not fall off directly with increasing distance, and may increase*

recovering a bird soon after it was ringed on migration. Those given in Fig. 9 are of the same order as those of homing birds, indicating that their lowness is due to similar causes.

Undoubtedly there can be little but speculation on such matters until there is information about the actual paths followed by homing birds. A few preliminary experiments have been made in America in following their flight from light aircraft. Great advances will be made when the latter, or better, helicopters, become more generally available. It is perhaps significant that the only recoveries of experimental birds on their way home, three starlings (Fig. 10), and one coot, have been on or near the direct line from the release point.

The evidence outlined above has indicated that landmarks are not essential for bird navigation. In addition a great deal of migration definitely occurs in the absence of landmarks. Many species travel entirely by night, often when there is no moon. Others fly or swim across many hundreds of miles of open sea. Some have been observed flying steadily over unbroken, country-wide cloud layers. In the absence of winds (or of oceanic currents in the case of the swimmers) such birds must at least have the ability to hold a straight compass course from the last landmark (Course I in Fig. 11). But once a bird is airborne (or afloat) it

cannot feel the movements of the medium which it is in. Therefore when there are no landmarks to serve as a check, the bird, if it could not

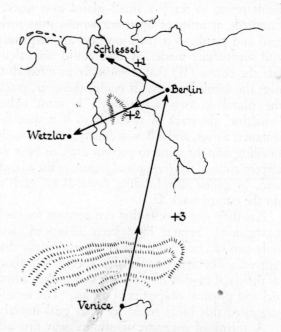

Fig. 10: Routes of homing starlings
Three birds found dead were 19, 19 and 87 miles from the direct line for home. The deviations can be explained by assuming the bird was following a river valley (1), or skirting mountains (2 and 3)

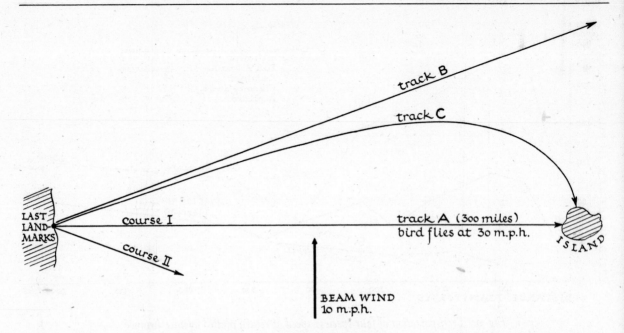

Fig. 11: Effect of a beam of wind on a bird flying without landmarks. For explanation see text

otherwise appreciate the "drift" imposed on it by a beam wind, would fly on a resultant track B. Birds trying to reach a small island over several hundreds of miles of open sea would miss their goal and perish. Yet such journeys are frequently and successfully made. A bird could not calcu/ late the course (II) that it must fly to offset drift over the whole journey. It could, therefore, reach the island in two ways only. It must either "visualise" the track A as clearly as if it was, for instance, a river, and follow it closely, automatically heading into the wind to prevent drift, or have an appreciation of the *geographical position* of the island, and, by continually heading towards it, reach it on the curved track C.

A re there any theories that can account for such navigation? Several have been advanced, and only two can be considered as experimentally dis/ proved. The first postulated a special sensitivity of the nasal cavities or of the air sacs to the chemi/ cal and physical properties of the air. The second suggested that birds could see their goal directly.

A theory of magnetic sensibility was first ad/ vanced at least 75 years ago, and is continually being "discovered" by the popular press. A sensi/ tivity to the magnetic North would be little use without a map. The birds were, therefore, con/

sidered to be able to appreciate the various com/ ponents into which the earth's magnetic field can be resolved. By joining the places where the components are equal a meshwork of lines is obtained, covering the globe. If this mesh was of straight lines intersecting at right angles, a "sensi/ tive" bird could home by following lines most similar to those by its nest and by "fixing" its position at points where two lines crossed. How/ ever the lines are not straight or regular, requiring the bird to know the whole mesh, and tend on the whole to run parallel, crossing if at all at oblique angles (giving poor "fixes") and sometimes re/ crossing each other several times, giving a confus/ ing series of identical points in different places. The theory is thus not impressive, but it has yet to be definitely disproved by experiment. Distur/ bance of the magnetic field in the neighbourhood of the bird has been tried, so far inconclusively. Thus one stork, of two with powerful magnets attached to their heads, flew back from Berlin to near Lwow. But two "control" birds, without magnets, both returned. Various anecdotes of a disorientation of birds by transmitting wireless stations have not been the subject of reliable tests.

A more plausible theory recently (1945) ad/ vanced suggests that birds appreciate their latitude and direction of flight relative to the surface by forces created by the rotation of the earth acting on the fluids in the semicircular canals of the inner ear. It is doubtful, however, whether the forces would be of detectable magnitude. Nothing has been done to test the theory experimentally so it remains a possibility.

Lastly there is the theory that a bird is able to register unconsciously all the component displacements that it undergoes on its outward journey, and from these maintain an appreciation of its total displacement, in direction and distance, from its point of origin. The semicircular canals are suggested as the means by which such displacements are recorded, assisted by "muscle memories" when the bird makes the outward journey under its own power. This is not impossible though an extremely complex neuro-muscular mechanism would be required. The theory has not yet been proved or disproved. Birds have been released after transport under heavy anaesthesia or in cages continually rotated on gramophone turntables, without apparent diminution of their homing powers. But so far these releases have been in areas the bird might have known, or from which known areas could easily be reached, even by a disorientated bird. If birds were released at much greater distances in completely unknown areas after such treatment, and still homed successfully, the theory would have been disproved so far as is possible.

This short review has only skimmed the subject. To summarise the main conclusions, it can be said that some young birds are possibly equipped with a readily modifiable "instinct" to migrate in a certain compass direction. Further, that return to a known goal cannot entirely be explained on the operations of the five senses plus an element of chance. The nature of this necessary "unknown factor" remains one of the deepest and most fascinating mysteries of biology.

REFERENCES:

The great majority of the important papers are published in foreign journals. The following selection of those appearing in English are not therefore at all representative but will serve to give the reader some further impressions on the subject:

D. R. GRIFFIN (1943) *Homing Experiments with Common Terns (Sterna hirundo) and Herring Gulls (Larus argentatus)*. Bird Banding, 14: 7.

D. R. GRIFFIN (1944) *The Sensory Basis of Bird Navigation*. Quart. Rev. Biol. 19: 21.

R. A. MCCABE (1947) *The Homing of Transplanted Young Wood Ducks*. Wilson Bull. 59: 104.

J. A. C. NICOL (1945) *The Homing Ability of the Carrier Pigeon, its Value in Warfare*. Auk, 62: 286.

W. H. THORPE and D. H. WILKINSON (1946) *Ising's Theory of Bird Orientation*. Nature, 158: 903.

Oystercatchers and herring-gulls, with a few lesser black-backed gulls, rest on Hilbre Island, Cheshire, on autumn migration

Eric Hosking

PETER SCOTT

THE MIGRATION
OF WILD GEESE

OF the migratory birds which come to Britain in winter few are more impressive than wild geese, for the great skeins in which they fly and the wild music of their call must catch the attention and often the imagination of those who normally show little interest in birds. It is surprising, therefore, that so much should remain unknown about them, and particularly about the methods and even the routes of their migration. One of the greatest additions to the study of migration was the development of the marking scheme by which an individual bird may be traced by affixing a numbered aluminium ring to its leg. This has been done with many species, including wild ducks which have been caught in various duck decoys in this country and in Holland; but until now it has not been attempted on a large scale with wild geese. The problem of catching the geese in bulk has hitherto appeared to be insuperable. It was to this problem that the newly formed Severn Wildfowl Trust turned its attention in 1947. It was thought that no better locality could be found for such an attempt than the wildfowl observation station at the New Grounds on the Severn Estuary, which had recently been established by the Trust and which was largely devoted to the study of the great flocks of White-fronted geese which frequent this area in winter. Special nets were made and experiments were carried out in throwing them by means of rockets. Early in 1948 the system was put into operation for the first time in the field and 31 geese—30 of them White-fronts and 1 Pink-foot—were caught at the first attempt.

The net has to be set out in the hurrying darkness before dawn. For 25 yards across the marsh it is laid in a straight line, and concealed as well as may be in a groove cut in the turf. At each end a rocket is attached and from each leads a length of wire flex towards the hide which conceals the netters. It takes at least 5 people to set the net, working feverishly by the light of a hurricane lamp. The team must make a very early start and by the time the preparations are complete the first geese have usually appeared and caused a headlong rush for cover. It is always a hectic introduction to a long and exciting wait.

The net has so far been placed in such a way that the geese first settle well out in front of it and then walk in towards the Catching Area—the square of 25 yards or so immediately down wind of the net itself. As the geese feed into this area quite slowly and as the numbers gradually increase, the suspense becomes terrific. For several hours—sometimes for a whole day—the watching netters are subjected to alternating paroxysms of optimism and disappointment. A phlegmatic disposition is essential for the successful goose-netter, for at any moment a false move, a cough or a sneeze from the hide, a passing farm worker, or a passing aeroplane, may put up the geese and ruin the day's chances to which the team has been devoting its energies since 4.30 a.m. But if all goes well the "pressure" of geese mounts in the Catching Area and only the leading birds have shown S.O.R., or "Strange Object Reaction". About 4 yards from the net they have suddenly noticed something which they do not like. How will they react? Will they go no closer, but continue to feed, or will they turn and walk out of the Catching Area? Upon this depends the pressure of geese behind them pushing forward into the C.A. And who shall say when there are enough in the C.A. to warrant a "pull"? The loud noise made by the rockets suggests that the apparatus should be used as little as possible. Should we ever pull for less than was caught at the first attempt? We thought not and since that time we have had 28 geese in the C.A. and at another time 20, and at yet another 14. In each case we waited in vain for more, and then in due course the geese set off on their northward migration.

But the triumph of the successful first attempt remains. Early observations have already been made of the birds which were ringed on that day and since then they have been watched frequently moving about among the remainder of the flock; but unfortunately on this first occasion we omitted to take certain details of the birds caught which would greatly have added to the interest of the subsequent observations. It is a curious fact that the black bars on the breasts and bellies of adult White-fronted geese vary from one bird to another. The extent of this individual variation appears to be infinite, so that the pattern can be used, like finger prints, to identify an individual bird. This identification appears to be absolute over the winter season, but minor alterations in the black patterns on the breast and belly take place during the summer moult. At present, however, it appears that these changes are only in degree and not in fundamental pattern, and there seems every likelihood that birds can in future be identified from season to season by this means. Had we recorded the breast patterns of those adult White-fronted geese which were ringed at the first attempt with the rocket net, we should subsequently have been able to identify the ring numbers in the field from the drawings of their breast patterns. Meanwhile the single Pink-footed goose which was ringed on the same day is, of course, recognisable.

He remained at the New Grounds until 15th March when he was in company with 19 White-fronts and 1 other Pink-foot, the last party to leave for the north on the spring migration. The bird was constantly present from the date of ringing, which already provides some useful information upon its movements.

The main flocks of geese which winter annually on the New Grounds on the Severn Estuary are White-fronted geese, although every species and subspecies of goose on the British List has been observed there at one time or another. These White-fronted geese belong to the typical race *Anser albifrons albifrons* which breeds in Northern Europe east of the White Sea, in Asia and in North America. Those which come to England in winter come from North Russia (so far as is at present known). Their migration line appears to follow the south side of the Baltic to Holland where they remain until frost drives them across the Channel to England. As is always the case with geese a few pioneer flocks (usually those with the highest proportion of young birds), strike onwards to the end of the migration line— to the terminus, as it might be called—early in the season. In the case of the New Grounds these flocks are only a few hundred strong. Just before Christmas they are augmented by flocks several thousands strong and the dates correspond very fairly with the departure of White-fronted geese from the big marshes in the south of Holland.

Drawing by the writer

Drawing by the writer

Left to right: typical White-front, Greenland White-front, immature Greenland White-front, Lesser White-front

On their return migration, however, the geese, which have arrived in autumn from an easterly and sometimes from a south-easterly direction, usually depart flying due north. There is some evidence that they may visit the Mersey for a short stop on the return migration. Thereafter all trace of them is lost, but it would not be surprising to find that they return northward by a different route from that which they took in the autumn. This is often the case with wildfowl; it has been observed with Canada geese passing through Jack Miner's big ringing station at Kingsville, Ontario, and also with Teal ringed in Western Europe. The north-ward migration from the New Grounds begins with the utmost regularity within 2 or 3 days of the 10th March. Only in an exceptional spring such as that of 1947 when snow-covered fields lay to the northward, was the migration delayed. On the other hand, however spring-like and warm the weather may be, there is no premature departure. The available evidence supports the theory that the amount of daylight rather than the seasonal temperature change is the stimulus which calls upon the flock to set out on its migratory flight.

Large flocks of White-fronted geese breed in North-West Greenland and until recently they were supposed to be indistinguishable from those breeding in Europe and Asia, and North America. Recently however, it has been shown that these birds which winter principally in Ireland are easily distinguishable from the typical White-fronted geese by their much darker plumage with a tendency to heavier barring on the belly, by their slightly larger bright orange-yellow instead of pink bills, and by the narrower white edging to the feathers of the tail. This bird has recently been described by the author and a colleague, C. T. Dalgety, as a new subspecies *Anser albifrons flavirostris*. Numbers of them have been ringed in Greenland by Doctor Finn Salomonsen of the Zoological Museum at Copenhagen, and recover-ies have been made in Ireland, a few in West Scot-land and in Wales and one on the eastern coast of Canada. The migration of these birds differs from that of the typical race in that the birds arrive all together in Ireland at the end of September or in the early days of October, and depart all together late in April. They cannot come south, neither can they return north, by easy stages, for they have long sea passages to make. In spring they must fly direct from Ireland across the sea to Iceland and thence across the Denmark Strait and the Greenland Ice Cap to their breeding ground. Observations have been made at the breeding ground indicating that the majority of the geese arrive and depart *over* the Ice Cap rather than round the coast by way of Cape Farewell.

Thus White-fronted geese of two races converge upon the British Isles in winter. In addition another form of White-fronted goose which is held by science to warrant the status of a full species—the Lesser White-fronted goose, *Anser erythropus*—is also recorded as a visitor to the British Isles. It was first identified in 1886 when an immature specimen was shot at Fenham Slakes in Northumberland by Alfred Chapman, the brother of the distinguished sportsman-naturalist, Abel Chapman. Several subsequent records exist but under the critical scrutiny of the late H. F. Witherby at the time of the publication of his *Handbook* none of them was considered to be "above reproach". Thus at the beginning of the war the Lesser White-front was the rarest of British birds—for you cannot have a rarer bird than one which has only been recorded once. It shared this distinction with some 25 other single-record species.

The Lesser White-front is only slightly smaller than the common White-front. Its plumage is a little darker and its general shape is slightly different; but its bill is little more than half the length and round its eye is a slightly swollen brilliant golden-yellow eyelid. The Lesser White-front breeds in Lapland very considerably closer to Great Britain than the common White-fronts of the Russian Arctic east of the White Sea, and these birds from Norway and Sweden and Finland migrate regularly southward through Hungary to the coasts of Dalmatia and Greece. It had always seemed to me strange that Lesser White-fronts did not come to this country more frequently and, indeed, I began to wonder whether perhaps they did not often pass unnoticed for there were few enough among ornithologists, as I believed, who would readily recognise this beautiful little goose among a large flock of its near relations. My theory was to some extent upheld by a record of a single Lesser White-front which, in 1942, visited the enclosures of a farmer friend, Mr. William Tinsley, in Lincolnshire, where he kept a pair of tame Lesser White-fronts which I had given him at the beginning of the war. There was no room for doubt in this identification for he was one of the few people in this country who was really familiar with the species, having kept it in captivity for several years, and it constituted the second authentic record of the Lesser White-front in Britain. Were the occurrence of this bird to prove regular the most likely place in which to find it would, I thought, be amongst the largest flocks in this country of the White-fronted geese

from North Russia, and these flocks were to be found at the New Grounds.

It was this theory which first led me to the Severn Marshes in the winter of 1945, and, among 2,000 wild geese (which included 7 different kinds), we found 2 Lesser White-fronts—the third and fourth records for the British Isles. In the following winter 3 of these birds were present among 4,000 White-fronted geese, so that the evidence seemed to indicate that Lesser White-fronts might come regularly to the British Isles in the approximate proportion of 1 per 1,000 common White-fronts or a little more. This theory has unfortunately not been upheld, since among nearly 3,000 Whitefronts on the New Grounds during the past winter no Lesser White-front made its appearance.

It is of interest that whereas the Northumberland Lesser White-front of 1886 was an immature bird the 6 subsequent records have all been adults. Unfortunately no record was made of the belly markings of the 1945–6 birds (these markings are as variable and individual in this species as they are in the common White-front). It was not possible, therefore, to say whether any of the three which were present in 1946–7 were those which we had observed in the previous year, and the complete absence of Lesser White-fronts during the present winter has prevented us from using the careful drawings made the year before. Each of these individual birds was independent of the other, and by means of their special markings they

Drawing by the writer

Adult Greenland White-front

were quite easily distinguished one from another. Certainly two and possibly all three were males. On the rare occasions when they met while wandering through the flocks they did not appear to recognise each other. They might, in fact, be said to have cut each other dead.

The presence of odd single birds of other species among a flock of wild geese is sufficiently common to warrant some special explanation. It seems probable that in winter the gregarious instinct is more powerful than that which links one member of a species to another. Thus a goose which has gone astray would rather take up with a flock of some other species of goose than remain alone. After a while the odd bird becomes so accustomed to seeing the other members of its flock around it that it comes to regard itself as belonging to the species of the flock. In the majority of cases these single birds are young ones of the year. It would seems that young birds go astray from their own flock more frequently than adults. The significance of the fact that the Lesser White-fronts were in all cases adults is not yet explained, if indeed any significance exists.

It seems possible that at a given time in the spring the instinct for rejoining its own species often reasserts itself, but this does not always happen. Two of the three Lesser White-fronts of 1946-7 were well mated with common White-fronted females and there is considerable evidence that wild hybrids regularly occur among various species of geese. As an example during the same winter a male Bean-goose and a female White-front were present at the New Grounds for several weeks in company with a juvenile bird which was quite clearly a hybrid between them. Two other juveniles were present which exhibited hybrid characteristics. Several years previously two hybrids between the Barnacle-goose and the White-front appeared at the New Grounds, in company with two pure Barnacle-geese, one of which may be supposed to have been one of the parents of the hybrids. In the winter of 1945-6 two and possibly three Blue Snow-geese made their appearance on the Wexford Slob in the south-east of Ireland. It has never been possible to establish for certain whether these birds were of wild origin or whether they were "escapes" from captivity, but they kept company with the White-fronted geese wintering in that area which belong, of course, to the Green-land subspecies. In the winter of 1946-7 one of the Blue Snow-geese was present again on the Slob in company with an immature bird which left little doubt that it was a hybrid Blue Snow × White-fronted. This leads to a fascinating field for conjecture; did the Blue goose travel to Greenland in company with the White-fronts and if so does this fact increase the likelihood of its wild origin in Northern Canada or did the White-front parent of the hybrid stay behind to mate somewhere in Ireland with a more sedentary escaped Blue goose which could have come from Whipsnade or from Mr. Bengt Berg's collection in Sweden?

However, ample evidence exists of hybridisation in the wild state and we may wonder what compensating force prevents the coalescence of these nearly related species. It may be that hybrid eggs are less likely to hatch, that hybrid young are less likely to survive or that, if they do survive, their fertility is likely to be less high. In any event the possibility of hybridisation between the common and Lesser White-fronted goose as a result of these aberrant migrations cannot be discounted and a doubtful bird sent from the New Grounds, where it was shot in 1936 by Captain R. G. Berkeley, to the British Museum of Natural History, may well be such a hybrid. It was sent because of its noticeable yellow eye ring, but by its measurements it was placed in a drawer among common White-fronts. When we found it there last year we had no doubt, until we came to measure it, that it was a typical Lesser White-front for so it seemed in every character; and yet the measurements are all outside the range of *Anser erythropus*.

It remains to be seen whether any Lesser White-fronts will return with the winter flocks to the New Grounds in December of 1948 and whether, if they do, we shall be able to recognise them as our friends of previous winters. It remains to be seen whether any of the ringed common White-fronts or the single Pink-foot are recovered from foreign lands or whether they in their turn will come back to their traditional winter home. Meanwhile we shall be getting ready with our rocket nets to catch many of them next winter and to send them away with their identifying rings so that we may learn more about the migrations and the movements and the length of life of these most fascinating and romantic of all our winter birds.

K. B. ASHTON

THE PROBLEM OF
THE CORN-CRAKE

THE Western Isles of Scotland share with the north-west of Ireland the distinction of being the only parts of the British Islands where the Corn-crake or Land-rail is now flourishing. There has been much speculation on the causes of the virtual disappearance from the south of a bird whose voice if not its form was once familiar to all country folk. Farmers who had seen the nests and young destroyed by their mowing-machines were the first to conclude where the responsibility lay, while ornithologists were quick to note that the Corn-crake showed no signs of diminution in numbers in just those areas where hand-scything still pre-dominates, and where the hay-harvest is normally later than the fledging time of the young.

An inquiry undertaken in 1938–9 by Mr. C. A. Norris revealed that 85 per cent of the territories occupied by Corn-crakes in Britain as a whole were regularly cut by machinery, and he concludes that the mowing-machine must stand convicted for the great and continual decrease of the Corn-crake that has taken and is taking place in the British Isles. Admittedly the case against the mowing-machine is very strong, but there are reasons for believing that it is only one of a number of mortality factors to which the species is vulner-able, and that the Corn-crake's present distribution is nearer to the norm than we have supposed.

The general distribution of the Corn-crake in Britain is shown on the map reproduced from Mr. Norris's paper.

It was Mr. E. M. Nicholson who first pointed out that the problem of the Corn-crake is not so much its present distribution as its phenomenal spread in the latter half of the nineteenth century. There were no Corn-crakes nesting near Selborne in Gilbert White's time, for he tells how "a man brought me a Land-rail or Daker-hen, a bird so rare in this district that we seldom see more than one or two in a season, and those only in Autumn."

Early writers, from William Turner (1544), and Francis Willughby (1678) to Montagu in 1802, all agree that it was rare in the south but more plentiful in the north and in Ireland. It is only in the latter half of the nineteenth century that references are found to Corn-crakes being common in southern England.

The truth is that the Corn-crake belongs to a species liable to fluctuation in numbers and in distribution. The vulnerability of the Corn-crake can be deduced from the fact that it lays a clutch of eight to fourteen eggs, which is double the

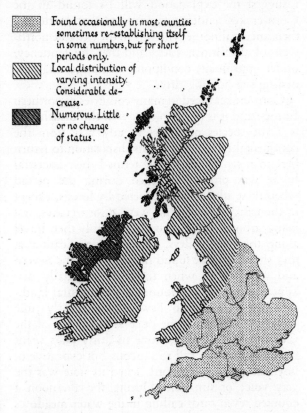

Found occasionally in most counties sometimes re-establishing itself in some numbers, but for short periods only.

Local distribution of varying intensity. Considerable de-crease.

Numerous. Little or no change of status.

The distribution of the corn-crake in the British Isles
After C. A. Norris

average of British breeding birds. The large clutch of the Corn-crake is an adaptation to meet one or more mortality factors and must have been determined far back in its evolutionary past. It is a species struggling to maintain its numbers against adverse factors in its environment, the perils of migration, of predators in its summer and winter quarters, and, in modern times only, of human interference in its chosen habitat of lush grass, now mown during its nesting season.

The great increase in the last century can only be a matter for conjecture. It is possible that the improvement in the quality of the grass-land was a contributory factor; if so it brought its own Nemesis in its train. But we are too prone to attribute the fluctuations in our bird populations to human agencies and to think of the population of the day as being the normal one. Species ebb and flow, they wax and wane and wax again. The essence of their existence, as of ours, is change.

How then do we account for the present distribution of the Corn-crake as shown on the map? I suggest the explanation will be found in the Corn-crakes' tendency to return to that portion of their ancestral home which is in the extreme north-west of the British Isles; and that this tendency, under appropriate conditions, is stronger than the nesting-site homing drive.

Corn-crakes breed in many countries of northern Europe and it is not suggested that the British race is a sub-species or differs in any way from the continental race, except in its disposition to return here to nest. What I have termed their ancestral home was probably formed during the period when these islands were covered by forests, except in the extreme north and west. Corn-crakes, not being arboreal birds, would probably then travel along the river valleys, and it is significant that they should still be found nesting along the Severn and other rivers when they have virtually disappeared from the surrounding agricultural land.

When on a visit to Tewkesbury in early June 1945, I heard again the once familiar call of the Corn-crake for the first time in thirty years spent in the south, that call so raucous but evocative of boyhood days in the north when its note was the very voice of summer. During the afternoon I counted seven birds calling in the water-meadows between the confluence of the Severn and the Avon, and was informed by local residents that

Corn-crakes had always been numerous in the vicinity. The grass of these water-meadows, known as the Severn Ham, is cut by local farmers by machines. The meadows are liable to flooding so that the land is never ploughed nor are artificial fertilisers used since the river silt renews the mineral content of the soil. It is safe to say that apart from the employment of mowing machines the use of these water-meadows has remained the same since agriculture began, and it seemed to me highly significant that Corn-crakes should be numerous in just this part of southern England. To test the significance it was desirable to take a census of the district and ascertain whether in fact the birds are confined to the water-meadows. Accordingly an inquiry was organised the following year as an activity of the Cardiff Naturalists' Society and a questionnaire issued to all the secondary schools in the district and to a number of local residents. The greatest concentration is in the Severn Ham at Tewkesbury, where eleven Corn-crakes were found in an area of 170 acres and where haymaking started on June 12. A count made in June the following year, 1947, showed that approximately the same number were present.

The question arises whether Corn-crakes are found in this locality because of the lush water-meadows or because it lies on a main migratory route. But until results of ringing experiments are available, we may allow ourselves to indulge in speculation as to what happens when the birds are on migration to this country. Let us start with the birds in their winter-quarters somewhere in North Africa. At about the end of March or early in April, the first male birds, in response to that urge which we call the migrating instinct, set out on the journey to their breeding quarters. They have an inherited disposition to fly in a north-westerly direction; a disposition to return to the neighbourhood of the previous year's nest; a disposition to prefer grassland; a disposition to bunch together in adjoining territories; and a disposition to make their presence known within a few days of arrival. Thus a male bird flying across the English Channel comes down early one morning to a meadow in southern England and, finding his normal food in good supply, spends a few days recovering from the fatigue of his journey. His trend to occupy a desirable

Corn-crake at nest, Orkney, June

Eric Hosking

territory over-rules his disposition to fly farther, and he starts to call in the late evening and early morning, and is heard by observers. Meanwhile, starting about a fortnight later, the first females have followed. They also have a disposition to fly north-west; a disposition to return to last year's nesting site; and a disposition to respond to the call of a prospective mate. Perchance one hears the call of the male so that the impulse to respond becomes dominant, and the pair remain to breed. But if no female responds after the male has called for a few days, his disposition to fly north-west will again become dominant and he will fly on. He arrives, perhaps, in North Wales, where—we will assume he bred or was bred last year, descends into the familiar meadow, feeds, and starts to call. If no female responds or no other males call from adjoining territories, again the impulse to fly north-west will become dominant, and he will proceed, perhaps to Anglesey, where he will find large numbers of his kind assembled and, like them, will fly across the Irish Sea. Ultimately he may reach the extreme west of Ireland, part of the ancestral home of his species, and can go no farther.

If this explanation is accepted, we can see how Corn-crakes nest occasionally in the Midland Counties but not in large numbers. The theory also explains the fact that in Ireland Corn-crakes are frequently seen on the roadsides and perched on the walls. We all know how difficult it is to catch sight of a Corn-crake in the south; the most is a glimpse of a snake-like head and neck extended for a moment above the grass, and every effort to find or flush the bird fails. It is curious that birds of the same species should act so differently in Ireland, and I suggest that they are unmated birds who are released from the urge to secrecy in those attached to the nest or young. Unmated birds will be rare in England since they will always tend to fly on, but when they reach the extreme west of the British Isles, they may find all territories already occupied, or all of the opposite sex already mated.

Let us now consider the case of a male Corn-crake with a directional disposition towards the west of Scotland which finds himself on the shores of the Bristol Channel. He will fly north up the Severn Valley, which is a favourite migratory route for many species. Arrived at the confluence of the Severn with the Avon, he hears another male calling on the Severn Ham and flies down to an adjoining part of the meadows. In his turn he begins to call, and being situated on one of the main routes of migration will soon attract a female, so that the impulse to fly farther will be inhibited. In this way we see how the water-meadows in the Severn Valley will be occupied by breeding pairs each year.

At the best all the speculations we make about bird life are pointers to the direction in which future investigations should be made. Among these I would place ringing first. Since the inauguration of the ringing scheme in 1909, the number of Corn-crakes ringed is 566, and of these only 9 have been returned. One was a bird ringed on migration by Ronald Lockley on Skokholm on April 29, 1940, which was recovered in Tipperary on June 20 of the same year. The others are all of young birds ringed in Ireland and Scotland and recovered in England, France and Spain the same year. If some local enthusiasts would undertake the ringing of Corn-crakes in the Severn valley results might be obtained in a few years, particularly if ringing were also continued on an increased scale in the west of Scotland.

Census work should also be continued in the Seven Valley because if the Corn-crake is going to rehabilitate itself in the south it is likely to be from these water-meadows that the spread will start. Such an increase is in my view by no means impossible, despite the continued toll which the mowing-machines will take. Many of the accounts of what happens when the last few swathes fall, either by scythe or machine, are not well authenticated and any careful observer will be struck by the agility with which some birds escape and hide. An increase is likely to show itself first in a greater density of population in the present sites, since the existing territories are no doubt compressible to a considerable degree; later, a spread into the water-meadows of the Warwickshire Avon, the Stour, the Trent, the upper reaches of the Thames, the Somerset and Hampshire Avons, the Wye, the lower reaches of the Severn, and the South Wales littorals adjoining the Severn Sea might be expected.

REFERENCE:

C. A. NORRIS (1945, 47) *Report on the Distribution Status of the Corn-Crake*. Brit. Birds, 38: 142–48, 162–68; 40: 226–44.

R. M. LOCKLEY

BIRD MIGRATION STATIONS IN BRITAIN

BIRD migration stations (as generally understood now) are places where the marking of migratory birds by means of numbered metal leg-rings is actively carried out. Britain, by her situation and topographical construction, with many small islands around her coasts, is well suited to the establishment of a chain of such stations. Britain lies in the path of many of the "long-distance" migratory species nesting in northern and western Europe, Iceland, the arctic islands and eastern Greenland; and her mild climate encourages many of the less migratory birds to winter along her shores.

Ringing (or banding as it is called in America) is quite a modern device; and although there are instances of the marking of a few or single wild birds almost as far back as history records, it was not until the year 1909 that the present types of neat numbered aluminium leg-rings were extensively used in Britain. In that year Dr. Landsborough Thomson started work at Aberdeen, and H. F. Witherby launched a ringing scheme in conjunction with the periodical *British Birds*. Hitherto most rings had had the year and place of ringing only stamped on them. Gurney, for example, marked gannets on the Bass Rock with rings embossed "Bass Rock 1904". To-day all rings are issued by the British Trust for Ornithology. Each ring bears a number and the inscription, "Inform British Museum Nat. Hist. London". Thus all recoveries and inquiries are dealt with by the secretary of the Bird-Ringing Committee whose office is at the Museum.

To be precise the earliest bird migration stations were the duck decoys, where wildfowl were lured by a trained dog and tame ducks until they passed under tunnels of netting suspended over a narrowing waterway, and were finally driven into a catching net. These decoy nets were used principally for marketing ducks for food, but are now also used for ringing waterfowl. The only one at present in regular use for this purpose in Britain is that at Orielton in South Pembrokeshire, where valuable results have followed the ringing of migrating ducks, notably of teal wintering in this country and breeding abroad.

The first permanent migration and bird-ringing station in Europe was established in 1903 by the German Ornithological Society, at Rossitten on the long sandy bar of the Kurische Nehrung. Then came the station on Heligoland made famous by Heinrich Gätke's book on the birds of that North Sea island. In the years preceding the war about ten thousand birds were annually trapped and ringed at Heligoland, and with this abundant material many homing and other experiments were made, the work being financed by the German State Biological Bureau. To-day Heligoland is a heap of rubble but the ornithological records are safely housed in the new base of the *Vogelwarte Helgoland* at Wilhelmshaven.

In the United States local bird-banding stations rapidly sprang up from 1909 onwards, and subsequently the Department of Agriculture recognised the economic importance of the work and, through its Biological Survey Bureau, became responsible for the issue of rings.

In Britain ringing has remained almost entirely in the hands of the unpaid amateurs, by whose efforts the first bird migration stations were established on islands off the coast. These began in a small way with the building of a Heligoland-type trap in the garden at Skokholm, Pembrokeshire, in August 1933 by the writer, assisted by H. Morrey Salmon and other ornithologists. A year later the Midlothian Ornithological Club built a large Heligoland trap on the Isle of May. In 1935 the traps at both island observatories were improved and other traps erected. Up to the beginning of the war some six thousand birds were

The Duck Decoy, Orielton, S. Pembrokeshire

annually ringed at or near Skokholm, and a smaller number at the Isle of May. The Isle of May was occupied by the War Department in 1938. Work continued at Skokholm until the island had to be evacuated in 1940, when it was also occupied by the Services.

These stations were extremely popular with ornithologists. The limited accommodation for six to eight persons at a time was in great demand. The work proved interesting and valuable, and the joys of island life in summer with congenial companions could be appreciated to the full. Apart from the pleasure of identifying and ringing birds, including some rarer species, *in the hand,* and releasing them again (as compared with the gun and glass case method of the old-time observer), there were vast numbers of sea-birds to be studied by the same method (of ringing the individual).

The day on the island observatory always proves too short, like all happy days. The work has its reward in the recovery of birds elsewhere and abroad, or year after year at home. Problems of migration, longevity, age at breeding, sexual relationships, nesting, rearing, fledging and moult can be studied most easily at these stations, and interesting information follows. At Skokholm for example extensive ringing of Manx shearwaters proved beyond all doubt that a breeding bird with egg or chick in a burrow on the island may fly as far as the north coast of Spain to feed, a journey of six hundred miles each way!

War suspended the work of the two observatories, but discussions went on among ornithologists, some of whom actually met and made plans in prisoner-of-war camps. In 1945 it was agreed to form a committee, composed of one representative from each observatory, for co-ordinating the work of bird observatories, as a sub-committee of

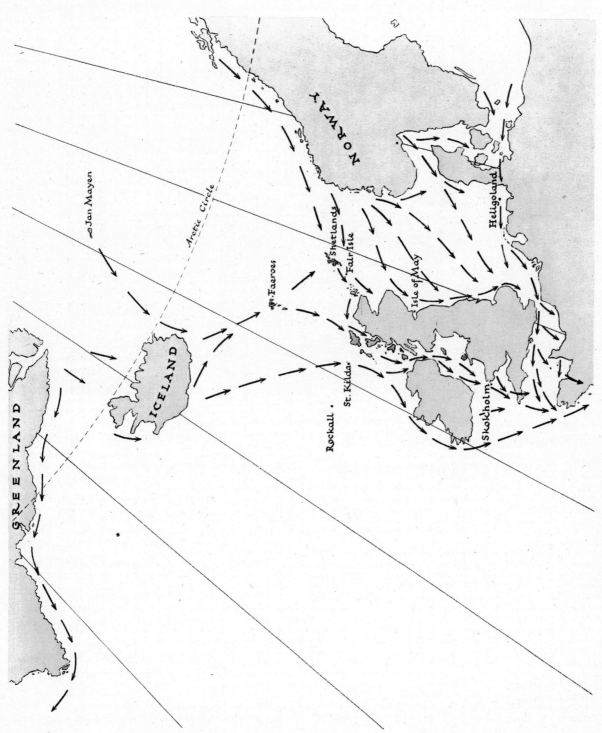

A sketch map to show general direction of autumn migration of birds breeding in northern Europe, which pass through the British Isles

R. M. Lockley

Heligoland trap on Skokholm. Cover, water and food in front of the trap invite passing birds to rest. They are then driven into the funnel of netting, caught in an enclosure at the end, ringed, and set free on their travels once more

the British Trust for Ornithology. The form and method of recording observations at migration stations was standardised—a great convenience for those who, as frequently happens, visit and work at more than one station.

In 1946 Skokholm was re-opened by the West Wales Field Society, which also made an experimental survey of the neighbouring island of Skomer; and 6,387 birds were ringed on this group of islands in 1946. In the same year the Isle of May Bird Observatory was re-opened and later it was announced that this observatory would be governed by a joint committee representing the Midlothian Ornithological Club, the Commissioners of Northern Lighthouses (the owners of the island) and the four Scottish Universities.

1946, too, was to see the Yorkshire Naturalists' Union build a Heligoland trap at Spurn Head, and place a cottage there at the disposal of ornitho-

logists. In the autumn of the same year Devon naturalists formed the Lundy Field Society and built a large Heligoland trap on Lundy Island. This has been successfully operated since.

On remote Fair Isle, half-way between Orkney and Shetland, George Waterston (who is now the owner of the island) was instrumental in erecting a Heligoland trap. This is available for ringing the numerous common and rare migrants for which this island is a famous stopping place. The main problem of the would-be visitor is to get there and to get back, for there is no reliable boat service!

Lastly, Peter Scott has established the Severn Wildfowl Trust, to build and maintain an observatory and sanctuary on the English side of the Severn, near Slimbridge, Gloucestershire. On the saltings here wild geese graze unmolested but observed from hides conveniently situated against the sea wall. There are large enclosures for breeding

R. M. Lockley

The catching-box of the new trap, showing sleeve for insertion of hand to extract bird

pinioned water fowl; there is a duck decoy; and the trapping and ringing of the resident as well as the migratory birds is contemplated.

We thus have three observatories widely dispersed on the east coast, and three others on the west coast, rather close together in or near the Bristol Channel. This is a very good start. It is more than likely that new stations will be set up elsewhere in the next few years, and these may well link up to form a chain with the established observatories. A glance at the map of Britain indicates the need for stations at Holy Isle, in Norfolk (Scolt Head or Blakeney?), Kent (Dungeness is famous for migration), the Isle of Wight (St. Catherine's is the obvious site), the Isles of Scilly (several sites here; Tresco has had many rare birds, but probably St. Agnes would be the best island for the necessary concentration within a small area for trapping purposes), Bardsey

Island (off North Wales, and on the migration route), and the Calf of Man (a National Trust property). The west of Scotland presents a difficult problem; since the whole coast abounds in small islands there are few places where migrants concentrate, save on the outer almost inaccessible and therefore unsuitable islands, such as North Rona and St. Kilda. In Shetland and Orkney again there is too great an area of islands

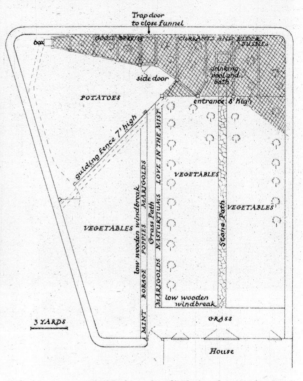

The garden at Skokholm: detail of the first Heligoland trap in Britain (1933)

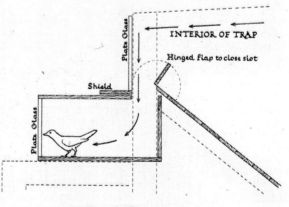

Detail of catching-box

Eric Hosking

The Fair Isle, Shetland, where the Atlantic meets the North Sea: an aerial view of the south-west end of this migration station. Half a gale was blowing when this photograph was taken on 29 September, 1947

to achieve much concentration, and it will be only by the efforts of enthusiastic individuals that any ringing will be done here. Islands such as Unst, Whalsey, and Out Skerries at times swarm with both common and rare species. Theo Kay has recorded in gardens in Shetland's capital, Lerwick, barred warblers, Greenland redpolls and numbers of other rare birds, many of which he has ringed.

Only those who wish to make a serious study of some branch of natural history are admitted to the present observatories, and preference is given to competent ornithologists. But the resident mammals, insects and flora also await study on these fascinating islands and headlands, where the ecology (or dependence of species upon species) is of special significance in isolated communities.

Students and learners should arrange to go in the company of an expert. This is no more than a necessary safeguard, for the identification of

migratory birds does call for the expert eye; and the technique of handling, ringing, examination for plumage phases, age, moult, parasites etc. needs to be acquired by careful training.

Those observatories at which there is a competent resident warden, as at Skokholm, are of most use to the beginners. Moreover a resident warden, with a changing team of visitors, can keep a line of research going and provide the essential continuity which a series of separate groups of workers cannot hope to do.

The work of the amateurs is often valuable, but all too often it is broken off for lack of financial support. Eventually, when ornithology and outdoor studies receive proper recognition, it is hoped that money will be made available to provide permanent wardens at bird observatories. These men would spend seven months, from mid-March to mid-October, at these island observatories entirely on ringing work, on field surveys, in conducting their own research, and in helping the researches of others; the remainder of the year (apart from the necessary annual holiday), would be spent in working up the information in the form of papers, and an annual report. Observatories on the mainland, as at Spurn Head and Slimbridge, would probably be open throughout the year.

Those desiring the latest information as to accommodation at any of the established observatories should write to: Mr. W. B. Alexander, Observatories Committee, British Trust for Ornithology, 91 Banbury Road, Oxford.

REFERENCES

BRITISH BIRDS Monthly Magazine, London, Witherby.

JAMES FISHER (1940) *Watching Birds*. Harmondsworth, Penguin Books.

R. M. LOCKLEY (1947) *Letters from Skokholm*. London, Dent.

A. L. THOMSON (1936) *Bird Migration*. London, Witherby.

▲ Fair Isle

▲ Isle of May

▲ Holy Isle

✠ Calf of Man

✠ Bardsey

▲ Spurn Head

✠ Blakeney

▲ Orielton Decoy

▲ Skokholm

▲ Slimbridge

Lundy ▲

✠ Dungeness

✠ St. Catherine's

✠ St. Agnes'

▲ Bird Observatories where Heligoland traps and/or Decoys are in use for the purpose of ringing migratory birds.

✠ Sites suitable for further Observatories

Sites of Bird Observatories in England, Scotland and Wales

R. M. Lockley

The rare Greenland Redpoll caught in a bird-ringing trap at the Isle of May

A. LANDSBOROUGH THOMSON

THE VALUE OF BIRD-RINGING IN THE STUDY OF MIGRATION

THE opportunities for direct observation of bird-migration are limited. Usually one can note only the seasonal appearances and disappearances of certain species or local fluctuations in numbers. In favourable circumstances migration may be seen in actual progress, but even where the phenomena are on a grand scale the record of particular birds or flocks is restricted to the short time and distance that these remain in view. (With the help of radar the track of a flock of geese has been followed for seventy-nine miles.) Although simultaneous watch may be kept at many stations, the correlation of the collected records presents many difficulties and uncertainties.

The marking of individual birds with numbered rings provides an indirect method of observation yielding supplementary information of a valuable kind. The recovery of a ringed bird implies that at two (occasionally more) dates in its life we know its exact whereabouts. These records of the particular individual may be separated by a period of months or years and by a space of up to thousands of miles—something which is obviously quite outside the scope of direct observation. When the bird has been ringed as a chick or nestling, one of the two records gives its place and approximate date of birth, with the desirable result that we know exactly with what we are dealing in our endeavour to interpret the later and possibly distant record.

The contrast between direct observation and the ringing method is, in a sense, one between studying migrants in the mass and studying the individual bird. This is, however, merely the initial approach, and it is to be emphasised that the ultimate value of ringing records lies in their aggregation and the possibilities of statistical analysis. An isolated record is open to the suspicion of some human error in the data, or of abnormal behaviour on the part of the particular bird. It is, therefore, important to have the confirmation of numerous records of the same kind. More than that, we want quantitative as well as qualitative information: we want to know not only that members of a certain species, and of a particular community of that species, may sometimes behave in the indicated manner, but also to what extent they actually do so.

The limitations of the method must be frankly recognised. The proportion of recoveries is often small, thus involving immense labour in ringing the total required for a useful yield: in British experience the figure is less than one per cent for some of the small passerines but rises as high as 21·8 per cent in the case of the cormorant. Of the records obtained, moreover, some may be uninteresting or difficult to interpret.

Again, there are both avian and human factors affecting the chances of recovery. There are seasonal differences in the rate of bird mortality; and the density and character of the human population will influence the extent to which dead birds bearing rings are reported from any area. Such indeterminate variables make it necessary to use statistical analysis with great caution.

The ringing method is accordingly one that must (like any other) be applied in a critical frame of mind. With this proviso, however, one may confidently claim that its positive advantages are important. To take the most general example, direct observation can tell us the breeding distribution, passage occurrence and winter-quarters of a species—or of a recognisable sub-species; but it cannot tell us to what part of the winter area the birds from a particular part of the summer area resort. Ringing, on the other hand, can give us just this type of information, which happens to be of great significance for a proper understanding of the nature of migration and for an approach to the biological problems which the phenomena present.

R. M. Lockley

How to hold a bird for ringing. This chaffinch is securely held with the first and second fingers while the third and fourth control the leg for the ring to be clipped on by the other hand of the observer

R. M. Lockley

White Wagtail about to be released, Skokholm

Valuable facts of this kind have already accrued from use of the ringing method. One of the most dramatic examples has been the mapping of the migration of the white stork south-eastwards across Europe, round the Levant, and southwards by an inland route through the eastern part of Africa—with an indication of an alternative direction from the more westerly parts of the European range south-westwards through Spain. A smaller number of records has demonstrated the winter-quarters, in the eastern half of South Africa, of many of the swallows native to the British Isles. Again, winter ringing of starlings in the British Isles has shown that our winter visitors are native to an area subtended by Holland and Arctic Norway and stretching eastwards to include the land adjacent on all sides to the Baltic Sea.

Another question which is fundamental in considering the nature of migration is that of the con-

stancy, or otherwise, of the individual's behaviour. Direct observation tells us only that the seasonal distribution of a species remains more or less constant, but ringing has abundantly shown that as a general rule the individual migrant returns annually to its native locality. There is also some evidence of the return of individuals to the same winter-quarters.

In most species for which adequate records exist, exceptions to the rule of constant return to the native locality are few. Among the ducks, however, it has been found that the exceptions are relatively numerous, suggesting a less firmly-fixed pattern of behaviour. The case is often one of "aberrant return" from winter-quarters to a new summer area; but it is sometimes one of "abmigration"—a spring movement on the part of a member of a resident community (e.g. British-bred mallard). It seems probable that such irregularities are

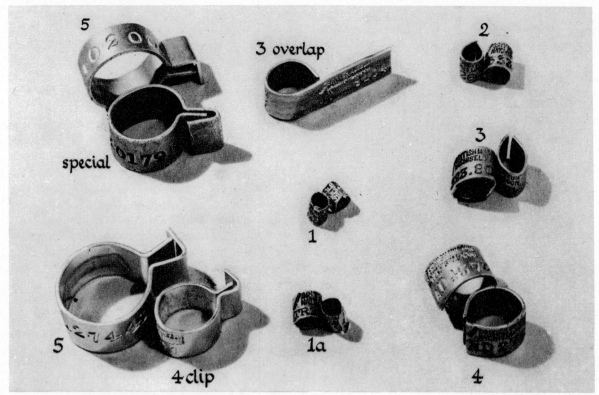

Aaprint

Bird-rings: aluminium bands stamped "INFORM BRITISH MUSEUM NAT. HIST. LONDON", *and numbered, issued by the British Trust for Ornithology to accredited workers for use in the British Isles*

Size: 1 finches, pipits, warblers, swallows, etc.; 1a thrushes, waders, terns, etc.; 2 cuckoo, plover, etc.; 3 crows, ducks, gulls, etc.; 3 overlap: sheer-waters and puffin; 4 birds of prey, grebes, etc.; 4 clip: raven, peregrine, sea-ducks, etc.; special: gannet and heron; 5 geese, cormorants and divers

imitative, being due to winter association, includ-ing pre-migratory pairing, with other members of the species belonging to different communities.

Ringing has clearly brought out that although a community may be faithful to its native area, the degree to which migration therefrom is developed may vary as between individuals. One of the earliest results of ringing in the British Isles was the finding that of lapwings native to the north-east of Scotland a few remained stationary through the winter, some migrated to Ireland, and others found winter-quarters further south, notably in Portugal. The method, however, rarely produces more than one distant recovery record for a single bird, and it is therefore not possible to say whether the individual repeats the same performance annually or whether in successive years it may adopt different alternatives from among the several types of movement exhibited by its community.

Analysis of the records according to age, never-theless, shows in some cases that the tendency differs at least in this respect. The ringing of gannets at various breeding stations round the British coasts, for instance, has shown that south-ward movement is more pronounced in the first year of life than subsequently, the proportion of recoveries from North African and tropical waters (as compared with European waters) being con-siderably higher than among second-year or older birds. Similar results have been obtained for other species, with the further point that in some of them the adult females as well as the juvenile birds show a greater tendency to migrate than the adult males.

This question of "partial migrants" has been specially studied by Lack on the basis of British ringing data. He has shown in the case of the song-thrush, for instance, that of recoveries show-ing movement from Great Britain to France and the Iberian Peninsula the proportion representing birds in their first winter is much higher than among recoveries showing absence of movement or showing movement only to Ireland. He also showed interesting regional differences in migratory behaviour.

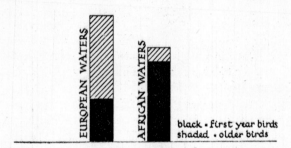

Winter recoveries (Nov.–Feb.) of British gannets ringed as nestlings

black = first year birds
shaded = older birds

Statistical analysis of ringing data has also served to emphasise the difference between a mere dispersal and a true migratory movement. In the former case the number of recovery records falls away progressively as distance increases. In the latter it falls away more steeply at first but the curve rises again to a second peak farther away. If the recovery records for herring-gulls and lesser black-backed gulls, ringed in the British Isles, are plotted in zones (by distance from point of origin) the two curves show this contrast quite clearly: the second not only extends farther but shows the two peaks characteristic of true migration, one at the native locality and the other at the focus of winter distribution.

Even where the records for a species are too few for statistical treatment they may yield new information. We could not otherwise have known, for instance, that transatlantic migration of kittiwakes native to the British Isles is a common occurrence. Again, a few records for the wigeon have shown that birds from Iceland may migrate either south-westwards to America or south-eastwards to Europe; that birds bred near the Caspian Sea and in Northern Russia may reach the British Isles; and that some from Siberia travel to India.

In the hands of those with opportunities for intensive work, ringing can be an aid to direct observation within a small area. For this purpose visible rings of different colours are used, in various combinations, instead of—or in addition to—the

usual numbered rings of light metal. Rings may also be used in certain types of experiment, such as in testing the homing powers of wild birds or in ascertaining the migratory behaviour of birds transported to another area. It may also be noted in passing that ringing has applications to facets of bird behaviour other than migration.

As a general conclusion it may be said that much of value has already been learnt from ringing, but that even more still remains unknown which further exploitation of the method may be expected to reveal. To obtain the best results, avoiding waste of effort, it is desirable that the experience which has now been gained should form the basis of careful planning, done with a clear conception of objectives and with a critical appreciation both of the potentialities and of the limitations of the ringing method.

REFERENCES:

LACK, D. (1943-44) *The problem of partial migration.* British Birds, 38: 122-30, 143-50.

LEACH, E. P. (1947) *Recovery of Marked Birds.* British Birds, 40: 360-68 (and many earlier lists in the same journal).

THOMSON, A. L. (1942) *Bird Migration: a short account,* second edition. London, Witherby.

C. A. Gibson-Hill

Immature gannet: the largest sea-bird of the North Atlantic truly migrates during its four years of immaturity, passing south in autumn as far as north-west Africa. Adult gannets appear, on the other hand, simply to disperse outside the breeding-season

JAMES FISHER

THE LAST HUNDRED BIRD BOOKS

A HUNDRED bird books have been published since 1943: twenty books a year in Britain, about British birds; excluding pamphlets, but including reprints and new editions of books published first before 1943.

When the British publishers first realised that the boom in natural history was quite separate from, and independent of, the book-boom, there was a great rush into print with nature books. Many of these were hastily written or compiled for a quick market, and it is a most remarkable tribute to the taste and restraint of most British publishers that half of the hundred—fifty books exactly—are, in my opinion, sound, and have been worth while. My analysis of the nature and value of the last hundred bird books is as follows:

excellent, and will be reprinted for many years. Some will be quoted scientifically and will become classics. Others will be *used*, for reference, by the student (whatever his stage) and are unlikely to be replaced by anything better for a long time.

Those in the "satisfactory" class will, I believe, not last long; and, while a lot of people have taken pleasure in them, or learned something from them, few will regard them as books to keep. Some authors of books in this category have clearly not read many other books on birds; some, on the other hand, have copied authority too closely and uncritically. Some have suffered from a complete misunderstanding of what is valuable or interesting, though they have written so carefully that they could not be classed as unsound.

	SOUND	SATISFACTORY	UNSOUND	TOTAL
Introductions to general ornithology or bird watching	8	—	11	19
Books on special birds or special bird subjects	14	—	4	18
Books on bird identification	5	4	5	14
Books on personal experiences with birds	7	—	6	13
Books on local birds	6	—	4	10
Pot-boilers, to go with photographs	4	1	3	8
Pot-boilers, to go with pictures	1	1	3	5
Magazines	2	2	1	5
Stories	1	3	—	4
Poems	1	1	—	2
Paper cut-outs	1	—	—	1
Lunatic fringe	—	—	1	1
	50	12	38	100

Naturally, the classification of these books is based on subjective judgment, and I have tried to restrain bias. Those which I have described as "sound" have done their self-appointed tasks with honesty and thoroughness. Some are quite

The remaining thirty-eight books are almost valueless. One, for instance, is a re-issue of a book on the status of British birds written before the first world war. Scarcely a word has been changed: the book, as it stands, is, to say the least of it, misleading, and an unfair reproach to the distinguished name it bears. Others are written by authors whose excessive consciousness of the exquisite nature of their prose, and the distinction conferred on the reader by a peep at their personalities, are so grotesque as to baffle description. In some such books you cannot see the birds for the words. Some of the bad writers take so much trouble in proving other people wrong, and in putting forward their "theories" that their prose makes better material for the psychiatrist than the bird-watcher.

It will be noted that the preceding paragraph has been written in some heat. This is because it seems, to the reviewer, a pity that well over a third of the bird books and, probably, about a quarter of the paper available for bird books, should have been devoted to worthless work, by uncritical or uncaring publishers. Some of these books, unduly praised under the general reviewers' formula that nature is somehow safe and charming, have enjoyed large sales, and have attracted the money of worthy students who can only afford limited sums. It must be galling to purchase a certain widely-praised book only to find that its author appears never to have heard of the *Zoological Record*, purports, without visible support, to criticise the *Handbook of British Birds* (fair enough game through its very excellence to those with fair intentions), neglects the work published in seven readily available British journals, misunderstands the nature of evidence, pooh-poohs the careful investigations of a trained scientific investigator with thousands of field-hours to his credit on one species, and suggests, roughly speaking, that scientists are a bad influence in ornithology.

The situation, however, must not be exaggerated. I suppose that any other subject that now enjoys a wide following suffers in the same way. There are bad novelists, bad journalists, bad historians and bad scientists who get their books published. In the long run, the public decides on the good, and the bad goes to the wall. All the same it is wrong that some bird writers do not try harder to find out what is already known, and say what they have to say with a little more point, and a good deal more fairness and scrupulousness.

What is good, the good half, is the really important thing, however; and there is nothing invidious about mentioning some of the books in this group. Among the eight sound introductions to bird-watching, for instance, are E. A. Armstrong's *The Way Birds Live*, and his *Bird Display and Behaviour*, E. A. R. Ennion's *The British Bird*, and Stuart Smith's *How to Study Birds*. Among the special-subject books quality is higher, because specialists are usually well-informed, and out of the fourteen sound ones I must choose, simply as samples, David Lack's excellent *Life of the Robin*, R. M. Lockley's *Shearwaters*, and A. Landsborough Thomson's *Bird Migration* (reprint). Those stand-bys on bird identification, Coward (in its various forms), Sandars, and Joy continue in print, and can sometimes be obtained in the shops. Among books about the "fun" of bird-watching I can single out Armstrong's *Birds of the Grey Wind*, Ennion's *Adventurer's Fen*, Lockley's *Letters from Skokholm*, Niall Rankin's *Haunts of British Divers*, and E. H. Ware's *Wing to Wing*. Good books on local birds include the Carlisle Natural History Society's *Birds of Lakeland*, A. W. Boyd's *Country Diary of a Cheshire Man*, R. S. R. Fitter's *London's Natural History*, A. J. Harthan's *Birds of Worcestershire*, and Richard Perry's studies on *Lundy* and *Lindisfarne*. Messrs. Eric Hosking and G. K. Yeates have produced a selection of beautiful and remarkable photographs in their *Birds of the . . .*, and *Bird Life in . . .* series; we hope they are busy on more. There has been one original and amusing bird story, J. K. Stanford's *The Twelfth*; and R. B. Talbot Kelly's clever cut-out Puffin book, *Paper Birds*, deserves a special mention. Throughout the period under review that remarkable publication, *The Handbook of British Birds*, has usually remained in print, though rationed by booksellers, and has put all other bird-books in the shade.

To sum up, the last hundred bird books are a mixed lot, but half of them have been definitely worth printing. This is not a bad proportion, by publishing standards. There is no doubt that the next hundred birds books will have been published by 1953, and it will be interesting to taste their quality and compare it with that of their predecessors.

THE NATURALIST's JOURNAL

Year / Selborne. Place. Soil.		Therm	Barom	Wind	Inches of Rain or Sn. Size of Hail-st.	Weather	Trees first in leaf. —Fungi first appear.	Plants first in flower: Mosses vegetate.	Birds and Insects first appear, or disappear.	Observations with regard to fish, and other animals.	Miscellaneous Observations, and Memorandums.
May 5.	Sunday. 8 / 12 / 4 / 8	44.	29 3·70½	N.		dark, & harsh.					Some swallows, & h. martins.
6.	Monday. 8 / 12 / 4 / 8	43.	29 4·10½	N.	32.	snow, sleet, cold rain.					No swifts. Some swallows.
7.	Tuesday. 8 / 12 / 4 / 8	43¾	29 6·10½	N. NW.		dark & cold. sun & clouds. pleasant even. distant clouds.			White throat appears. No swifts. Cucumber sets, & swells. Two Nightingales sing in my outlet.		
8.	Wednes. 8 / 12 / 4 / 8	44.	29 4·10½	SE. S.		frost. ice. sun & clouds. louring.			Mowed the grass-walks for the first time. Some swallows. No swifts. Tortoise awakes.		
9.	Thurs. 8 / 12 / 4 / 8	49.	29 2·70½	E.		grey & mild. dark & mild.			A few beeches in the hanger show leaves. Swallows on every chimney. Seven Swifts. Radishes.		

An English spring: recorded in Gilbert White's Journal for 1779

THE NEW NATURALIST

A JOURNAL OF BRITISH NATURAL HISTORY

WINTER

THE LOCAL NATURALIST

CONTENTS

BRIAN VESEY-FITZGERALD: *On Being a Local Naturalist* 181

J. S. GILMOUR: *A Directory of Natural History Societies* 186

H. K. AIRY SHAW: *The Natural History Societies of the British Isles* 188

DAVID STAINER: *School Natural History Societies* 207

W. H. PEARSALL, F.R.S.: *Local Journals* 211

L. C. LLOYD: *Naturalists on the Air* 214

EDITOR: JAMES FISHER • ASSISTANT EDITOR: ELISABETH ULLMANN

BRIAN VESEY-FITZGERALD

ON BEING
A LOCAL NATURALIST

"MEN that undertake only one district are much more likely to advance natural knowledge than those that grasp at more than they can possibly be acquainted with; every kingdom, every province, should have its own monographer." The words are those of Gilbert White. The full force of such a sentence can hardly be felt by one who reads him in the light of our modern knowledge. It is, indeed, an invaluable warning for all time, and every man who puts pen to paper to write on natural history would do well to learn it by heart.

But, it may be said, in Gilbert White's day the accurate study of the life and habits of animals was almost unknown, and the facts which are now the common property of naturalists were then awaiting discovery or verification. In ornithology, for example—and ornithology was White's favourite study—no important contribution to the science had been made by an Englishman for a hundred years before the publication of the *Natural History of Selborne*. White, so far as England was concerned, had to take up almost exactly where Willughby and Ray had left off. If you read Willughby's account of any of the insignificant-looking little birds that are so numerous in our woods and fields, you will find that the study of their songs and habits and movements had then scarcely begun, and that naturalists were still to a very great extent under the tyranny of tradition. White had almost a clear field.

It is true enough. It was all new for White. But let me quote again from his writings. He says: "Though there is endless room for observation in the field of nature, which is boundless, yet investigation, where a man endeavours to be sure of his facts, can make but slow progress and all that one could collect in many years would go into a very small compass." And again, in 1779, he wrote: "It is now more than forty years that I have paid some attention to the ornithology of this district,

without being able to exhaust the subject; new occurrences still arise as long as any inquiries are kept alive." Both sentences are still true to-day, even though we now have a vast accumulation of knowledge stored up in the books. There is still room, there will always be room, for the local naturalist.

Now, what do I mean by a "local naturalist"? There are hundreds of local natural history societies in the country—I believe that if the membership of these societies were to be added up it would be found to exceed one hundred thousand —and in a sense it would be true to say that all the members of such societies are local naturalists. I would prefer to say that all the members should be local naturalists; but that, unfortunately, only few of them are. I would narrow down the definition considerably. More is needed than mere membership of a local society to qualify for the proud title of "a local naturalist". Essentially, a local naturalist should be an amateur (as Gilbert White was) and a man whose natural history interests are confined (as were those of Gilbert White) to his own immediate district. He should be a man of *parochial* interests. He should be a man who studies natural history as a hobby, for pleasure. He should be a man unconcerned with fame in the scientific world, indifferent to profit, content with that profit, physical and mental, that accrues to those who pursue a hobby intelligently. Needless to say, he will be a man with a lively and inquiring mind; he would not otherwise be interested in natural history at all. He will not be a specialist, for the specialist is above local, parochial, boundaries. But he should not (as I shall hope to show presently) be a man of no ambition.

Such a man can contribute, even in these days, a great deal to the general store of knowledge. We live in the hey-day of the specialist. We are inclined to forget, on so high a pedestal have we

"Men that undertake only one district. . . . ." Selborne from the Hanger

placed him, that the specialist no less than other men must have food in order to live. Pennant and Daines Barrington were the specialists of Gilbert White's day. Both were Fellows of the Royal Society, and both were distinguished zoologists. Both realised (Pennant especially so, for Barrington was a man of much wider interests and addicted to dabbling in all sorts of pools) that Gilbert White was nourishing food for scientific minds, and Pennant, in particular, waxed fat on White's letters. The essence of the position has altered but little since then. There are modern specialists, who do go out into the woods and the fields, who are themselves excellent field naturalists, but in the great army of specialism that has grown up they are few and far between. Modern specialisation is a hard taskmaster, and few modern specialists have the time—even when they have the inclination—to be anything but specialists, talking a language of their own, breathing the rarefied air of the Museum or the Laboratory or the Lecture Room. But they must still have food.

It is the local naturalist that, as often as not, provides it to-day as White provided it nearly two hundred years ago. The trouble is that he does not provide nearly enough. For this, the specialists are themselves largely to blame. With the growth of modern specialisation there has come, in far too many cases, superiority, a conscious condescension to the amateur, an attitude of mind that would have been quite outside the understanding of men like Pennant or Barrington, even of men who lived a century later, men like Darwin or T. H. Huxley. As a result there has grown up the idea that there is now, in natural history, only work for the specialist, that the rest of us can amuse ourselves if we like playing with natural history, but that there is no excuse or justification for the serious amateur. You can see this attitude of mind, the inevitable result of the ill-concealed superiority of the professional, in half the local natural history societies in the country. (I exclude societies like the London Natural History Society, which has a large membership of specialists—and famous names at that—and which, despite its title, covers a very large area. I exclude also a number of similar societies, which are local only in name. I have in mind the truly local society, the society centred round a small town and which calls itself as often as not a "Field Club".) Too many of them have

become no more than occasional social gatherings; a monthly meeting during the spring and summer, a "ramble" (sparsely attended) with tea and buns at some café in a neighbouring town or village; in the winter a few lectures, if the finances will run to it. Serious work? None. And yet, in every society of this nature, there are a number of keen members, vitally interested in some branch of natural history or in natural history generally, and who would be only too glad to do some constructive work, given the guidance and encouragement.

What work is there to do? So much that I could not even begin to list it in the space at my disposal. In general there is to-day, as there has been in the past, too great a concentration on birds, butterflies and the larger moths, and flowers. Despite all that we do know about birds, there is still a great deal to be discovered and in this connection the British Trust for Ornithology encourages amateurs to take part in its various inquiries. This organisation, indeed, does invaluable work quite outside its Inquiries, by making the amateur feel that he is wanted by the specialist and thereby training him, albeit unconsciously, in field-work. I know of no similar work in the fields of Botany or Entomology, no such organised work. Records are kept of the immigrations of butterflies and moths— and the amateur may send his own records in—but there the matter appears to end. In both these fields there is an immense and yawning gap between the specialist and the amateur which, in ornithology at least, the British Trust is trying to bridge.

But what happens when we come to mammals, to spiders, to the microlepidoptera, to reptiles, to the amphibia, to fish, to snails, to beetles? Nothing happens at all. And yet in each there is a vast amount of work crying to be done—and plenty of people to do it, and keen to do it, were they only given the encouragement and some guidance from specialists, especially in the matter of correct identification.

Take mammals, for example. We do not know the full distribution in this country of all our bats. Indeed, for more than half our twelve species we have but the sketchiest idea of their distribution. It would be quite true to say that for no area in this country have we a complete list of the mammalian species. You have only to get a man interested in bats moving into a new area, and almost immediately the list of species for that area will be increased. Leisler's Bat has recently been found in Cambridgeshire—far to the east of any previously known haunt—and Bechstein's Bat has recently been found in Dorset. Our knowledge of the distribution of our spiders is also sketchy in the extreme. Here, indeed, is work for the local naturalist, and food for the specialist.

But, first, the local naturalist must know his country. Knowing a country, even a small area, takes time. It is not a matter of knowing merely the boundaries or the footpaths over fields and through woods. To be a really good local naturalist you must know the geography of your district as well as you know the geography of your own house; not just the paths through the woods, but the woods themselves; not just the paths across fields, but every fold in the ground in every field; not the hedges alone, but the lie of the hedgerows to the compass, their "set" to the prevailing winds (if you had to live on what you could trap, you would soon realise the supreme importance of that point); the streams and their depths and eddies; the local weather and the local signs foretelling it; and so on and so on. A working knowledge of these things is acquired only slowly and over years, and at the same time the keen local naturalist will be learning the movements of the animals in his district. It is not often, in this country, that one may see a wild animal in person and by chance, but no animal can move over ground without leaving some sign of its passing. Too little attention is paid to such signs in this country. Of course, all these things will not be learnt by any one man in a lifetime (the man interested in spiders will find spiders which would be overlooked by another naturalist, equally observant, but interested in some other animal) but a good all-round working knowledge can be gained with just a little trouble taken.

Thereafter some serious work could be combined with the hobby. I firmly believe that natural history should never cease to be a hobby, a pleasant relaxation for spare time, for the local man, but that does not mean that it cannot also be made to serve some larger and useful purpose. For example, one could work out the spider population (species and distribution) for a small area: the information gained would I am sure be of great value to the specialists, and especially if a number of local naturalists in different parts of the country were to do so. Similarly with bats or snails or beetles, with any number of creatures. There would be no falling-off of interest for the local naturalist, indeed his interest would be increased, and the sum total of knowledge would inevitably be advanced.

But it is asking too much of the local naturalist to do such work without encouragement and without specialist guidance, particularly as regards identification. (Have you ever thought what would have happened had Pennant not encouraged Gilbert White?) I have myself a considerable distrust of organisation where it means centralisation, but I believe that the time is ripe for some such movement in British natural history. At present all the many little field clubs and local natural history societies struggle along by themselves, and the enthusiasm that makes young people join is gradually atrophied. In most counties there is a County Archaeological and Natural History Society, among whose members there is a nucleus of specialists. Beyond these societies there are the National organisations, the Universities and the Museums. If these latter took a little more interest in the county societies and the county societies in the local societies (I have recently found a county society that was unaware of the existence of two local societies within its boundaries!) then there might be brought into being a proper ladder stretching from the field to the specialist to the great benefit of both. And the local amateur would not feel quite so unwanted as is now too frequently the case. But the initiative must come from the top. The British Trust for Ornithology has shown what can be done. I should like to see something of the same sort done with the mammals and other groups. What better medium for some such plan as this than through the columns of THE NEW NATURALIST?

Knowledge is built up slowly—as Isaiah said, "Line upon line, here a little, and there a little"— as the specialist knows. It is the little that the local naturalist could so often provide, if he dared. There would be a lot of chaff, of course, but here and there also a grain. There would be a lot of questions asked—and many foolish, maybe—and that no doubt would be a strain on the patience of the learned, but as Eddington, a great and courteous man, said, "Progress is marked not so much by the problems we are able to solve as by the questions we are enabled to ask."

THE RIVER MOLE

BELOW BOX HILL

described by G. E. Hutchings

The Mole is the type and model of all the Wealden rivers. Rising in the forest country of the Central Weald its upper waters are gathered together in the Vale of Holmesdale and thence find their way northward to the Thames through a magnificent gap in the Chalk range of the North Downs. In this picture the river is shown at the place where it sweeps hard against the foot of the escarpment just before entering the gap. In the background is seen a small piece of the open down near the summit of Box Hill. Between this and the river is an almost precipitous slope, the end portion of an eroded river cliff of great age. It is clothed with a growth of box and yew, with here and there a scar of bare chalk where even these tenacious plants have failed to maintain a root-hold. The woods of box and yew on the scarp face and over the top of Box Hill are regarded as a genuine unspoilt relic of the native forest of the southern English Chalk.

Here, then, is the Mole entering upon its passage across the chalk country through one of the loveliest tree-clad valleys of southern Britain. And here by Burford Bridge we have a typical scene—on one side of the river the wall of the Chalk Hills with their mantle of dark green, on the other a quiet meadow. The trench of the stream is lined with overhanging trees—elms, poplars, alders, limes and sycamores. Wherever there is a break in their shade the banks are clothed with waterside plants, seen at their best perhaps in the late summer, starred with the bright flowers of balsam, tansy and the great hairy willow-herb.

The river and its belt of vegetation afford livelihood and cover to a whole world of animal life. Its inhabitants in their pursuit of the stern affairs of food, reproduction and the avoidance of enemies are in general inconspicuous and of secretive habits. They enter little into the readily visible scene of the riverside. Even of the great host of insects in high summer we see but a tiny fraction, and there is but little to show that this river belt is the haunt of a multitude of mammals from small mice to ponderous badgers. Only the birds have a demonstrative way of life, and with them this ribbon of water with its trees and thickets becomes a noisy, turbulent aviary.

A short distance from Burford Bridge, in the heart of the Chalk country bordering the Mole Gap, is Juniper Hall, one of the new Field Centres opened by the Council for the Promotion of Field Studies. Broadly its purpose is to foster the scientific understanding and aesthetic appreciation of nature and rural life in this delectable region. With the residential Centre as their base students from schools and universities, naturalists, artists and research workers will have at hand for their study and their delight a rich and varied countryside, one of the best-preserved and scientifically one of the most interesting in all Southern England.

Robert Atkinson

J. S. L. GILMOUR

A DIRECTORY OF
NATURAL HISTORY SOCIETIES

ON another page of this Journal we print a List of British Natural History Societies abstracted from the *Directory of Natural History Societies*, recently published by the AMATEUR ENTOMOLO-GISTS' SOCIETY. The appearance of this list will, I hope, induce many to acquire the original Directory, which contains a great deal of additional information, and a Foreword by Dr. Julian Huxley and Mr. R. S. R. Fitter.

The oft-repeated claim that amateurs have contributed more to science in Britain than in any other country is, no doubt, well-founded. As far as I know, however, no detailed statistics have hitherto been available to support or refute it. In the field of natural history, the A.E.S.'s Directory, with its impressive list of national and local amateur societies, past and present, covering 134 pages, now provides a quantitative backing to the British claim that would certainly be difficult to rival outside this country.

The Directory is divided into the following sections: British Isles—General; British Isles—Unions (i.e. regional unions of local societies, such as the Northern Naturalists' Union); England; Wales; Scotland; Isle of Man; and Ireland. The last five sections each have a "general" sub-section and one arranged alphabetically under counties. There are appendices covering the Channel Isles and the Forces in the Middle East, followed by an excellent index of places and societies. Under each society the information given includes date of foundation, area covered, address, membership and subscriptions, activities, facilities (i.e. library, collections, etc.) and publications. These particulars are based on answers to questionnaires sent out during and just after the war and it is not surprising that there are many entries consisting only of the bare name of the society, marked with an asterisk signifying that no reply to the questionnaires has been received. It is particularly

disappointing to find an asterisk against the Manchester Literary and Philosophical Society, founded in 1781, which must be one of the oldest societies of its kind in the country.

The lists are well arranged and easy to consult, once the large number of abbreviations (clearly necessary to save space) has been mastered. Defunct societies are printed in a special type. At first sight the number of these is surprising but the majority, no doubt, became merged or transformed into other bodies and must be looked upon as births rather than deaths.

In their foreword, Dr. Huxley and Mr. Fitter rightly stress the value of local societies in keeping, and printing, records of the wild life of their areas. This function has often been neglected in the past and a mass of data on distribution must now lie buried in local collections, inaccessible without a long journey and a time-consuming examination of labels and notes. Printing is, of course, expensive and this must have prevented many societies from publishing their records. In his Introduction, the Editor, Mr. B. A. Cooper, suggests the foundation of a "National Union of Naturalists"; one of its functions should certainly be to organise the financing of publications by its constituent societies.

A glance at the dates of foundation given in the Directory reveals a mass birth of societies during the second half of the nineteenth century. Now that research into Victorian manners and motives has become fashionable, I hope that someone will investigate this phenomenon. Broadly, no doubt, it was a result of the increased scope given by the spread of popular education to the back-to-nature element in the Romantic Revival. But the details would be fascinating. What kind of people founded these societies? Were they more frequently working-class naturalists, professional men such as doctors and clergymen, or leisured squires with a hobby? Why did one town produce a society fifty years earlier than another? These and similar questions are worth asking and many of them could be answered by searching the archives of the societies listed in the Directory.

The AMATEUR ENTOMOLOGISTS' SOCIETY and the Compiler, Mr. H. K. Airy Shaw, are to be warmly congratulated on their vision in realising the need for such a Directory, and on their courage in tackling it under war-time conditions. I hope that there will be a good response to their appeal for further information, so that a second and more complete edition can be brought out in the near future.

THE

Gil: White. 1768.
The gift of the Honourable
Mr. Barrington the Inventer.

NATURALIST'S

JOURNAL.

The Insects are named according to
Linnaeus:
The plants according to the sexual
system:
The birds according to Ray.

LONDON:
Printed for W. SANDBY, in FLEET-STREET.

M.DCC.LXVII.

I solitary court
Th' inspiring breeze; & meditate the book
of Nature ever open — *Thomson's Seasons.*

This quarto book, with ruled lines, columns and headings, was designed by Daines Barrington, one of Gilbert White's two correspondents in The Natural History of Selborne. *In his neat writing White enters his name; thanks his friend and correspondent for the gift; enters the basis of his nomenclature and, very typically, writes out an apt literary quotation. The reader who turns this page, and reads on, finds twenty-five years of record; twenty-five years of the same fine writing, of meticulous observation, of learned and literary quotations, of new facts and discoveries, of realisations and disappointments. From the pages of this journal, one of which heads this number of our Journal, the personality of England's greatest local naturalist comes more warmly, more humanly, than from the Letters. Perhaps this is because they reveal all that he saw and recorded, not only just what he judged worthy of handing on to others. Those who read these MS. journals in the British Museum often feel the thrill of meeting the first entry of a new discovery, but the chief emotion with which they close the volumes is affection for the gentle naturalist who wrote them.*

H. K. AIRY SHAW

THE NATURAL HISTORY SOCIETIES

OF THE BRITISH ISLES

THE list of British Natural History Societies that follows is compiled, with permission of the Amateur Entomologists' Society, from the *Directory of Natural History Societies*, recently published by that Society, which is reviewed on another page. The reader in search of full information is referred to this work, which may be obtained from the A.E.S. at 1 West Ham Lane, London, E.15, price 7s. 6d. post free.

The A.E.S. list contains the available information for each society as to its date of foundation, the area which it covers, its affiliations, membership, meetings, amenities, collections and publications. It also contains the more important school natural history societies, which I have had to omit from this summary.

In the present list the name (when known) of the secretary or some officer who handles correspondence is given; and the address of the Society's offices or, failing that, the private address of the officer.

BRITISH ISLES: GENERAL

AMATEUR ENTOMOLOGISTS' SOCIETY *1 West Ham Lane, London, E.15*

ASSOCIATION OF BRITISH ZOOLOGISTS *Dr. J. Smart, Zoology Department, Cambridge University*

AVICULTURAL SOCIETY *86 Regent's Park Road, London, N.W.1*

BIOLOGICAL ASSOCIATION OF THE UNITED KINGDOM *The Laboratory, Citadel Hill, Plymouth, Devon*

BOTANICAL SOCIETY OF THE BRITISH ISLES *Miss M. S. Campbell, c/o Dept. of Botany, British Museum (Natural History), Cromwell Road, London, S.W.7*

BRITISH ASSOCIATION FOR THE ADVANCEMENT OF SCIENCE *Burlington House, Piccadilly, London, W.1*

BRITISH BEE-KEEPERS' ASSOCIATION *19 Church Crescent, Whetstone, London, N.20*

BRITISH BRYOLOGICAL SOCIETY *E. C. Wallace, 2 Strathearn Road, Sutton, Surrey*

BRITISH ECOLOGICAL SOCIETY *Prof. A. R. Clapham, Department of Botany, The University, Sheffield 10*

BRITISH EMPIRE NATURALISTS' ASSOCIATION Honorary Secretary: *22 South Drive, Ruislip, Middx.*

BRITISH HERPETOLOGICAL SOCIETY *Alfred Leutscher, 5 St. Margaret's Court, London, E.12*

BRITISH MYCOLOGICAL SOCIETY Secretary: *Imperial Mycological Institute, Kew, Surrey*

BRITISH ORNITHOLOGISTS' CLUB *W. E. Glegg, Zoological Museum, Tring, Herts.*

BRITISH ORNITHOLOGISTS' UNION *Miss P. Barclay-Smith, Bird Room, British Museum (Natural History), Cromwell Road, London, S.W.7*

BRITISH PTERIDOLOGICAL SOCIETY *P. Greenfield, Beech Bank, Stuart Road, Warlingham, Surrey*

BRITISH SNAIL-WATCHING SOCIETY *14 Ladbroke Square, London, W.11*

BRITISH SOCIETY FOR THE HISTORY OF SCIENCE *F. H. C. Butler, Ravensmead, Keston, Kent*

BRITISH SPELAEOLOGICAL ASSOCIATION Spelaeo-Biology Section. *Association Headquarters: Duke Street, Settle, Yorks.*

BRITISH TRUST FOR ORNITHOLOGY *91 Banbury Road, Oxford*

CHALLENGER SOCIETY *c/o British Museum (Natural History), Cromwell Road, London, S.W.7*

COMMONS, OPEN SPACES AND FOOTPATHS PRESERVATION SOCIETY *71 Eccleston Square, London, S.W.1*

CONCHOLOGICAL SOCIETY OF GREAT BRITAIN AND IRELAND *Manchester Museum, The University, Manchester 13*

COUNCIL FOR BRITISH ARCHAEOLOGY: NATURAL SCIENCES COMMITTEE *Miss Kathleen M. Kenyon, Institute of Archaeology, Inner Circle, Regent's Park, London, N.W.1*

COUNCIL FOR THE PRESERVATION OF RURAL ENGLAND *4 Hobart Place, London, S.W.1*

COUNCIL FOR THE PROMOTION OF FIELD STUDIES *F. H. C. Butler, 10 Exhibition Road, London, S.W.7*

grey: *Vice-counties covered by local natural history societies*
hatched: *Vice-counties covered by a printed local natural history journal or periodic report*

100 Miles

The Natural History Societies of the British Isles

FLORA'S LEAGUE *Lady Abbot-Anderson, c/o C.P.R.E., 4 Hobart Place, London, S.W.1*

FRESHWATER BIOLOGICAL ASSOCIATION OF THE BRITISH EMPIRE *Wray Castle, Ambleside, Westmorland*

GEOGRAPHICAL ASSOCIATION *c/o Municipal High School of Commerce, Princess Street, Manchester 1*

GEOLOGICAL SOCIETY OF LONDON *Burlington House, Piccadilly, London, W.1*

GEOLOGISTS' ASSOCIATION *University College, Gower Street, London, W.C.1*

GILBERT WHITE FELLOWSHIP *6 Queen Square, Southampton Row, London, W.C.1*

GREY OWL SOCIETY *Honorary Secretary: P. Burden, Norton, Cuckney, Mansfield, Notts.*

LINNEAN SOCIETY OF LONDON *Burlington House, Piccadilly, London, W.1*

MALACOLOGICAL SOCIETY OF LONDON *c/o British Museum (Natural History), Cromwell Road, London, S.W.7*

MARINE BIOLOGICAL ASSOCIATION OF THE UNITED KINGDOM *The Laboratory, Citadel Hill, Plymouth, Devon*

MINERALOGICAL SOCIETY OF GREAT BRITAIN AND IRELAND *c/o British Museum (Natural History), Cromwell Road, London, S.W.7*

NATIONAL AQUARISTS' SOCIETY *Kathleen Cooke, 28 Poulett Gardens, Twickenham, Middx.*

NATIONAL TRUST FOR PLACES OF HISTORIC INTEREST OR NATURAL BEAUTY *42 Queen Anne's Gate, London, S.W.1*

PALAEONTOGRAPHICAL SOCIETY *c/o Geological Society Burlington House, Piccadilly, London, W.1*

PEAK DISTRICT AND NORTHERN COUNTIES FOOTPATHS PRESERVATION SOCIETY *Thomas Boulger, 29 Brown Street, Manchester 2*

QUEKETT MICROSCOPICAL CLUB *Burlington House, Piccadilly, London, W.1*

RAY SOCIETY *c/o British Museum (Natural History), Cromwell Road, London, S.W.7*

ROMANY SOCIETY *Miss J. M. Graham, 45 Kirklees Road, Hillside, Southport, Lancs.*

ROYAL ENTOMOLOGICAL SOCIETY OF LONDON *41 Queen's Gate, South Kensington, London, S.W.7*

ROYAL GEOGRAPHICAL SOCIETY *Kensington Gore, London, S.W.7*

ROYAL METEOROLOGICAL SOCIETY *49 Cromwell Road, London, S.W.7*

ROYAL MICROSCOPICAL SOCIETY *B.M.A. House, Tavistock Square, London, W.C.1*

ROYAL NAVAL BIRD-WATCHING SOCIETY *Major N. A. G. H. Beal, R.M., 1 Auriol Road, London, W.14*

ROYAL SOCIETY FOR THE PROTECTION OF BIRDS *82 Victoria Street, London, S.W.1*

SCHOOL NATURE STUDY UNION *Honorary Editor: Rosamund F. Shove, 13 Burlington Avenue, Kew Gardens, Richmond, Surrey*

SELBORNE SOCIETY LIMITED *W. Mark Webb, The Hermitage, Hanwell, London, W.7*

SOCIETY FOR THE BIBLIOGRAPHY OF NATURAL HISTORY *F. J. Griffin, 29 Bushey Park Gardens, Teddington, Middx.*

SOCIETY FOR BRITISH ENTOMOLOGY *S. L. S. Brown, 454 Christchurch Road, Bournemouth, Hants.*

SOCIETY FOR FREEDOM IN SCIENCE *Dr. J. R. Baker, University Museum, Oxford*

SOCIETY FOR GENERAL MICROBIOLOGY *R. St. John-Brooks, Lister Institute, Elstree, Herts.*

SOCIETY FOR THE PRESERVATION OF THE FAUNA OF THE EMPIRE *H. G. Maurice, c/o Zoological Society of London, Regent's Park, London, N.W.8*

SOCIETY FOR THE PROMOTION OF NATURE RESERVES *c/o British Museum (Natural History), Cromwell Road, London, S.W.7*

SOCIETY FOR THE PROTECTION OF WILD FLOWERS AND PLANTS *A. L. Onslow, Mount Severn, Llanidloes, Montgomeryshire*

SOCIETY FOR VISITING SCIENTISTS *5 Old Burlington Street, London, W.1*

SYSTEMATICS ASSOCIATION *Botanical Secretary: Royal Botanic Gardens, Kew, Surrey. Zoological Secretary: British Museum (Natural History), Cromwell Road, London, S.W.7*

UNIVERSITIES' FEDERATION FOR ANIMAL WELFARE ("UFAW") *Capt. C. W. Hume, 284 Regent's Park Road, Finchley, London, N.3*

WILD FLOWER SOCIETY *Miss H. S. A. Dent, Flass, Maulds Meaburn, Penrith, Cumberland*

ZOOLOGICAL SOCIETY OF LONDON *Regent's Park, London, N.W.8*

BRITISH ISLES: UNIONS

ASSOCIATION OF SCHOOL NATURAL HISTORY SOCIETIES *David Stainer, Salisbury House, St. Thomas' Hill, Canterbury, Kent*

FEDERATION OF BRITISH AQUATIC SOCIETIES *H. J. Dunbar, 16 Friern Barnet Road, New Southgate, London, N.11*

LINCOLNSHIRE NATURALISTS' UNION *F. T. Baker, City and County Museum, Lincoln*

MIDLAND NATURALISTS' UNION *G. Brian Hindle, Avebury House, 55 Newhall Street, Birmingham 3*

NORTH-EAST LANCASHIRE NATURALISTS' UNION *Frank Hodson, 152 Cleaver Street, Burnley, Lancs.*

NORTHERN NATURALISTS' UNION *Dr. K. Blackburn, King's College, Newcastle-upon-Tyne 2*

NORTH-WESTERN NATURALISTS' UNION *G. J. Kerrich, The Manchester Museum, University, Manchester 13*

SOUTH-EASTERN UNION OF SCIENTIFIC SOCIETIES *H. M. Montford, 23 Mountside, Guildford, Surrey*

SOUTH-WESTERN NATURALISTS' UNION *Stanley Smith, The University, Bristol 8*

YORKSHIRE NATURALISTS' UNION *Chris. A. Cheetham, Austwick, via Lancaster*

ENGLAND: COUNTIES

Bedfordshire

BEDFORD NATURAL HISTORY AND ARCHAEOLOGICAL SOCIETY *W. N. Henman, 38 Western Street, Bedford*

BEDFORDSHIRE NATURAL HISTORY SOCIETY AND FIELD CLUB *H. A. S. Key, 61b Goldington Road, Bedford*

LUTON AND DISTRICT AQUARIST AND PONDKEEPERS' SOCIETY *R. Gee, "South View", 539 Hitchin Road, Stopsley, Luton*

Berkshire

NEWBURY DISTRICT FIELD CLUB *C. J. Raymond, Rathlyn, Donnington, Newbury*

READING AND DISTRICT NATURAL HISTORY SOCIETY *W. C. Fishlock, 19 South View Avenue, Caversham, Reading*

READING ORNITHOLOGICAL CLUB *J. D. Wood, 74 Shinfield Road, Reading*

Buckinghamshire

BUCKINGHAMSHIRE ARCHAEOLOGICAL SOCIETY *W. F. Serby, The Museum, Church Street, Aylesbury*

CHILTERN CLUB OF ARTS AND HANDICRAFTS, NATURAL HISTORY GROUP, Ornithology Section *J. Hardiman, Hyrons Cottage, Woodside Road, Amersham*

SLOUGH NATURAL HISTORY SOCIETY *Peter R. Marler, 6 Oakley Crescent, Slough*

Cambridgeshire

CAMBRIDGE BIRD CLUB *c/o E. N. Willmer, Clare College, Cambridge*

CAMBRIDGE NATURAL HISTORY SOCIETY Honorary Secretary: *Zoology Museum, Downing Street, Cambridge*

CAMBRIDGE PHILOSOPHICAL SOCIETY

CAMBRIDGE UNIVERSITY BOTANY CLUB

WICKEN FEN COMMITTEE

Cheshire

ALTRINCHAM AND DISTRICT NATURAL HISTORY AND LITERARY SOCIETY *P. Newton, 57 Bloomsbury Lane, Timperley, Altrincham*

CHESTER NATURALISTS' GROUP *F. Burke, 42 Kingsmead, Upton-by-Chester*

CHESTER SOCIETY OF NATURAL SCIENCE, LITERATURE AND ART *Grosvenor Museum, Chester*

MACCLESFIELD SCIENTIFIC ASSOCIATION *Dr. Mary Cunningham, 27 Clarence Cottages, Bollington, near Macclesfield*

MARPLE FIELD CLUB *A. Barrington, Ruscott, Ridge Road, Marple*

WALLASEY AQUARIUM SOCIETY *W. Bailey, 9 Kenwyn Road, Wallasey*

WILMSLOW GUILD NATURAL HISTORY SOCIETY *1 Bourne Street, Wilmslow, near Manchester*

Cornwall

CORNISH AQUARISTS' AND POND-KEEPERS' ASSOCIATION *Mrs. Howard Spring, Hoopers Hill, Flushing, near Falmouth*

CORNWALL BIRD WATCHING AND PRESERVATION SOCIETY *Lieut.-Col. B. H. Ryves, Mawgan, Newquay, and Dorothea Valentine, Lelant*

PENZANCE NATURAL HISTORY AND ANTIQUARIAN SOCIETY *c/o Morrah Road Library, Penzance*

ROYAL CORNWALL POLYTECHNIC SOCIETY *Falmouth*

ROYAL INSTITUTION OF CORNWALL *County Museum, Truro*

ROYAL GEOLOGICAL SOCIETY OF CORNWALL *St. John's Hall, Penzance*

Cumberland

CARLISLE NATURAL HISTORY SOCIETY *c/o Corporation Museum, Tullie House, Carlisle*

CUMBERLAND NATURE CLUB *c/o Friends' Meeting House, Cockermouth*

PENRITH AND DISTRICT NATURAL HISTORY SOCIETY *W. F. Davidson, 9 Castlegate, Penrith*

Derbyshire

DERBY AND DISTRICT AQUARISTS' SOCIETY *T. S. White, 25 Riddings Street, Derby*

DERBYSHIRE ARCHAEOLOGICAL AND NATURAL HISTORY SOCIETY *W. H. Hansbury, St. Mary's Bridge-Chapel House, Derby*

DERBYSHIRE ENTOMOLOGICAL SOCIETY Secretary: *Laurel Bank, 20 Kedleston Road, Allestree*

L.M.S. (DERBY) NATURAL HISTORY SOCIETY *The Derby Railway Institute*

Devonshire

DEVON BIRD WATCHING AND PRESERVATION SOCIETY *Rev. F. C. Butters, Stockland Vicarage, Honiton*

DEVONSHIRE ASSOCIATION FOR THE ADVANCEMENT OF SCIENCE *Prof. W. J. Harte, City Library, Exeter*

ILFRACOMBE FIELD CLUB *Miss D. Jameson, 13 Bicclescombe Gardens, Ilfracombe*

LUNDY FIELD SOCIETY *Prof. L. A. Harvey, University College, Exeter*

NATURALIST CLUB OF THE UNIVERSITY COLLEGE OF THE SOUTH-WEST *University College of the South-West, Gandy Street, Exeter*

PLYMOUTH AND DISTRICT FIELD CLUB *O. G. Watkins, 20 Torr View Avenue, Peverell, Plymouth*

PLYMOUTH INSTITUTION AND DEVON AND CORNWALL NATURAL HISTORY SOCIETY *Secretary, 49 Amherst Road, Plymouth*

ROYAL NAVAL COLLEGE DARTMOUTH FIELD CLUB *A. M. C. Nicholl, Royal Naval College, Dartmouth*

SOUTH DEVON BRANCH, BRITISH EMPIRE NATURALISTS' ASSOCIATION *M. B. B. Heath, Urania, Firleigh Road, Kingsteignton*

TEIGN NATURALISTS' FIELD CLUB *E. F. Windeath, The Elms, Totnes, Devon*

TORQUAY NATURAL HISTORY SOCIETY, Ornithological Section *The Museum, Torwood Street, Torquay*

UNIVERSITY COLLEGE FIELD CLUB, EXETER *—. Frankiss, 8 Topsham Road, Exeter*

Dorsetshire

DORSET NATURAL HISTORY AND ARCHAEOLOGICAL SOCIETY *Dorset County Museum, Dorchester*

Durham

ANNFIELD PLAIN AND STANLEY NATURALISTS' CLUB *Mrs. F. Wade, 36 South View, Annfield Plain*

BISHOP AUCKLAND GEOGRAPHICAL ASSOCIATION *Girls' County School, Bishop Auckland*

CONSETT AND DISTRICT NATURALISTS' FIELD CLUB. *W. Ellerington, 10 Maudville, Castleside, Consett*

DARLINGTON AND TEESDALE NATURALISTS' FIELD CLUB *Friends' School Premises, Skinnergate, Darlington*

EASTBOURNE (DARLINGTON) GIRLS' YOUTH CENTRE FIELD CLUB *187 Yarm Road, Darlington*

SUNDERLAND TECHNICAL COLLEGE SCIENTIFIC ASSOCIATION *Miss M. L. W. Stirk, Biology and Physiology Department, The Technical College, Sunderland*

UNIVERSITY OF DURHAM PHILOSOPHICAL SOCIETY *King's College, Newcastle-upon-Tyne*

WEARDALE AND DISTRICT NATURALISTS' FIELD CLUB *Dr. R. Hughes, The Grammar School, Wolsingham, via Bishop Auckland*

Essex

BENHURST AQUARISTS' SOCIETY *V. F. Swettenham, 5 Devonshire Road, Hornchurch*

CHELMSFORD AND DISTRICT AQUARIST SOCIETY *Mrs. R. Tappenden, 33 Prykes Avenue, Chelmsford*

DAGENHAM AQUARISTS' SOCIETY *D. F. Eyres, 83 Wren Road, Dagenham*

EPPING FOREST GROUP, AMATEUR ENTOMOLOGISTS' SOCIETY *C. B. Pratt, 1 West Ham Lane, London, E.15*

EPPING FOREST GROUP, BRITISH EMPIRE NATURALISTS' ASSOCIATION *C. Cheshire, 11 Portman Drive, Woodford Green*

ESSEX FIELD CLUB *P. G. Thompson, The Essex Museum of Natural History, Romford Road, Stratford, London, E.15*

ILFORD AQUARISTS' AND PONDKEEPERS' SOCIETY *S. H. Carter, 13 Kenwood Gardens, Ilford*

LEIGH AND DISTRICT AQUARIST SOCIETY *E. H. Sarll, 35 Rectory Grove, Leigh-on-Sea*

SOUTH ESSEX NATURAL HISTORY SOCIETY *S. E. Adams, 11 Drake Road, Westcliff-on-Sea*

Gloucestershire

BRISTOL AQUARISTS' SOCIETY *Honorary Secretary: 46 Wolseley Road, Bristol 7*

BRISTOL NATURALISTS' SOCIETY *Miss M. D. Hiley, Museum and Art Gallery, Queen's Road, Bristol 8*

CHELTENHAM SCIENCE SOCIETY *Lieut.-Col. A. M. Cockshott, Colaba, Ryeworth Road, Charlton Kings, Cheltenham*

COTTESWOLD NATURALISTS' FIELD CLUB *G. Makins Smith, Hamilton House, Brookway Road, Charlton Kings, Cheltenham*

NORTH COTSWOLD BRANCH, BRITISH EMPIRE NATURALISTS' ASSOCIATION *Mrs. A. B. Lane, Blackdowns, Moreton-in-Marsh*

SEVERN WILDFOWL TRUST *M. Bratby, 8 Edwardes Square, London, W.8*

STROUD SCIENTIFIC SOCIETY *J. Webber, Police Station, Kings Stanley, near Stroud*

UNIVERSITY OF BRISTOL SPELAEOLOGICAL SOCIETY *The University, Bristol 8*

Hampshire

BOURNEMOUTH NATURAL SCIENCE SOCIETY *39 Christchurch Road, Bournemouth*

HAMPSHIRE FIELD CLUB AND ARCHAEOLOGICAL SOCIETY *F. Warren, Staple Garden, Winchester*

ISLE OF WIGHT NATURAL HISTORY AND ARCHAEOLOGICAL SOCIETY *Honorary Secretary: 6 Watergate Road, Newport, I.O.W.*

NEW FOREST ASSOCIATION *Captain Cecil Sutton, Estate Offices, Brockenhurst*

PORTSMOUTH PHILOSOPHICAL SOCIETY

SOUTHAMPTON NATURAL HISTORY SOCIETY *"Glengarriff", Pinehurst Road, Basset Heath Avenue, Southampton*

WINCHESTER AND HAMPSHIRE SCIENTIFIC AND LITERARY SOCIETY *G. Crompton, 12 Kingsgate Street, Winchester*

Herefordshire

WOOLHOPE NATURALISTS' FIELD CLUB *G. Marshall, The Manor House, Breinton, Hereford*

Hertfordshire

BARNET AND DISTRICT NATURAL HISTORY SOCIETY *R. J. Griffiths, 7 Netherlands Road, New Barnet*

BISHOP'S STORTFORD AND DISTRICT NATURAL HISTORY SOCIETY *Derek A. Ashwell, "The Heights", Galloway Road, Bishop's Stortford*

HERTFORDSHIRE AQUARISTS' SOCIETY *J. H. Gloyne, 2 Cowper Road, Welwyn Garden City*

HERTFORDSHIRE NATURAL HISTORY SOCIETY AND FIELD CLUB *Miss Eileen Gibbs, Houndspath, Upper Marlborough Road, St. Albans*

HITCHIN AND DISTRICT REGIONAL SURVEY ASSOCIATION

HOCKERILL COLLEGE NATURAL HISTORY SOCIETY *The Diocesan College, Dunmow Road, Bishop's Stortford*

LETCHWORTH AND DISTRICT NATURALISTS' SOCIETY *A. T. Clarke, The Museum, Town Square, Letchworth*

WATFORD AQUARISTS' SOCIETY *Mrs. Tennant, 120 St. George's Drive, Carpender's Park, Oxhey*

Huntingdonshire

NIL

Kent

EAST KENT BRANCH, BRITISH EMPIRE NATURALISTS' ASSOCIATION *C. N. Pope, 256 Hythe Road, Ashford, Kent*

EAST KENT NATURAL HISTORY AND SCIENTIFIC SOCIETY *F. M. Williamson, Royal Museum, Canterbury*

FOLKESTONE NATURAL HISTORY SOCIETY *J. W. Walton, Tower House, 16 Manor Road, Folkestone*

GRAVESEND AND DISTRICT SCIENTIFIC AND ARCHAEOLOGICAL SOCIETY

GRAVESEND SOCIETY FOR THE PROMOTION OF ARCHAEOLOGY, SCIENCE, LITERATURE AND ART, with INVICTA ART AND CRAFT SOCIETY *Public Library, Gravesend*

IDEN NATURAL HISTORY SOCIETY *Miss K. Wratten, 7 Udimore Road, Rye*

ISLE OF THANET FIELD CLUB *Rev. Laurens Sargent, The Vicarage, St. Peter-in-Thanet*

MAIDSTONE SCIENTIFIC AND ANTIQUARIAN SOCIETY *The Museum, Maidstone*

MID-KENT BRANCH, BRITISH EMPIRE NATURALISTS' ASSOCIATION *Miss J. Nisbett, Borough Green House, Borough Green, Sevenoaks*

NORTH-WEST KENT BRANCH, BRITISH EMPIRE NATURALISTS' ASSOCIATION *D. Stoyel, 38 Lancing Road, Orpington*

see London, South-east: NORTH-WEST KENT GROUP, AMATEUR ENTOMOLOGISTS' SOCIETY

PIONEER CLUB, FIELD AND ARCHAEOLOGICAL CIRCLE *Miss T. Ray, 24 Longmeads, Rustball, Tunbridge Wells*

ROCHESTER AND DISTRICT NATURAL HISTORY SOCIETY *C. G. Appleton, 12 Temple Gardens, Cuxton Road, Rochester*

SIDCUP LITERARY AND SCIENTIFIC SOCIETY *C. S. Bryant, 4 Priestlands Park Road, Sidcup*

TUNBRIDGE WELLS NATURAL HISTORY AND PHILOSOPHICAL SOCIETY *Dr. J. Lister, Heronsgate, Speldhurst*

WELLING AND DISTRICT AQUARISTS' AND PONDKEEPERS' CLUB *E. Starnes, 36 Cornwall Avenue, Welling*

WEST KENT SCIENTIFIC SOCIETY *C. C. Newell, 52 Hardy Road, London, S.E.3*

Lancashire

ACCRINGTON NATURALISTS' AND ANTIQUARIAN SOCIETY *Miss E. Crawshaw, 285 Dill Hall Lane, Church, Accrington*

ASSOCIATED LEARNED SOCIETIES OF LIVERPOOL AND DISTRICT *Miss E. Wayhurst, 3 Argyle Road, Liverpool 4*

BACUP NATURAL HISTORY SOCIETY *Zion Buildings, Bacup*

BARROW NATURALISTS' FIELD CLUB AND PHOTOGRAPHIC SOCIETY *G. E. Williams, c/o Technical College, Abbey Road, Barrow-in-Furness*

BELLE VUE (MANCHESTER) AQUARIUM SOCIETY *Zoological Gardens, Manchester 12*

BLACKBURN NATURALISTS' FIELD CLUB *J. W. Nixon, 12 Coniston Road, Blackburn*

CASTLETON LITERARY AND SCIENTIFIC SOCIETY *M. Froggatt, 6 St. Martins Street, Castleton, Rochdale*

COLNE NATURALISTS' SOCIETY *E. Binns, 4 Edward Street, Colne*

EAST LANCASHIRE AQUATIC SOCIETY *H. Loder, 59 Standish Street, Burnley*

LANCASHIRE AND CHESHIRE ENTOMOLOGICAL SOCIETY *The Royal Institution, Colquitt Street, Liverpool*

LIVERPOOL BOTANICAL SOCIETY *Secretary: 3 Argyle Road, Anfield, Liverpool 4*

LIVERPOOL GEOLOGICAL SOCIETY *J. C. Harper, Geological Dept., The University, Liverpool*

LIVERPOOL MARINE BIOLOGICAL ASSOCIATION

LIVERPOOL MICROSCOPICAL SOCIETY *H. J. Harper, Royal Institution, Colquitt Street, Liverpool*

LIVERPOOL NATURALISTS' FIELD CLUB *Miss M. Henderson, 44 Higher Bebington Road, Bebington, Wirral, Cheshire, and Miss Ellis, 201 Portland Court, Wallasey*

LIVERPOOL UNIVERSITY BIOLOGICAL SOCIETY *Zoology Dept., University of Liverpool*

MANCHESTER ENTOMOLOGICAL SOCIETY *R. J. Wigelsworth, 117 Hulme Hall Road, Cheadle Hulme, Cheshire*

MANCHESTER FEDERATION OF SCIENTIFIC SOCIETIES *Dr. E. H. Rodd, Imperial Chemical Industries, Ltd. (Dyestuffs Division), Blackley, Manchester*

MANCHESTER FIELD NATURALISTS' AND ARCHAEOLOGISTS' SOCIETY *H. Weston Jackson, Heathbank, Edgeley, Stockport, Cheshire*

MANCHESTER GEOGRAPHICAL SOCIETY *A. Marsham, Geographical Chambers, 16 St. Mary's Parsonage, Manchester 3*

MANCHESTER GEOLOGICAL ASSOCIATION *Geological Survey Office, 250 Oxford Road, Manchester 13*

MANCHESTER GEOLOGICAL AND MINING SOCIETY *L. C. Timms, Queen's Chambers, 5 John Dalton Street, Manchester 2*

MANCHESTER LITERARY AND PHILOSOPHICAL SOCIETY *Miss H. R. Corbishley, 36 George Street, Manchester*

MANCHESTER MICROSCOPICAL SOCIETY *T. Warburton, 29 Birch Hall Lane, Rusholme, Manchester 13*

MANCHESTER UNIVERSITY BIOLOGICAL SOCIETY *The University, Manchester 13*

MANCHESTER UNIVERSITY SETTLEMENT ART MUSEUM FIELD CLUB *B. Green, 25 Edge Lane, Manchester 21*

MERSEYSIDE AQUARIST SOCIETY *L. Plant, 66 Ferguson Road, Liverpool 11*

MERSEYSIDE BRANCH, BRITISH EMPIRE NATURALISTS' ASSOCIATION (MERSEYSIDE NATURALISTS' ASSOCIATION) *Eric Hardy, 47 Woodsorrel Road, Wavertree, Liverpool 15*

MOSS AND LICHEN CLUB (?) *Miss Ackerley, Milton Vicarage, Whalley, Blackburn*

NELSON AND DISTRICT NATURAL HISTORY SOCIETY *A. Turner, 140 Pine Street, Nelson*

NORTH LANCASHIRE BRANCH, BRITISH EMPIRE NATURALISTS' ASSOCIATION *Miss E. E. Hastings, 5 Great John Street, Lancaster*

NORTH LONSDALE FIELD CLUB *H. Postlethwaite, 21 Alexander Road, Ulverston, N. Lancs.*

OLDHAM MICROSCOPICAL SOCIETY AND FIELD CLUB *The Lyceum, Union Street, Oldham*

OLDHAM NATURAL HISTORY SOCIETY *Natural History Museum and Study Centre, Werneth Park, Oldham*

PRESTON SCIENTIFIC SOCIETY, Microscopical and Natural History Section *Miss E. M. Yates, 43 Mulgrave Avenue, Ashton-on-Ribble, Preston*

RAVEN ENTOMOLOGICAL AND NATURAL HISTORY SOCIETY *Mrs. B. M. Gearey, 27 Dale Street, Liverpool*

ROCHDALE LITERARY AND SCIENTIFIC SOCIETY *Dr. J. R. Ashworth, 55 King Street South, Rochdale*

SOUTHPORT SCIENTIFIC SOCIETY *R. Kay Greswell, 28 Albert Road, Southport, Lancs.; J. T. Rigby, 13 Hoghton Street, Southport*

UNITED FIELD NATURALISTS' SOCIETY *B. Green, 15 Lichfield Terrace, Rochdale*

WARRINGTON FIELD CLUB AND SCIENTIFIC SOCIETY *J. Newton, "Newlam", 18 Higher Knutsford Road, Grappenhall, Warrington*

WARRINGTON LITERARY AND PHILOSOPHICAL SOCIETY *D. P. Bayley, Oban, Greenbank Road, Latchford Without, Warrington*

WIGAN AND DISTRICT FIELD CLUB *c/o Biology Dept., Mining and Technical College, Wigan*

Leicestershire

BARROW-ON-SOAR ENTOMOLOGICAL CLUB *C. J. Tatham, "Charnwood", Barrow-on-Soar*

LEICESTER AQUARISTS' SOCIETY *W. A. Budden, 15 Gort Crescent, Hinckley Road, Leicester*

LEICESTER GEOLOGICAL SOCIETY *c/o Museum and Art Gallery, Leicester*

LEICESTER LITERARY AND PHILOSOPHICAL SOCIETY, Botany, Biology, Entomology, Geology, Ornithology, and Zoology Sections *Museum and Art Gallery, New Walk, Leicester*

LEICESTERSHIRE BRANCH, BRITISH EMPIRE NATURALISTS' ASSOCIATION

LEICESTERSHIRE AND RUTLAND BIOLOGICAL SOCIETY *F. Sowter, 9 North Avenue, Leicester*

LEICESTERSHIRE AND RUTLAND ORNITHOLOGICAL SOCIETY *The Museum and Art Gallery, Leicester*

LEICESTER UNIVERSITY COLLEGE BIOLOGICAL SOCIETY *University College, Leicester*

Lincolnshire

GRANTHAM MUSEUM GUILD *The Curator, Public Library and Museum, Grantham*

GRIMSBY AND DISTRICT ANTIQUARIAN AND NATURALISTS' SOCIETY *W. T. Gayfer, The Museum, Corporation Buildings, Convamore Road, Grimsby*

GRIMSBY AND DISTRICT AQUARISTS' SOCIETY *A. T. Baskcomb, Kilgerran, 59a Bargate, Grimsby*

LINCOLN NATURAL HISTORY SOCIETY

LOUTH NATURALISTS' AND ANTIQUARIAN SOCIETY

London

ACTON SCIENTIFIC AND NATURAL HISTORY SOCIETY

BATTERSEA FIELD CLUB *W. Johnson, 5 Barber Road, Clapham Common, S.W.11; Miss L. B. Morris, 21 Ruskin Walk, S.E.24*

BLAIR AQUATIC CLUB *T. Wyber, 85 Richmond Avenue, N.1*

BOTANICAL SOCIETY, UNIVERSITY COLLEGE, LONDON

CHELSEA POLYTECHNIC GEOLOGICAL FIELD CLUB *Chelsea Polytechnic, Manresa Road, S.W.3*

EALING SCIENTIFIC AND MICROSCOPICAL SOCIETY *Y.M.C.A. Buildings, 14 Bond Street, Ealing, W.5*

EAST LONDON AQUARISTS' AND POND-KEEPERS' ASSOCIATION *T. E. Butt, 25 Humberstone Road, Plaistow, E.13*

ENTERPRISE AQUATIC SOCIETY *W. T. Jefferies, 4 The Broadway, Friern Barnet, N.11*

HAMPSTEAD SCIENTIFIC SOCIETY *Mrs. H. Baily, 74 Lawn Road, N.W.3*

LAMBETH FIELD CLUB *W. Rivers, 48 Overton Road, Brixton, S.W.9*

LIONEL JACOB SCIENTIFIC SOCIETY *The Working Men's College, Crowndale Road, London, N.W.1*

MALHAM

The Field Centre at Malham Tarn is ideally placed. Within little more than fifty miles are all the greater cities of the Industrial North—Liverpool, Manchester, Huddersfield, Leeds. Students from these cities and from many beyond will be able to study the animals and plants of the Pennines, from this new base, with the least trouble or inconvenience.

Malham is almost on the water-parting between west and east. It is, actually, in Airedale; but the visitor can reach it by taking the road up Ribblesdale through Clitheroe and Settle, as easily as up Airedale through Skipton and Kirkby Malham. The approach up the Aire is the more dramatic. Between Kirkby Malham and Malham the dale closes in, and a tributary valley, containing the Gordale Beck, enters from the east. The main dale continues to ascend to the north, but is blocked, three-quarters of a mile north of the Malham village, by a limestone wall about a hundred feet high which is the steepest part of a sudden three-hundred-foot rise, and is known as Malham Cove.

This grey wall, curved like the side of an amphitheatre, embraces a little wood. A tributary of the River Aire flows straight out from under the bottom of the wall, after an underground passage from the Smelt Mill (and from other sinks): the water, running from the water-parting at Capon Hall, enters the ground a mile and a half to the north-west of the Cove. A mile to the east of Capon Hall lies the square lake Malham Tarn, at 1,229 feet above sea-level. The waters from this lake, which plunge below at Water Sinks (only a mile north of the Cove) do not join the Aire at the Cove, but much further south at Aire Head Springs beyond the village.

A mile to the east of Malham Cove is another great piece of natural limestone architecture, Gordale Scar. Here the beck has cut back through the limestone, the roof of a previous water-tunnel has collapsed, and at a sharp corner is found a dramatic waterfall. In one place the stream plunges through a limestone window.

It is in this region of striking natural scenery, and near these two remarkable geological "monuments", that men and women will soon be engaged on serious projects of field study and research, and on courses in field education. Their material will be the animals and plants of mountain and limestone moorland. The stream flowing from under the great wall of the Cove has many interesting stoneflies, mayflies and caddis-flies. The wall itself houses nesting jackdaws, house-martins and stock-doves; on the meadows and moors above breed yellow wagtails and ring-ouzels. Nearly all the typical moorland-breeding waders of Britain are found on the fells and marshes—curlew, snipe, dunlin, redshank, ringed plover, golden plover and lapwing. Of these the ringed plover only has not yet been proved to nest. The great crested grebe breeds on Malham Tarn.

The interesting—and beautiful—plants of upland limestone are well represented at Malham. On the cliffs and slopes of the Cove and the Scar grow many rare species. Some, like the baneberry, the narrow-leaved bittercress, and Jacob's ladder are confined to, and rare in, North England. Others are plants of the rocky north and west of Britain, like alpine meadow-rue, hoary whitlow-grass, mountain heartsease, vernal sandwort, wood cranesbill, cut-leaved saxifrage, heath bedstraw, bird's-eye primrose, blue Sesleria, lesser clubmoss, and the rare currant Ribes pubescens. One plant, the milkwort, Polygala amara, is extremely rare; in Britain its bright blue or pink flowers are seen only in Yorkshire.

In 1671 John Ray looked for Jacob's ladder at Malham. He found it, and wrote that it "grows about Malham Cove, a place so remarkable that it is esteemed one of the wonders of Craven, in a wood on the left-hand of the water as you go to the Cove from Malham, plentifully, and also at Cordill* or the Whern, a remarkable cove where comes out a great stream of water, near the said Malham." Jacob's ladder is still plentiful at Malham Cove, though now it grows on the right-hand of the water.

* Gordale

John Markham

LONDON NATURAL HISTORY SOCIETY *H. A. Toombs, British Museum (Nat. Hist.), S.W.7*

LONDON SCIENTIFIC FILM SOCIETY

MORLEY COLLEGE SCIENTIFIC SOCIETY *Waterloo Road, S.E.1*

see Essex, Epping Forest: NORTH-EAST LONDON GROUP, AMATEUR ENTOMOLOGISTS' SOCIETY

NORTH LONDON AQUARISTS' SOCIETY *J. Gregg, 15 Regent Square, King's Cross, W.C.1*

NORTH-WEST LONDON GROUP, AMATEUR ENTOMOLOGISTS' SOCIETY *B. J. L. Byerley and M. H. Port, 31 Pinner View, Harrow, Middx.*

ROYAL COLLEGE OF SCIENCE NATURAL HISTORY SOCIETY *Miss M. H. Platt, Imperial College Union, South Kensington, S.W.7*

SHOOTERS HILL AND DISTRICT AQUARIUM AND POND-KEEPERS' SOCIETY *N. L. G. Taylor, 89 Blackheath Hill, S.E.10*

SOUTH-EAST LONDON AND NORTH-WEST KENT GROUP, AMATEUR ENTOMOLOGISTS' SOCIETY *K. H. Bobe, 182 Kingsground, S.E.9*

SOUTH LONDON AQUARISTS *A. H. Hoare, 179 Stoneleigh Ave., Worcester Park, Surrey*

SOUTH LONDON BOTANICAL INSTITUTE *323 Norwood Road, S.E.24*

SOUTH LONDON ENTOMOLOGICAL AND NATURAL HISTORY SOCIETY *c/o Royal Society, Burlington House, Piccadilly, W.1*

SOUTH WEST LONDON AQUARISTS' SOCIETY *G. F. Pengilly, 5 Pursers Cross Road, Parsons Green, Fulham, S.W.6*

see Surrey: SOUTH-WEST LONDON GROUP, AMATEUR ENTOMOLOGISTS' SOCIETY

STREATHAM ANTIQUARIAN AND NATURAL HISTORY SOCIETY *Col. Sir G. R. Hearn, 52 Woodbourne Avenue, S.W.16; J. E. Lousley, 7 Penistone Road, Streatham Common, S.W.16*

TROPICOLD AQUATIC SOCIETY *D. Kerrison, 26 Georgina Street, Camden Town, N.W.1*

TWENTY CLUB (AQUARIST) *G. Frier, 29 Melrose Avenue, Wimbledon Park, S.W.19*

WILLESDEN AND DISTRICT AQUARISTS' CLUB *R. O. B. List, 31 Coronation Court, Willesden Lane, N.W.6*

WIMBLEDON NATURAL HISTORY SOCIETY *C. P. Castell, 52 Graham Road, Wimbledon, S.W.19*

WOOLWICH HISTORICAL AND SCIENTIFIC SOCIETY *C. Foster, 71 Rectory Place, Woolwich, S.E.18*

Middlesex

ENFIELD AND DISTRICT AQUARISTS' SOCIETY *Mrs. Frances Perry, Bulls Cross Cottage, Enfield*

HARROW AQUARISTS' CLUB *F. J. Boardman, 10 Roxeth Grove, Harrow*

KODAK ENTOMOLOGISTS' SOCIETY *Kodak Works, Headstone Drive, Wealdstone*

POTTERS BAR AQUARISTS' SOCIETY *M. D. Cluse, 78 The Walk, Potters Bar*

TWICKENHAM AND THAMES VALLEY BEEKEEPERS' ASSOCIATION *24 Vincam Close, Whitton, Middlesex*

WEST MIDDLESEX AQUARISTS' SOCIETY *R. A. Scarbrow, 21a Uxbridge Road, Hanwell, London, W.7*

WEST MIDDLESEX AND SOUTH BUCKINGHAMSHIRE SCIENTIFIC SOCIETY *C. J. S. Bromfield, Dingle Combe, Potters Cross, Iver Heath, Bucks.*

Monmouthshire

NEWPORT AND DISTRICT NATURALISTS' SOCIETY *A. Rowland, 54 St. Julian's Avenue, Newport*

Norfolk

GREAT YARMOUTH NATURALISTS' SOCIETY *P. E. Rumbelow, 27 Rodney Road, Great Yarmouth*

KING'S LYNN SOCIETY OF ARTS AND SCIENCES *J. H. Pratt, 29 Tower Street, King's Lynn, Norfolk*

NORFOLK BRANCH, BRITISH EMPIRE NATURALISTS' ASSOCIATION *Miss R. T. Heward, "O'Fids", Hall Road, Cromer*

NORFOLK NATURALISTS' TRUST *Victoria Chambers, Bank Plain, Norwich*

NORFOLK AND NORWICH NATURALISTS' SOCIETY *Castle Museum, Norwich*

Northamptonshire

KETTERING AND DISTRICT NATURALISTS' SOCIETY AND FIELD CLUB *E. Osborn, 76a Wood Street, Kettering*

NORTHAMPTON AND DISTRICT AQUARISTS' SOCIETY *R. F. Perrett, 9 Peverels Way, St. James, Northampton*

NORTHAMPTONSHIRE NATURAL HISTORY SOCIETY AND FIELD CLUB *A. E. Tyrrell, 32 Bridge Street, Northampton*

PETERBOROUGH NATURAL HISTORY, SCIENTIFIC AND ARCHAEOLOGICAL SOCIETY *The Museum, Peterborough*

Northumberland

HEXHAM NATURAL HISTORY AND ANTIQUARIAN SOCIETY *Miss L. E. Barnett, Silcoates, Whitby Avenue, Hexham*

KENTON LODGE TRAINING COLLEGE NATURAL HISTORY SOCIETY *Kenton Lodge, Newcastle-on-Tyne*

KING'S COLLEGE NATURALISTS' SOCIETY *D. Morgan, King's College, Newcastle-upon-Tyne 2*

LITERARY AND PHILOSOPHICAL SOCIETY OF NEWCASTLE-UPON-TYNE *A. Holmes*

NATURAL HISTORY SOCIETY OF NORTHUMBERLAND, DURHAM AND NEWCASTLE-UPON-TYNE *Hancock Museum, Barras Bridge, Newcastle-upon-Tyne 2*

NEWCASTLE-UPON-TYNE AND DISTRICT AQUARISTS' SOCIETY *C. L. Crighton, 14 Middle Street, Walker, Newcastle-upon-Tyne*

TYNESIDE GEOGRAPHICAL SOCIETY *G. H. J. Daysh, c/o Department of Geography, King's College, Newcastle-upon-Tyne*

WALLIS CLUB *L. C. Beadle, King's College, Newcastle-upon-Tyne 2*

Nottinghamshire

NOTTINGHAM BIOLOGICAL SOCIETY *Miss S. M. Harris, 1 Franklyn Gardens, Western Boulevard, Nottingham*

NOTTINGHAM AND DISTRICT AQUARISTS' SOCIETY *S. H. Scott, 15 Tithby Drive, Sherwood, Nottingham*

NOTTINGHAM NATURALISTS' SOCIETY *Miss B. Jeffries, University College, Nottingham*

NOTTINGHAM NATURAL SCIENCE FIELD CLUB *W. J. Leighton, 86 Wimbledon Road, Sherwood*

TRENT VALLEY BIRD WATCHERS *J. Staton, The Falcons, Besecar Avenue, Gedling*

Oxfordshire

ASHMOLEAN NATURAL HISTORY SOCIETY OF OXFORDSHIRE *University Museum, Oxford*

OXFORD AND DISTRICT AQUARISTS' SOCIETY *F. Alderton, 8 Kilbourne Road, Cowley, Oxford*

OXFORD ORNITHOLOGICAL SOCIETY *G. H. Spray, Exeter College, Oxford*

OXFORD UNIVERSITY ENTOMOLOGICAL SOCIETY *Hope Department, University Museum, Oxford*

OXFORD UNIVERSITY JUNIOR SCIENTIFIC CLUB *University Museum, Oxford*

Rutland

see Leicestershire: LEICESTERSHIRE AND RUTLAND BIO-LOGICAL SOCIETY, LEICESTERSHIRE AND RUTLAND ORNITHOLOGICAL SOCIETY

RUTLAND ARCHAEOLOGICAL AND NATURAL HISTORY SOCIETY *H. F. Trayler, Stamford, Lincs.*

Shropshire

CARADOC AND SEVERN VALLEY FIELD CLUB *L. C. Lloyd, The Groves, Wenlock Road, Shrewsbury*

Somersetshire

BATH NATURAL HISTORY SOCIETY *Honorary Secretary: 10 Laura Place, Pulteney Street, Bath*

SOMERSET ARCHAEOLOGICAL AND NATURAL HISTORY SOCIETY *Somerset County Museum, Taunton Castle, Taunton*

Staffordshire

BURTON-ON-TRENT NATURAL HISTORY AND ARCHAEOLOGICAL SOCIETY *Mrs. H. J. Wain, The Museum, Burton-on-Trent*

EAST STAFFORDSHIRE BRANCH, BRITISH EMPIRE NATURALISTS' ASSOCIATION *Honorary Secretary: 13 Carless Avenue, Harborne, Birmingham*

NORTH STAFFORDSHIRE FIELD CLUB *Lloyds Bank Chambers, Kingsway, Stoke-on-Trent*

WOLVERHAMPTON AND DISTRICT AQUARIST SOCIETY *D. Bowles, Dudley Zoological Society Ltd., Dudley, Worcs.*

Suffolk

IPSWICH AND DISTRICT NATURAL HISTORY SOCIETY *H. E. P. Spencer, The Museum, High Street, Ipswich*

SUFFOLK AQUARISTS' AND POND-KEEPERS' ASSOCIATION *C. W. Shute, 7 Beechcroft Road, Ipswich*

SUFFOLK NATURALISTS' SOCIETY *C. Morley, Monks' Soham House, Framlingham*

Surrey

CAMBERLEY NATURAL HISTORY SOCIETY *Miss Jean Armitage, Sumner Lodge, The Avenue, Camberley*

Local societies purely devoted to Botany

Local societies purely devoted to Entomology

CROYDON AQUARISTS' CLUB *G. Saunders, 5 Blenheim Gardens, Wallington*

CROYDON NATURAL HISTORY AND SCIENTIFIC SOCIETY Honorary Secretary: *Eldon House, 2 Lansdowne Road, Croydon*

GODALMING NATURAL HISTORY, FOOTPATH AND RAMBLING SOCIETY *E. B. Bishop, Lindfield, Marshall Road, Godalming*

GUILDFORD NATURAL HISTORY AND LITERARY SOCIETY *E. T. Fulk, 145 High Street, Guildford*

HASLEMERE NATURAL HISTORY SOCIETY *Educational Museum, High Street, Haslemere*

HOLMESDALE NATURAL HISTORY CLUB *Miss D. Powell, The Museum, Croydon Road, Reigate*

PURLEY NATURAL HISTORY AND SCIENTIFIC SOCIETY *H. F. Haskins, 39 Windermere Road, Coulsdon; J. F. Parker, 42 High-field Road, Purley*

SURREY AND SOUTH-WEST LONDON GROUP, AMATEUR ENTOMOLOGISTS' SOCIETY *E. L. Bean, 121 Queen's Road, W. Croydon*

SUTTON AND DISTRICT NATURAL HISTORY SOCIETY *C. J. Paton, Ormley, 7 Cavendish Road, Sutton*

WEST SURREY PONDKEEPERS' AND AQUARISTS' CLUB *T. Fitzgerald, 8 Orchard Way, Aldershot, Hants.*

Sussex

BOGNOR REGIS NATURAL SCIENCE SOCIETY *E. M. Venables, Norman's Gate, Elm Grove, Barnham, nr. Bognor Regis*

BRIGHTON AND HOVE NATURAL HISTORY SOCIETY *P. G. Simmonds, Booth Museum, Dyke Road, Brighton 5*

EASTBOURNE NATURAL HISTORY, PHOTOGRAPHIC AND ARCHAEOLOGICAL SOCIETY *F. C. Bing, 18 Sancroft Road, Eastbourne*

EAST GRINSTEAD AND DISTRICT NATURAL SCIENCE SOCIETY *County Grammar School, East Grinstead*

HASTINGS NATURAL HISTORY SOCIETY *Miss A. D. Kaye-Smith, 23 Charles Road, St. Leonard's-on-Sea*

LITTLEHAMPTON NATURAL SCIENCE AND ARCHAEOLOGY SOCIETY *The Museum, Littlehampton*

Warwickshire

BIRMINGHAM BIRD CLUB *W. E. Groves, 4 Lyttleton Road, Edgbaston, Birmingham 16*

BIRMINGHAM FIELD NATURALISTS' CLUB *H. Potter, Digbeth Institute, Digbeth, Birmingham 5*

BIRMINGHAM MICROSCOPICAL AND NATURALISTS' SOCIETY
The University, 10 Great Charles Street, Birmingham 1

BIRMINGHAM AND MIDLAND INSTITUTE SCIENTIFIC SOCIETY
W. B. Chivers, Birmingham and Midland Institute, Paradise Street, Birmingham 1

BIRMINGHAM NATURAL HISTORY AND PHILOSOPHICAL SOCIETY *55 Newhall Street, Birmingham*

COVENTRY NATURAL HISTORY AND SCIENTIFIC SOCIETY
2 Roland Mount, Coventry

MIDLAND AQUARIUM AND POOL SOCIETY *D. E. H. Knights, 58 Frederick Road, Wylde Green, Sutton Coldfield*

Westmorland

see Cumberland: CARLISLE NATURAL HISTORY SOCIETY, CUMBERLAND NATURE CLUB, PENRITH AND DISTRICT NATURAL HISTORY SOCIETY

Wiltshire

WILTSHIRE ARCHAEOLOGICAL AND NATURAL HISTORY SOCIETY *The Museum, Long Street, Devizes*

Worcestershire

DUDLEY ZOOLOGICAL SOCIETY LTD. *Dudley*

MALVERN FIELD CLUB *S. E. Warner, Wanganui, Upper Wyche, Malvern*

WORCESTERSHIRE NATURALISTS' FIELD CLUB *Education Offices, Worcester*

Yorkshire

AUSTWICK AND DISTRICT FIELD CLUB *Chris. A. Cheetham, Austwick, via Lancaster*

BARNSLEY NATURALIST AND SCIENTIFIC SOCIETY *Cass's Buildings, St. Mary's Place, Barnsley*

BRADFORD NATURAL HISTORY AND MICROSCOPICAL SOCIETY *Bradford Technical College, Great Horton Road, Bradford*

BRADFORD SCIENTIFIC ASSOCIATION *The Mechanics' Institute, Bradford*

CENTRAL YORKSHIRE BRANCH, BRITISH EMPIRE NATURA-LISTS' ASSOCIATION *E. G. Todd, Askern, near Doncaster*

CLEVELAND LITERARY AND PHILOSOPHICAL SOCIETY *Lieut.-Col. E. L. Johnson, Corporation Road, Middlesbrough*

Local Bird societies, excluding "ornithological sections"

Local Aquarist and Pond societies

CLEVELAND NATURALISTS' FIELD CLUB *J. K. Thomas, 30 Cranbourne Terrace, Stockton-on-Tees, Co. Durham*

CRAVEN NATURALISTS' SOCIETY *T. H. Holmes, 20 Castle View Terrace, Skipton*

CROSS HILLS NATURALISTS' SOCIETY *A. Butterfield, Yew Cottage, Green Lane, Glusburn, near Keighley*

DONCASTER SCIENTIFIC SOCIETY *Art Gallery and Museum, Waterdale, Doncaster*

GREETLAND AND WEST VALE NATURALISTS' SOCIETY *W. Moore, 51 Briscoe Lane, Greetland, Halifax*

HALIFAX AND DISTRICT AQUARISTS' SOCIETY *F. M. Slater, 63 Green Park Road, Sidercoat Green, Halifax*

HALIFAX SCIENTIFIC SOCIETY *J. H. Lumb, 1a Clarendon Place, Halifax*

HAREHILLS NATURALISTS' CLUB *C. Large, 9 Broughton Terrace, Harehills, Leeds 9*

HEBDEN BRIDGE LITERARY AND SCIENTIFIC SOCIETY, Natural History Section *W. Uttley, 8 Prospect Terrace, Savile Road, Hebden Bridge*

HUDDERSFIELD NATURALIST, PHOTOGRAPHIC AND ANTI-QUARIAN SOCIETY *C. Ridgwick, 6 Tower Fold, Honley, Huddersfield*

HULL GEOLOGICAL SOCIETY *H. C. Green, Royal Institution, Hull*

HULL LITERARY AND PHILOSOPHICAL SOCIETY *Royal Institution, Hull*

HULL SCIENTIFIC AND FIELD NATURALISTS' CLUB *Miss E. Crackles, 28 Devon Street, Hull*

ILKLEY NATURAL HISTORY SOCIETY

LEEDS CO-OPERATIVE FIELD NATURALISTS' CLUB *W. A. Wilson, Ridgemont, Hartley Avenue, Leeds 6*

LEEDS AND DISTRICT AQUARISTS' SOCIETY *C. Graham, 171 Thornes Road, Lupset, Wakefield*

LEEDS GEOLOGICAL ASSOCIATION *Department of Geology, The University, Leeds 2*

LEEDS NATURALISTS' CLUB AND SCIENTIFIC ASSOCIATION *D. Fisher, Botany House, University Road, Leeds 1*

LEEDS PHILOSOPHICAL AND LITERARY SOCIETY, Scientific Section *The Museum, Park Row, Leeds 1*

OVENDEN NATURALISTS' SOCIETY *F. Schofield, 2 Glen View, Clover Hill, Halifax*

ROTHERHAM NATURALISTS' SOCIETY *Miss Newell, 3 Rencliffe Avenue, Moorgate, Rotherham*

SCARBOROUGH FIELD NATURALISTS' SOCIETY *G. B. Walsh, 22 Stepney Drive, Scarborough*

SCARBOROUGH PHILOSOPHICAL AND ARCHAEOLOGICAL SOCIETY *H. H. Farwig, The Hermitage, Green Lane, Newby, Scarborough*

SHEFFIELD AND DISTRICT AQUARISTS' SOCIETY *E. Chapman, 170 Gibraltar Street, Sheffield 2*

SORBY NATURAL HISTORY SOCIETY *Alan Ward, 24 Chapel Walk, Sheffield 1*

SOUTH-WEST YORKSHIRE ENTOMOLOGICAL SOCIETY *M. D. Barnes, 12 Dudley Road, Marsh, Huddersfield*

SPEN VALLEY LITERARY AND SCIENTIFIC SOCIETY Honorary Secretary: *Healds Hall, Leeds Road, Liversedge*

STEETON FIELD NATURALISTS' SOCIETY *4 Stone Grove, Steeton, near Keighley*

WAKEFIELD NATURALISTS' SOCIETY Honorary Secretary: *The Quinta, 145 Lincoln Street, Wakefield*

WHITBY NATURALISTS' CLUB *Percy Burnett, Longmynd, Ruswarp Lane, Whitby*

YORK AND DISTRICT FIELD NATURALISTS' SOCIETY *c/o Yorkshire Philosophical Society, The Museum, York*

YORKSHIRE CONCHOLOGICAL SOCIETY *W. Thurgood, 16 Moss Gardens, Alwoodley, Leeds*

YORKSHIRE GEOLOGICAL SOCIETY *Dr. H. C. Versey, The University, Leeds*

YORKSHIRE NATURALISTS' TRUST LTD. *The Yorkshire Museum, York*

YORKSHIRE PHILOSOPHICAL SOCIETY *C. E. Elmhirst, York-shire Museum, York*

WALES: GENERAL

COUNCIL FOR THE PRESERVATION OF RURAL WALES

WALES: COUNTIES

Anglesey; Breconshire

NIL

Caernarvonshire

LLANDUDNO, COLWYN BAY AND DISTRICT FIELD CLUB *L. S. Underwood, Ashmore, Carroll Place, Llandudno*

UNIVERSITY COLLEGE OF NORTH WALES BIOLOGICAL SOCIETY *Biological Department, Memorial Buildings, Bangor*

Cardiganshire

see Pembrokeshire: WEST WALES FIELD SOCIETY

Carmarthenshire

see Pembrokeshire: WEST WALES FIELD SOCIETY

CARMARTHENSHIRE ANTIQUARIAN SOCIETY AND FIELD CLUB *T. Gwyn Jones, Curator, County Museum, Carmarthen*

Denbighshire

see Caernarvonshire: LLANDUDNO, COLWYN BAY AND DISTRICT FIELD CLUB

Flintshire

DYSERTH AND DISTRICT FIELD CLUB *S. Cronshaw, Elderslie, St. Asaph Road, Dyserth*

Glamorgan

CARDIFF NATURALISTS' SOCIETY *c/o National Museum of Wales, Cardiff*

SWANSEA SCIENTIFIC AND FIELD NATURALISTS' SOCIETY *E. R. Brown, 71 Rhyddings Park Road, Swansea*

Merionethshire; Montgomeryshire

NIL

Pembrokeshire

WEST WALES FIELD SOCIETY *Lieut.-Col. H. Allen, The Red House, Heywood Lane, Tenby*

Radnorshire

NIL

SCOTLAND: GENERAL

ASSOCIATION FOR THE PRESERVATION OF RURAL SCOTLAND *E. McGegan, 44 Queen Street, Edinburgh*

BOTANICAL SOCIETY OF EDINBURGH *Prof. R. G. D. Graham, Royal Botanic Garden, Edinburgh 4*

EDINBURGH GEOLOGICAL SOCIETY *Miss K. Stewart, Synod Hall Buildings, Castle Terrace, Edinburgh*

OUTDOOR STUDIES COUNCIL *Dr. G. Absolom, Kelvingrove Museum, Glasgow*

ROYAL PHYSICAL SOCIETY OF EDINBURGH *Dr. A. C. Stephen, Synod Hall, Castle Terrace, Edinburgh*

ROYAL SOCIETY OF EDINBURGH *22-24 George Street, Edinburgh 2*

SCOTTISH AQUARIUM SOCIETY *Strachan Kerr, 42 Aytoun Road, Glasgow, S.1*

SCOTTISH MARINE BIOLOGICAL ASSOCIATION *185 St. Vincent Street, Glasgow. Marine Station: Keppel Pier, Millport, Great Cumbrae, Bute*

SCOTTISH ORNITHOLOGISTS' CLUB *George Waterston, 35 George Street, Edinburgh*

SCOTTISH SOCIETY FOR THE PROTECTION OF WILD BIRDS *J. M. MacKellar, 131 West Regent Street, Glasgow, C.2*

SCOTTISH SOCIETY FOR RESEARCH IN PLANT-BREEDING *Craigs House, Corstorphine, Edinburgh 12*

ZOOLOGICAL SOCIETY OF SCOTLAND *T. H. Gillespie, Zoological Park, Corstorphine, Edinburgh 12*

SCOTLAND: COUNTIES

Aberdeenshire

ABERDEEN NATURAL HISTORY AND ANTIQUARIAN SOCIETY *Dr. David Clouston, West Sefton, Bieldside; Alexander McGregor, 78 Cairnfield Place, Aberdeen*

DEESIDE FIELD AND NATURALISTS' CLUB *Miss Alice Copeland, 5 Union Terrace, Aberdeen; Alex. McGregor, 78 Cairnfield Place, Aberdeen*

Angus

NIL

Argyllshire

KINTYRE SCIENTIFIC ASSOCIATION *Campbeltown Museum, Mull of Kintyre*

Ayrshire

AYR FIELD CLUB *Miss Helen Johnston, 37 St. Leonards Road, Ayr*

AYRSHIRE SCIENTIFIC FILM SOCIETY *John Grainger, Department of Plant Pathology, West of Scotland Agricultural College, Auchincruive, by Ayr*

KILMARNOCK GLENFIELD RAMBLERS *James Bain, c/o The Curator, Dick Institute, Kilmarnock*

Banffshire

BANFF FIELD CLUB *Dr. W. M. Barclay, Editor, Banffshire Journal, Banff*

Berwickshire

BERWICKSHIRE NATURALISTS' CLUB *H. Hargrave Cowan, The Roan, Lauder*

Buteshire

BUTESHIRE NATURAL HISTORY SOCIETY *Castle Street, Rothesay*

Caithness; Clackmannanshire

NIL

Dumbartonshire

DUMBARTONSHIRE NATURAL HISTORY SOCIETY *Mrs. E. R. Ewing, 6 Glenan Gardens, Helensburgh; James Gibson, Bank of Scotland, Helensburgh*

Dumfriesshire

DUMFRIESSHIRE AND GALLOWAY NATURAL HISTORY AND ANTIQUARIAN SOCIETY *Professor F. Balfour-Browne, Ewart Public Library, Dumfries*

East Lothian

NIL

Edinburgh

see Midlothian

Fifeshire

DUNFERMLINE NATURALISTS' SOCIETY *J. Gordon, c/o The Curator, The Museum, Abbot's House, Maygate, Dunfermline*

KIRKCALDY NATURALISTS' SOCIETY *A. Melville, Kirkcaldy Museum*

Forfarshire

NIL

Glasgow

see Lanarkshire

Inverness-shire

INVERNESS FIELD CLUB —. *Peters, Librarian, Inverness*

Kincardine; Kinross

NIL

Kirkcudbrightshire

see Dumfriesshire: DUMFRIESSHIRE AND GALLOWAY NATURAL HISTORY AND ANTIQUARIAN SOCIETY

Lanarkshire

CITY OF GLASGOW ORNITHOLOGICAL ASSOCIATION

GEOLOGICAL SOCIETY OF GLASGOW *D. B. Duncanson, 207 Bath Street, Glasgow*

GLASGOW AND ANDERSONIAN NATURAL HISTORY AND MICROSCOPICAL SOCIETY *Jean C. D. Craig, Societies Room, Royal Technical College, Glasgow, C.1*

HAMILTON NATURAL HISTORY SOCIETY

ROYAL PHILOSOPHICAL SOCIETY OF GLASGOW *John Boyd, 207 Bath Street, Glasgow; F. T. Gertenberg*

ZOOLOGICAL SOCIETY OF GLASGOW *S. H. Benson, Zoological Park, Calderpark Estate, Broomhouse, Glasgow*

Linlithgow

NIL

Midlothian

EDINBURGH FIELD NATURALISTS' AND MICROSCOPICAL SOCIETY

EDINBURGH NATURAL HISTORY SOCIETY *A. A. Pinkerton, Goold Hall, St. Andrew Square, Edinburgh*

EDINBURGH UNIVERSITY BIOLOGICAL SOCIETY *Miss C. Scott, 4 Burgess Terrace, Edinburgh 9*

EDINBURGH ZOOLOGICAL SOCIETY *Dr. A. M. Cockburn, 53 Ladysmith Road, Edinburgh*

MIDLOTHIAN ORNITHOLOGICAL CLUB

Morayshire

ELGIN AND MORAYSHIRE LITERARY AND SCIENTIFIC ASSOCIATION *W. E. Watson, The Museum, 1 High Street, Elgin*

MORAY FIELD CLUB   —. *Millar, Headmaster, Rothes*

Nairnshire

ELGIN AND MORAYSHIRE LITERARY AND SCIENTIFIC ASSOCIATION

NAIRN FIELD CLUB   —. *Bain, The Nairnshire Telegraph, Nairn*

see also Morayshire

Orkney

ORKNEY NATURAL HISTORY SOCIETY   *Stromness Museum*

Peebles

NIL

Perthshire

PERTHSHIRE SOCIETY OF NATURAL SCIENCE   *T. J. Simpson, Museum and Art Gallery, George Street, Perth*

Renfrewshire

GREENOCK PHILOSOPHICAL SOCIETY   *James J. Innes, Mansion House, 1 Ardgowan Street, Greenock*

PAISLEY NATURALISTS' SOCIETY   *John McKim, The Museum, High Street, Paisley*

PAISLEY PHILOSOPHICAL INSTITUTION   *J. Gardner, The Museum, Paisley*

PORT GLASGOW NATURALISTS' SOCIETY

Ross and Cromarty; Roxburghshire; Selkirkshire; Shetland

NIL

Stirlingshire

FALKIRK ARCHAEOLOGICAL AND NATURAL HISTORY SOCIETY   *Mrs. D. V. Hereward, Cartief, Redding, by Falkirk*

STIRLING AQUARIUM SOCIETY

STIRLING NATURAL HISTORY AND ARCHAEOLOGICAL SOCIETY   *D. B. Morris, 15 Gladstone Place, Stirling*

Sutherland

NIL

Wigtownshire

see Dumfriesshire: DUMFRIESSHIRE AND GALLOWAY NATURAL HISTORY AND ANTIQUARIAN SOCIETY

ISLE OF MAN

AEGLAGH VANNIN (THE YOUNG MANX) Natural History Section   *Mrs. A. J. Davidson, Summerland, Brunswick Road, Douglas*

ISLE OF MAN NATURAL HISTORY AND ANTIQUARIAN SOCIETY   *W. H. Capper, 19 Western Avenue, Douglas*

ISLE OF MAN SCIENTIFIC SOCIETY   *R. K. Matthews, The Sycamores, Tromode Road, Douglas*

MANX FIELD CLUB   *W. S. Cowin, Kenwood, Brunswick Road, Douglas*

IRELAND: GENERAL

GEOGRAPHICAL SOCIETY OF IRELAND   *c/o Department of Geography, Trinity College, Dublin.* Honorary Secretary: *J. A. K. Grahame, 95 Upper Leeson Street, Dublin*

IRISH SOCIETY FOR THE PROTECTION OF BIRDS   *c/o Thomas H. Mason & Sons, 5/6 Dane Street, Dublin*

ROYAL DUBLIN SOCIETY   *Ballsbridge, Dublin*

ROYAL IRISH ACADEMY   *19 Dawson Street, Dublin*

ROYAL ZOOLOGICAL SOCIETY OF IRELAND   *Phoenix Park, Dublin*

IRELAND: PROVINCES

Ulster

see Antrim: BOTANICAL SOCIETY OF NORTHERN IRELAND *Queen's University Scientific Society*

ULSTER AQUARIUM SOCIETY   *S. Woods, 59 Stranmillis Gardens, Belfast*

ULSTER SOCIETY FOR THE PROTECTION OF BIRDS

IRELAND: COUNTIES

Antrim

ROUTE NATURALISTS' SOCIETY

BELFAST NATURAL HISTORY AND PHILOSOPHICAL SOCIETY   *A. Deane, The Museum, College Square North, Belfast*

BELFAST NATURALISTS' FIELD CLUB *J. Skillen, Municipal Museum and Art Gallery, Stanmillis, Belfast*

MID-ANTRIM NATURALISTS' FIELD CLUB *c/o J. E. Stirling, Waveney Road, Ballymena*

QUEEN'S UNIVERSITY SCIENTIFIC SOCIETY (formerly BOTANICAL SOCIETY OF NORTHERN IRELAND) *T. Jackson, Department of Botany, Queen's University, Belfast*
see also Derry

Armagh

see Down: ROSTREVOR AND DISTRICT NATURALISTS' FIELD CLUB

Belfast

see Antrim

Carlow; Cavan

NIL

Clare

see Limerick: LIMERICK AND CLARE FIELD CLUB

Cork

CORK UNIVERSITY BIOLOGICAL SOCIETY *Honan Biological Institute, University College, Cork*

Derry

LIMAVADY NATURALISTS' FIELD CLUB *W. D. Cousins, Regional Education Office, Limavady; S. J. Courtney, Technical School, Limavady*

LONDONDERRY NATURALISTS' FIELD CLUB *F. W. Logan, 54 Abercorn Road, Londonderry*

ROUTE NATURALISTS' SOCIETY *W. P. Brown, Beresford House, Coleraine*

Donegal

NIL

Down

ROSTREVOR AND DISTRICT NATURALISTS' FIELD CLUB *L. H. Liddle, Carpenham, Rostrevor*

Dublin

DUBLIN NATURALISTS' FIELD CLUB *J. F. Haughton, Charleville, Dundrum, Co. Dublin*

UNIVERSITY COLLEGE, DUBLIN, BIOLOGICAL SOCIETY *Science Buildings, University College, Merrion Street, Dublin*

UNIVERSITY COLLEGE NATURAL HISTORY CLUB *Merrion Street, Dublin*

UNIVERSITY OF DUBLIN EXPERIMENTAL SCIENCE ASSOCIATION *Dr. Bryan P. Beirne, Trinity College, Dublin*

Fermanagh; Galway; Kerry

NIL

Kildare

SOUTH KILDARE NATURALISTS' FIELD CLUB *S. J. Cullinan, Vocational School, Athy*

Kilkenny; King's County; Leitrim

NIL

Londonderry

see Derry

Limerick; Longford

NIL

Louth

see Down: ROSTREVOR AND DISTRICT NATURALISTS' FIELD CLUB

Mayo; Meath; Monaghan; Queen's County; Roscommon; Sligo; Tipperary

NIL

Tyrone

OMAGH NATURALISTS' FIELD CLUB

TYRONE NATURALISTS' FIELD CLUB *Thos. Greer, The Bungalow, Sandholes, Cookstown*

Waterford; Westmeath; Wexford; Wicklow

NIL

CHANNEL ISLANDS

SOCIÉTÉ GUÉRNESIAISE *Guille-Allès Library, St. Peter Port, Guernsey*

SOCIÉTÉ JERSIAISE *The Museum, 9 Pier Road, St. Helier, Jersey*

DAVID STAINER

SCHOOL NATURAL HISTORY SOCIETIES

ONE of the pleasant aspects of the present day is the great increase in the number, scope and activities of Natural History Societies in schools. It is true that certain schools trace the origins of their present societies well back into the last century, but most of such beginnings, on closer scrutiny, show themselves as poor things indeed— as gatherings of self-conscious eccentrics alternately perishing as entities and undergoing brief and transient resurrection.

A short article must, of necessity, give only a narrow view. It is the writer's privilege to hold office in the Association of School Natural History Societies. The initiative in its formation was taken by a small group of Boys' Public Schools. The Association has not yet celebrated its first birthday, and is, hence, still predominantly representative of this small and highly specialised group of schools, and still almost entirely masculine. This is a pity, as there is some evidence that girls' schools are keener and more active in the pursuit of field studies, and display, on the whole, greater enterprise.

The Association's first Annual Journal has just been issued. It is a modest work in typescript, privately circulated among members. It contains contributions from fourteen boys' schools. This is the sort of work that is being done:—

Berkhamsted School N.H.S. is carrying out an ecological survey of part of Berkhamsted Common. Its botanists are making a permanent quadrat, and carrying out a belt transect. Soil, weather, plants, insects, birds, pond life and agriculture are being systematically studied. Clayesmore School N.H.S. have ringed 533 birds, contributed to the British Trust for Ornithology's Starling investigation, and Hatching and Fledging inquiry, and are completing schedules for the Insect Immigration Committee. In the holidays, parties from the school have worked at the Marine Biological Station at Plymouth and the Ornithological Station in the Isle of May, and studied marine biology in Brittany.

Of the activities of the Natural History Society of Dauntsey's School much could be written. The work done on the biology of the Wiltshire Dew Ponds by Dauntsey's boys while still at school is a real contribution to scientific knowledge, and the frequent bulletins issued by the society on such diverse groups as the Odonata, Lepidoptera, Arachnida, Amphibia, Reptiles and Birds are monuments of careful observation. Felsted School, who have included a visit to Wicken Fen in their activities, contribute matter on aquatic insects, insect migration, and birds. King's School, Canterbury, N.H.S. is suffering temporarily from a loss of senior members, but is continuing its study of an area on the lower Stour, flooded as a result of mining operations, whose claims to become one of the new Nature Reserves are powerful and insistent.

In Herefordshire, Lucton School N.H.S. are making a detailed study of the ecology of the Croft Ambrey Ridge, with special relation to the factors of soil, slope, height, and human interference. It is also carrying out a survey of the bird life of the district. Marlborough College N.H.S. one of the oldest and most active in the country, in addition to its regular work on the flora and fauna of the county, is specialising in the study of the Mollusca within ten miles of the school. Oundle, among other things, are completing phenological returns for the Meteorological Office, and assisting with the B.T.O.'s Hatching and Fledging inquiry, Bird Ringing scheme, and Heron count.

From C. R. Shoesmith of the Shrewsbury School Darwin Society comes a most interesting and scholarly article upon the weighing of young robins, carried out at the suggestion of Mr. David Lack. Tonbridge School N.H.S. has recently held an exhibition, containing, among other features, a tame jackdaw, tawny owl and hedge-hog, a reproduction in miniature of a Yorkshire Bog, a large collection of spiders, and a demonstration of milk-testing experiments.

Wellington contribute an article on a Praying Mantis kept in captivity, and a special study of the bees, wasps and ants in their district. From St. Edward's School, Oxford, come interesting articles on the display of the cock chaffinch, the irregularity of eggs in a blackbird's nest, a Camberwell Beauty taken in Jersey, the rearing in captivity of the larvae of the Clouded Yellow, and the Convolvulus Hawk Moth.

In a foreword to the Journal, Mr. Eric Parker, one-time editor of the *Field*, refers to his life at Eton sixty years ago, when to be a field-naturalist was to be "a frightful scug".

The above notes indicate something of what is going on. Very many other schools are doing equally good work, as is shown by the piles of admirably produced Annual Reports from all over the country, which cover a large area of the floor space of the writer's study.

The following inferences may safely be drawn: a large number of schools possess active and well-organised societies; school naturalists are no longer "frightful scugs"; mere collecting, as an end in itself, is becoming a thing of the past; many schoolboys, and girls, are actively aware of what is going on in adult research, and are co-operating, in some degree, in work sponsored by the B.T.O., the Insect Immigration Committee, the Meteorological Office, the Freshwater Biological Association, and other authoritative bodies; distinguished naturalists

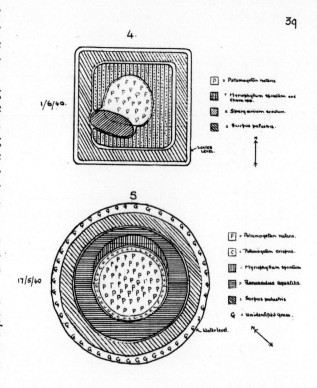

Zonation of plants in four dew-ponds surveyed by

are giving their valuable time in helping boys and girls; many of the younger generation are keenly interested in field-studies and in the preservation of our flora and fauna.

This is all immensely to the good. Although, year by year our rural amenities are being destroyed, an increasing number of young people are finding pleasure and profit in field-studies. More and

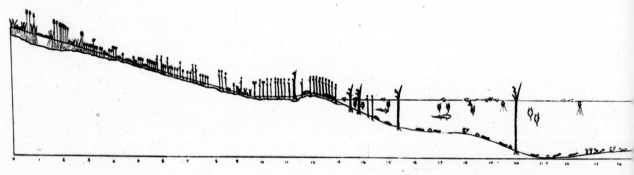

The plant-profile of another dew-pond,

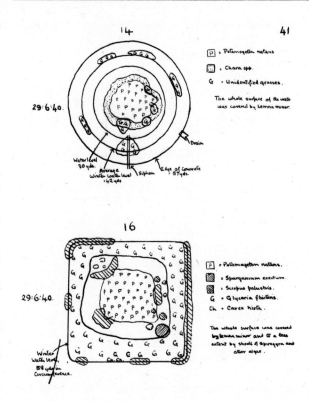

Dauntsey's school, and sketched in the school field-book

better popular works on Natural History (especially ornithology) are being published, and sold, than ever before. The outlook is not one of unrelieved gloom.

At a not-so-imaginary Rugby a hundred years ago Tom Brown and Harry East spent a half-holiday stoning blackbirds from hedge to hedge, unrebuked by their sincerely high-minded author.

The Tom Browns and Harry Easts of to-day try to remove the oil from stranded sea-birds, warm and nourish exhausted migrants, campaign against egg-collectors, and are Junior Bird-Recorders attached to the Royal Society for the Protection of Birds.

For all this, inertia, ignorance, wanton destructiveness and cruelty still exist. The shoddy amusements of the town call louder than ever before. Too many young people still drift through life blind and deaf to the best it has to offer. Wild things are still destroyed with wanton cruelty.

The chief purpose of a School Natural History Society is, of course, educational. A few, a very few, of its members may eventually become professional naturalists.

It is the rank and file that the Society really helps. One of the great services to the community performed by the Church of England has been the placing of an educated man in every parish: a Gilbert White, a Stephen Hales, a C. A. Johns. The School Natural History Society aims at sending educated men and women into the world, such as, in the grime of a bombed city, will hear with delight the song of the black redstart, and find on the sea-shore and in the waste places "that something", to quote Richard Jefferies, "that the ancients called divine".

Our Societies differ in a number of ways from their adult prototypes. Membership is constantly changing. The life of a public schoolboy is, unfortunately, a very short one: at most, a span of five years, from the irresponsible child of thirteen, fresh from his Prep. School, to the grave and authoritative young man of eighteen: from fag to

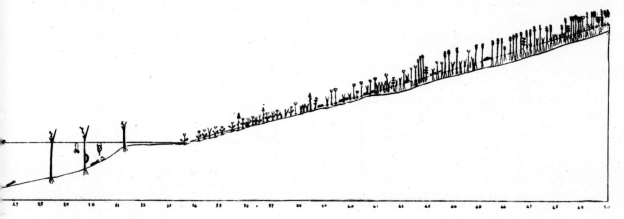

showing also some of its animals

monitor. The change is a very big one. The Society must cater for all intermediate stages.

Then, our Society is a society within a society. It operates within the framework of school economy. Its members are not completely free. Even so superficially unimportant a person as Smith Minimus is watched, during his uneasy leisure, by many pairs of eyes. His House authorities are prepared to spring upon him for some low task, some necessary piece of fagging; large and powerful men and boys are determined to turn him into a cricketer, footballer, boxer, or cross-country runner; conscientious pedagogues are devising for him extra classes in Latin or mathematics; the music-master wants him for the choir; everybody wants him, for Parade, for Confirmation Class, for Swimming, for . . .

School societies are nominally, and to a very great extent actually, run by the pupils themselves, under the patronage of a master, who is answerable to higher authority. In addition to the usual officers, honorary secretary, treasurer, report editor, etc., there is a committee, each member of which usually represents one particular branch. The difficulty of securing continuity will be understood when it is realised that all these officials are transitory. By the time he is sufficiently experienced and responsible, a boy is nearly at the end of his school career, and will soon be gone for ever. His loss is particularly disastrous when he represents one of the less popular branches of natural history.

The master is, thus, the only permanent official. Nevertheless, his hand must not, too obviously, be seen in the organisation of the society. It is a boys' society, not a masters'. Even in the present day of easy friendships between teachers and taught, the master is, so to speak, an emissary from another camp, no longer, happily, hostile, but, none the less, foreign. The vital force in the Society must come from the non-commissioned ranks.

The master holds office by the invitation of the boys, and one of his functions is to confer respectability. He is the buffer between the society, his colleagues, and the headmaster.

He must rescue Smith Minimus from Sergeant-Major and Chaplain, and make it possible for him to spend his afternoon dredging for aquatic larvae. He must secure a "late leave" for Jones to go mothing. He must cultivate local landowners,

farmers and gamekeepers, secure their interest, and see that their courtesy is not abused.

A school society is admirably self-contained. The honorary secretary can reach all his members, easily and quickly, by means of the school notice-board. A room is always available for meetings, and there is probably a biology laboratory with books and apparatus, and a projector or cinematograph. There are the school grounds and playing fields.

Where there is enthusiasm, very much can be accomplished. The task is to keep the torch alight and handed on from swift-disappearing generation to generation; to compete successfully for the boys' interest against many and varied rival spare-time activities, and to make each member really feel he is doing something useful. The work may be sometimes, let it be confessed, disheartening, but it is always interesting, and always worth while.

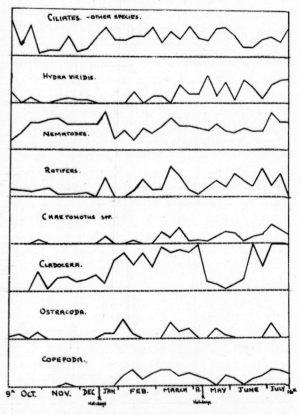

Seasonal changes in the abundance of Protozoa and animals in a dew-pond; surveyed by Dauntsey's school. (Note interruptions in observations during school holidays)

W. H. PEARSALL

LOCAL JOURNALS

THE local journal of natural history is a peculiarly British institution. Generally it originated about 100 years ago. Often it has led an on-and-off sort of existence since, and sometimes it has outlived the need that brought it into existence. Local journals were, in the first place, a result of the tremendous interest in things scientific that followed the Industrial Revolution. They acquired a biological basis after the enunciation of the theory of natural selection and the great intellectual upheaval which followed that event. It so happened that there was then available a field of biological work which was admirably suited to the somewhat sporadic activities of amateur naturalists, the recording of the major facts of the distribution of the local faunas and floras. Thus, for a time, local naturalists and their journals flourished and did good work. By the beginning of the new century, however, most of this work of recording had been completed, or at any rate, that part of it that could be done without a microscope and special experience. Except, therefore, for occasional additions and for some revision of critical groups, the local journals fell upon leaner times, a condition which has operated with increasing force as the years have passed. What then is to be their future? Are they to persist as the expression of a harmless interest or have they and their contributors and readers a part to play in the future development of biological knowledge?

The answer to these questions depends no doubt upon one's particular point of view, and if, of necessity, I write as a professional biologist, it is also as one with much sympathy for the problems a local journal involves and with much appreciation of the efforts and accomplishments of my amateur colleagues.

One must recognise firstly, that like almost any other journal run by a society, a local journal depends very largely on its contributors, chiefly the members of the society. The question of what scientific contribution a local journal can make, thus depends quite simply on what the society (or its members) *is prepared to do*. The day has long since passed when any large scientific interest centred around detailed county records, though they have uses.

On the other hand, biology is turning once again from the laboratory to the study of the living organism in nature. The orientation of its field interests has, however, changed and developed. In the search for reasons behind the facts of distribution and of survival in a particular habitat, biologists have come to look rather at the details of the environment and of the mode of life of the organism. It is realised that the correct way to tackle these problems is usually to study a common plant or animal, simply because worth-while data can be more quickly collected. We have thus had one or two admirable studies of single birds and mammals while the compilation of a "biological flora" by botanists is based on the study of single species.

The new biology has thus also come to focus attention far more largely on what is called ecology, the study of the relation of the organism to its environment, and this may concentrate, of course, either on the life-history, on the habitat factors or on the inter-relations of the organisms making up the plant or animal community. It is not, I think, generally realised that there is here also a field of work in which local scientific societies could excel —the description of the composition of mixed plant and animal communities, mainly those of the soil, plant cover and invertebrate populations. One such description, that of heather moor, is already being tackled by a northern union. This type of study can bring in almost any field interest, effects of season, weather data, geology and soil science as well as the life cycles of plants and animals. Sooner or later it would lead to the re-recording of the distribution of every local animal

or plant on an ecological basis, a work which could, of course, be undertaken independently. If work of these types were available, local journals would acquire a considerable scientific value, enabling comparisons to be made between different parts of the country.

The view has often been expressed that local journals as a class are too restricted in their outlook and that they should aim at a greater variety of material. Very often, in the attempt to meet this criticism, the editor includes material of very wide range which has little or no local bearing. He is driven towards this broadening of outlook also by another frequently expressed wish. There is evidently a very real desire among naturalists that their local journal should help them to keep up to date in the scientific fields adjacent to those in which they are interested. I have often been asked, for example, when lecturing to a local society, why material of the type I have used should not be reported in the Society's journal. How is this type of reporting to be done? One method that is quite feasible is to choose a President each year who could be asked to cover a suitable field of recent work—his address to appear in the journal. This is not perhaps a common way of choosing a President—but it is one which will appeal to the editor of the journal. The editor himself usually tries to do something towards meeting this need by reviewing books, but he is often handicapped by limitations of knowledge and interest, and more frequently still by the character of the books he gets for review. A considerable proportion of those received are of little interest or value, yet he is likely to feel that if he ignores them he will fall out of favour with publishers and will not get the more valuable publications he would like to have. Nevertheless, the most useful help an editor can have in maintaining varied interest is a panel of

suitable reviewers and a steady flow of books to review.

When all is said and done, however, a local journal should be *local*. It finds its greatest value in giving a complete record of the whole field of natural history in one locality. Let it not be thought that the limitation of space means limitation of interest. One restricted area, Selborne, yielded enough material to fill a classic volume and to acquire immortal fame. Of recent years, other similar localities have yielded equally rich dividends to active investigation. Some, it is true, like Wicken and Studland, have unique advantages of flora and fauna, but others like Aldenham and Austwick owe their reputation mainly to the keenness of their residents.

Lastly, there is the suggestion that local journals should also be "educational", a term that seems to cover a multitude of sins and perhaps few virtues. From this aspect, the real value of natural history is that one has to learn from nature and not from books, from things and not from the written word. The justification, educational or otherwise, for a local journal is thus that it gives to every naturalist the opportunity of recording what he has seen and learnt. He should feel that if his observations are worth while they ought to be recorded. Nothing has impressed me more than the vast stores of unrecorded wisdom that accumulate in the minds of my naturalistic friends. It should be the editor's duty to tap these stores for his journal and to get distilled from them some of the integrated knowledge they contain.

May we say, then, that our journals will persist and will justify themselves only as long as they continue to be based on naturalistic field-work? If they turn only to the dissemination of the written word or to provide an additional source of light literature, they will quickly descend into the limbo of forgotten things, "unwept, unhonoured and unsung".

A "run" of local journals on the shelves of the Zoological Society of London

By courtesy of the Society

L. C. LLOYD

NATURALISTS ON THE AIR

BECAUSE its appeal is largely visual, natural history does not at first sight appear to be a particularly promising subject for broadcasting. Such, at any rate, seems to be the conclusion arrived at by the programme planners of the B.B.C., for natural history is but meagrely represented on the air. Each month the B.B.C. puts out in its three programmes a thousand hours of broadcasting. Of these, during the past year, natural history has accounted for an average of about four hours per month, made up as follows:

	Minutes
"Bird-Song of the Month"	15
"The Naturalist"	20
"Country Questions"	30
"Nature Parliament"	30
Schools Nature Study (four sessions, during term only)	60
Various talks and features (say)	90
Total	245

Natural history also figures to some extent in such programmes as "Country Magazine" and the Midland Regional "Countrylover" series, but these, I think, are adequately provided for in the last item of my table.

Natural history, it will be seen, accounts for approximately 0·4 per cent of programme time, which may fairly be taken as an indication of the B.B.C.'s assessment of its importance, or of its suitability as radio material. For a nation like ours, in which a love of nature and the countryside looms large in the life of the people, this seems inadequate. It is, of course, true that broadcasting deals only with sound, whereas the appreciation of nature makes demands upon all the senses. But it is only on a superficial view that it is dismissed as unsuitable for radio treatment.

Natural history broadcasts seem to me to fall into four main classes, differentiated by their methods of presentation. One presents the actual sounds of nature—which, obviously, must usually be recorded—linked together by a spoken commentary. This is the method used in "Bird-Song of the Month" and in the periodical "live" broadcasts of bird-song. The second method is the "straight" talk, perhaps illustrated by recordings of bird-song, animal noises, and so on. Thirdly comes the discussion between two or more speakers, one of whom commonly acts as a kind of interlocutor. Examples of this technique are "The Naturalist" series and the schools broadcasts. Lastly, there is the method adopted in such programmes as "Country Questions" and the Children's Hour feature, "Nature Parliament", in which a team of experts in the studio answer questions previously sent in by listeners. Each of these classes of broadcast has its own advantages and disadvantages; each is particularly well adapted for certain purposes and less well adapted for others. Let us briefly consider them in turn.

So far as the reproduction of the actual sounds of nature is concerned, the B.B.C. appears to rely upon one man: Ludwig Koch. By his remarkable patience, skill and enterprise, and by the sheer quality of his recordings, Dr. Koch has made this field incontestably his own, and his recordings constantly turn up in the programmes. Sometimes he puts on a programme of his own, of which a notable example was "Sea Birds Calling", the illustrated narrative of a summer expedition to the Channel Islands to record the voices of sea-birds breeding on Little Burhau, three miles off Alderney. Dr. Koch's bird-song records—some of them well-known to bird-lovers since their publication in 1936—form the basis of the series "Bird-Song of the Month", which originated in the West Region, was promoted to the Third Programme, and finally reached the Home Service, where it is available to an audience commensurate with its merits. Ralph Whitlock is usually the commentator, and his West Country voice has all the cadences of the countryside in it.

For certain subjects the "straight" talk is probably the most satisfactory method of presenting natural history on the air, but for some reason or other it does not seem to be greatly favoured by the B.B.C. The reason is, I suspect, that few B.B.C. officials—on the programme side, at any rate—are naturalists, and they seem to feel that natural history must be to some extent "dressed up" if it is to appeal to the ordinary listener. In this I think they are mistaken. A plain, straightforward exposition, especially if it is based on personal experience, will always arrest the listener's attention, provided that the subject-matter is worth while and that the speaker is on friendly terms with the microphone. I remember, for instance, a delightful talk on riverside life by E. A. Ellis, the distinguished Norwich naturalist, in a Midland Regional programme on the River Yare in the series "Midland Roads and Rivers". His voice is not of the quality usually considered suitable for broadcasting, but his profound knowledge and his genuine enthusiasm made this an outstandingly effective broadcast. I remember, too, a good Third Programme talk by Stuart Smith on bird migration, in which he dealt with the obscure mystery of the underlying causes of migration. It was a spoken essay rather than a talk, but perhaps such an approach was justified by the subject-matter.

Roland Green, the well-known painter of birds, gave a first-rate talk on "Sketching Birds" in the Midland Regional "Countrylover" series. He made a particularly good point when he remarked that coloured illustrations in books usually show close-ups of birds in a good light, but that in the field we hardly ever see them like that. In the same programme Mary Laurie gave an interesting summary of some of her work on mouse populations, and J. Wentworth Day contributed a vivid and exciting account of a nocturnal punt-gunning expedition. Another contributor of good "straight" talks is Dr. Geoffrey Vevers, who has succeeded David Seth-Smith as the "Zoo Man" of the Children's Hour.

My third class of natural history broadcast is the discussion, which is best exemplified in "The Naturalist" series—another product of the West Region which has been promoted to the Home Service. In this series Brian Vesey-FitzGerald, the editor, takes part with (usually) two guest speakers, who have expert knowledge in some branch or other of natural history, and whom he stimulates (or restrains) with questions and comments. The programme is, in my opinion, a highly successful one, and much of its success is due to Desmond Hawkins, the producer, and to Vesey-FitzGerald himself. He is, of course, a first-rate all-round naturalist, and he is also an admirable broadcaster, with just the right blend of friendliness and authority. As editor of the series he has brought to the microphone Professor A. G. Tansley on nature reserves, W. B. Turrill and H. Godwin on bogs, A. D. Middleton on squirrels, Peter Scott on wild geese, and many other leading experts. Among other subjects which have been dealt with in this excellent series are caves and their flora and fauna, warblers, insect populations, animal scent, and birds at lighthouses—a mixed bag, indeed, but all of lively interest to the nature-lover. Miscalculations occur sometimes—there was an obviously absurd attempt to deal with pond-life in twenty minutes—but they are quite exceptional.

Only rarely am I able to listen to the schools broadcasts. In those I have heard Scott Kennedy and his young disciple Tom, the blacksmith's son, seem to have some quite exciting adventures which provide ample opportunities for Kennedy to impart a good deal of sound information about the birds and beasts of the countryside. Personally, I find the method a little trying, but I realise that these programmes are not meant for me, and if I insist on eavesdropping I must not complain of what I hear. I am no authority on education, and I presume that the method (which I find irritatingly "phoney") has the approval of those who are expert in instructing the young. Scott Kennedy certainly performs his part with admirable grace and aplomb.

A Home Service programme devoted to Hickling Broad, that East Anglian paradise for the ornithologist, used a variant of the discussion technique, but did not quite come off because it lacked spontaneity. Several of the people who took part doubtless knew their subject from A to Z, but they were unable to come to terms with the microphone, so that their contributions sounded stilted and unnatural. This is a difficulty that radio producers of "actuality" programmes are always up against; it may be summarised in a sentence: "Those who know can't broadcast, and those who can broadcast don't know." The only remedy is for the producer to go on searching until he finds somebody who both knows and can broadcast. Such people *do* exist—several have already been mentioned in this article—but they are rare birds and deserve tender handling when they have been captured. In this Hickling Broad programme a remarkable thing happened. It suddenly came to life in the last couple of minutes, when Anthony Buxton and the keepers started bird-spotting—an apparently spontaneous and un-rehearsed episode, which only goes to show that in broadcasting, as in so many other departments of human activity, you never can tell.

In the fourth class of natural history broadcasts there are two series of monthly programmes—"Country Questions" and the Children's Hour "Nature Parliament". In the former the team of experts comprises Brian Vesey-FitzGerald, Eric Hobbis, Ralph Wightman, and a tactful and witty question-master in Jack Longland. This, again, is a programme that originated in the West Region, which seems to be considerably more "nature-conscious" than any other part of the B.B.C.'s organisation. In the Children's Hour programme we again meet Vesey-FitzGerald, with Peter Scott, whose special field is, of course, birds, and L. Hugh Newman, who deals with matters entomological. Derek McCulloch ("Uncle Mac"), the director of the Children's Hour, occupies the chair. Of the popularity of these programmes there can be no doubt; both receive many more questions than they can answer in the limited time at their disposal. They are also interesting to listen to, and the members of the panels display an amazing readiness in finding answers to the posers that are put to them. Perhaps the "Country Questions" team is a little less confidence-inspiring than usual when it is occasionally called upon to answer questions about archaeology and folklore, but as this article is concerned with natural history I need say no more about that aspect of the matter. Very rarely are the experts stumped, and when they are an honest avowal of ignorance may beget more confidence than an unhesitating reply of doubtful validity. In "Nature Parliament", for instance, somebody asked for a list of the birds that eat mistletoe berries, and Peter Scott said quite frankly that he could not supply the answer off-hand, and that he would have to look it up. One's heart warmed at such a confession, and one's confidence in his authority was rather strengthened than weakened.

There remains to be noticed an important series of natural history programmes which do not quite fall into any of the four classes we have been considering. This was James Fisher's series produced by Stephen Potter in the Third Programme—a series which one hoped would be continued, because the author seemed to be working towards a technique that promised considerable possibilities. He began rather uncertainly with "The Natural History of Salcey Forest", but rapidly gained sureness of touch and a grasp of the significant in programmes devoted to Inverpolly Forest, St. Kilda and the Kite. A sound-mosaic of description, explanation, personal experience and the sounds of nature was contrived to convey to the listener a picture which had both clarity and coherence. These programmes were not only interesting and successful in themselves, but seemed to me to point the way to a whole series in which the natural history of various characteristic regions or species might be presented from the ecological point of view. The method is obviously capable of development, and one hopes that the idea may commend itself to the powers-that-be.

To sum up the main impressions of a year's fairly intensive listening, I suggest (a) that natural history is inadequately represented in the B.B.C. programmes; (b) that the natural history broadcasts that find a place in the programmes are generally satisfactory so far as they go; and (c) that there is room for considerable development in the presentation of natural history on the air.

THE NEW NATURALIST—a Journal of British Natural History—*is published by Collins, 14 St. James's Place, London S.W.1, and is designed and produced by Adprint. The Journal is edited from 51a Rathbone Place, London W.1, by James Fisher with the help of Elisabeth Ullmann, and it is supervised by the editorial board responsible for the New Naturalist* books—*James Fisher, John Gilmour, Julian Huxley, L. Dudley Stamp and Eric Hosking (photographic editor).*

New Naturalist books *are published by Collins and produced in conjunction with Adprint.*

Printed in Great Britain by Jarrold and Sons Limited, Norwich.